CODE NAME:
A M N O N

THE LIFE AND TIMES OF A
HAGANAH FIGHTER
1943 – 1949

BY DANIEL ROSENFELD

ROSENFELD BOOK PUBLISHING

Daniel Rosenfeld

"Code Name: Amnon. The Life And Times Of A Haganah Fighter" by Daniel Rosenfeld. ISBN 0-9716008-2-1

Library of Congress Control Number:Txu000982-668

Published 2003 by Rosenfeld Book Publishing, 3145 N.E. 210th Street, Aventura, Florida 33180 U.S. 2003 Daniel Rosenfeld. All rights reserved. No part of this publication may be reproduced, stored in a retrieval system, or transmitted in any form or by any means, electronic, mechanical, recording or otherwise, without the prior written permission of Daniel Rosenfeld

Printed in the United States of America

Amnon

To my brother Benjamin

Daniel Rosenfeld

OTHER BOOKS BY DANIEL ROSENFELD

WHAT IF

THE FALL OF THE SPANISH INQUISITION

PREFACE

I wrote this book to remind my children that during the entire course of Jewish history, from Biblical times to the present, Jews have always been a vulnerable people. However, not being an historian, I have not written an historical treatise, and this story covers only the personal involvement of one young man, a member of the Haganah, in the struggle to formally establish the State of Israel. This story details his thoughts and feelings about events occurring from 1943 to 1949 in the context of his military experience.

It is important the reader understand that Amnon's thoughts and feelings were his own and not always compatible with the rest of the population of Palestine. The book, therefore, concentrates on Amnon, his personality, and his beliefs, some of which differ from real historical facts.

It covers Amnon's enlistment in the Resistance movement in Palestine during World War II, and ends with his discharge from the Israel Defense Forces after the War of Independence.

While writing this, it occurred to me that very possibly today's readers might not be familiar with the tumultuous history of Palestine and the State of Israel. So, to help the reader fully understand the whys and wherefores of the issues, events, and developments surrounding Amnon's military experiences, a brief summation of the decades from the 1880's through the 1940's appears in Book One.

The reader is respectfully requested to note that this story is intensely personal. Not only is it the story of an idealistic young man who devotedly served his country [very often above and beyond the call of duty] in a cause for which he was willing to fight to the death, but indirectly, it is a memorial to those thousands of young men and women who willingly sacrificed their lives in the struggle to create a Jewish Homeland, not only for all the world's Jews, but especially for survivors of the Nazi Holocaust, as well as a memorial to the innocent six million who perished in that unspeakable horror. The story details a dream, as well as the accompanying belief, commitment, devotion, and personal sacrifice in and for a cause that was greater than us all.

Daniel Rosenfeld

BOOK ONE

THE PIONEERS

Daniel Rosenfeld

The following is the text of the historical Declaration of Independence of the State of Israel, made by David Ben Gurion who headed the National Council and who became the first Prime Minister of the State of Israel.

"In the Biblical 'Land of Israel' the Jewish people came into being. In this Land was shaped their spiritual, religious and national character. Here they lived in sovereign independence. Here they created a culture of national and universal import, and gave to the world the Bible, the eternal Book of books.

Exiled by force, still the Jewish people kept faith with their Land in all the countries of their dispersion, steadfast in their prayer and hope to return to Israel here to refresh their spirits and revive their political and personal freedom. Fired by this attachment of history and tradition, Jews in every generation strove to renew their roots in the ancient Homeland, and in recent generations they came home in their multitudes.

Veteran pioneers and defenders, and newcomers braving blockade, they made the wilderness bloom, revived their Hebrew tongue, and built villages and towns. They also founded a thriving society, master of its own economy and culture, pursuing peace but able to defend itself, bringing the blessing of progress to all the inhabitants of the Land, dedicated to the attainment of sovereign independence.

In 1897, the First Zionist Congress met at the call of Theodore Herzl, seer of the vision of the Jewish State, and gave public voice to the right of the Jewish people to national restoration of their Land. The right was acknowledged in the Balfour Declaration on November 2, 1917, and confirmed in the Mandate of the League of Nations, which accorded national validity to the historical connection of the Jewish people with the Land of Israel, and to their right to reestablish their National Home.

The Holocaust, that in our time destroyed millions of Jews in Europe, proved beyond doubt the compelling need to solve the problem of Jewish homelessness and dependence by the renewal of the Jewish State in the Land of Israel, which would open wide the gates to the Homeland to every Jew and endow the Jewish people with the status of a nation with equality of rights within the family of nations.

Despite every hardship, hindrance and peril, the remnant that survived the grim Nazi slaughter in Europe, together with Jews from other countries, pressed on with their exodus to the Land of Israel and continued to assert their right to a life of dignity, freedom and honest toil in the Homeland of their people.

8

In the Second World War the Jewish community in the Land of Israel played its full part in the struggle of the nations championing freedom and peace against the Nazi forces of evil. Its war effort and the lives of its soldiers won it the right to be numbered among the founding peoples of the United Nations.

On November 29, 1947, the General Assembly of the United Nations adopted a Resolution calling for the establishment of a Jewish State in the Land of Israel, and required the inhabitants themselves to take all measures necessary on their part to carry out the Resolution. The recognition by the United Nations of the right of the Jewish people to establish their own State is irrevocable.

It is the natural right of the Jewish people, like any other people, to control their own destiny in their sovereign State. Accordingly, we, the members of the National Council representing the Jewish people in the Land of Israel and the Zionist movement, have assembled on this day of the termination of the British Mandate for Palestine, and by virtue of our natural and historic right and the Resolution of the General Assembly of the United Nations, to hereby proclaim the establishment of a Jewish State in the Land of Israel -- the State of Israel.

WE RESOLVE that, from the moment the Mandate ends at midnight on the Sabbath the sixth of Iyar 5708 [the fifteenth day of May 1948] until the establishment of the duly elected authorities of the State in accordance with a Constitution to be adopted by the Elected Constituent Assembly not later than October 1, 1948, the National Council shall act as the provincial Council of the State, and its executive arm, the National Administration, shall constitute the Provisional Government of the Jewish Statem, and the name of that State shall be Israel.

The State of Israel will be open to Jewish immigrants and the ingathering of exiles. It will devote itself to developing the Land for the good of all its inhabitants. It will rest upon the foundations of liberty, justice and peace as envisioned by the Prophets of Israel. It will maintain complete equality of social and political rights for all its citizens without distinction of creed, race or sex. It will guarantee freedom of religion and conscience, of language, education and culture. It will safeguard the Holy Places of all religions. It will be loyal to the principles of the United Nations Charter.

The State of Israel will be prepared to cooperate with the organs and representatives of the United Nations in carrying out the General Assembly Resolution of November 29, 1947, and will work for the establishment of the economic union of the whole Land of Israel.

We appeal to the United Nations to assist the Jewish people in the building of their State, and to admit the State of Israel into the family of nations.

Even amidst the violent attacks launched against us for months past, we call upon the sons of the Arab people dwelling in Israel to keep the peace and to play their part in building the State on the basis of full and equal citizenship and due representation in all institutions, provisional and permanent.

We extend the hand of peace and good-neighborliness to all the states around us and to their peoples, and we call upon them to cooperate in mutual helpfulness with the independent Jewish nation in its Land. The State of Israel is prepared to make its contribution in a concerted effort for the advancement of the entire Middle East.

We call upon the Jewish people throughout the Diaspora to join forces with us in immigration and construction, and to be at our right hand in the great endeavor to fulfill the age-old longing for the redemption of Israel.

We trust in the Rock of Israel, we set our hands in witness to this Declaration at this session of the Provisional Council of State, on the soil of the Homeland, in the City of Tel Aviv, this Sabbath eve, the fifth day of Iyar, 5708, the fourteenth day of May, 1948."

This was not, however, where it all began.

We cannot isolate the creation of the State of Israel from the rest of the world during a time when many countries around the world also gained their independence, and when formerly great empires were crumbling. However, the form of the establishment of the State of Israel was entirely unique, and different from that of so many other countries that jumped on the wagon of independence during the course of the twentieth century.

None of the other people then clamoring for their independence had been forcibly exiled from their homeland, dispersed by their conquerors to face an indeterminate Diaspora, as the Jewish people had been forced out of the Land of Israel to wander homeless for more than 2000 years. No other people had faced and lived with baseless and senseless discrimination, hatred, intolerance, persecution, restrictions, or expulsion and total massacre at the whim of despotic or maniacal rulers, as had the Jewish people.

For countless years the Jewish peoples' revolution was a mental one, for it was just not possible for them to mount revolutions in the cause of independence when the countries in which they lived were not their own. Despite their constant longing to return to their lost Homeland, no matter what country they lived in during their enforced Diaspora, it was not the longing alone that engendered the Jewish peoples' revolution. The longing was only the key factor motivating the vision of certain enlightened men.

Theoretically, the American Revolution in the 1770's and the French Revolution in the 1780's inspired numerous cultural and political changes, especially in Europe. Revolutions, however, do not spontaneously erupt. They require due cause and strong-minded men and women with devoted beliefs, dreams, and ideals, coupled with purpose, vision and an unswerving willingness to sacrifice life and limb to the cause.

Moreover, some causes or revolutions are neither equal nor sensible. Witness the depraved insanity of Hitler's violently extreme German Aryan nationalism, without even the minimum degree of true idealism on any level, and the end to which it ultimately led him and his Aryan nation.

Theodore Herzl was a Hungarian Jew who enjoyed some renown as a playwright and journalist. He had formerly paid scant attention to the plight of Europe's Jews until the infamous Dreyfus affair shook him into rethinking the so-called "Jewish problem." In the course of his deliberations, he concluded the best possible solution would be the establishment of a Jewish State. With this objective in mind, he immediately began calling upon Jewish artists, scholars, writers and the leaders in Jewish communities in Europe and the rest of the world, which ultimately resulted in the First Zionist Congress convening in Basle, Switzerland in 1897.

During the period from 1880 to 1890, which became known as the First Aliya [first period of Jewish immigration to Palestine], many controversial issues faced the Zionist Organization. The worst of these involved the settlement of Palestine, which was under the rule of the Ottoman [Turkish] Empire and continued to be so until after World War I, at which time Palestine and the rest of the Holy Land came under the rule of Great Britain.

Thus, a priority Agenda item of that First Zionist Congress was a discussion of the problems imposed by the fact that Turkish law prohibited immigration to Palestine by the simple expedients of refusing to issue visas for more than 90 days, and also by prohibiting the sale of land there. The combined prohibitions made immigration to Palestine illegal. Russian delegates to the Congress vociferously demanded urgent action be undertaken to establish a permanent Jewish Homeland because of the continuing pogroms against Russian Jews. In consequence, the Zionist Congress was forced to consider the necessity for an alternative site for the proposed Jewish Homeland.

A notable delegate to the Congress was Dr. Chaim Weitzman, an ardent Zionist who lived and worked in England where many of his friends were influential British politicians whose major focus was on colonization in British Uganda in Africa. At their instigation, very likely in the course of his correspondence with Theodore Herzl, Dr. Weitzman might have suggested British Uganda as a temporary site for the proposed Jewish Homeland to house the suffering East European Jewish refugees. Herzl, who opposed illegal Jewish immigration to Palestine, then proposed British Uganda to the Congress as a temporary alternative site for the projected Jewish Homeland, and the resulting violent debate split the Congress.

The dissident faction in the debate, led by Herzl, argued unsuccessfully in favor of British Uganda becoming the temporary site of a Jewish Homeland so as to bypass the Ottoman Empire's prohibitions against Jewish immigration to Palestine, thereby avoiding 'illegal' immigration. The winning faction successfully argued in favor of Palestine in the Land of Israel as being the only acceptable site for the projected permanent Jewish Homeland. They vehemently stated Jews had a right to return to their Homeland, whether legally or illegally, and the Turks could jolly well lump it! Thereafter, Jewish immigration became the major objective, despite the inevitability that it would be illegal.

Although the Ottoman Empire ruled Palestine through the end of World War I, the Empire was seen to be suffering a continuing decline. By contrast, the British Empire, which had the greatest number of world territories, appeared much stronger. It was, therefore, widely believed the British Empire would sooner or later become the new ruler of Palestine. In the continuing belief this would ultimately take place, Dr. Weitzman diligently worked with his friends in the British Government, hoping their cooperation would aid his efforts to successfully smooth the way for Jewish immigration.

The decision taken at the First Zionist Congress proved costly, in terms of lives lost during those stubborn early pioneer years. Nevertheless, by the end of the nineteenth century, numerous Jewish farm settlements -- Petah Tikva, Hedera, Rosh Pina, Rehovot, Zichron Ya'akov, Mikve Israel and Yesod Hamaale, to only name a few -- were successfully established, and stand to this day.

But even before that momentous First Zionist Congress, records in Israel disclose the return of Jews to the Land of Israel had begun nearly five centuries earlier. Their return, in groups as small as a few hundred at a time, fired the continuing development of revolutionary thought. Nor should it be overlooked that small Jewish communities stubbornly existed in the Land of Israel throughout more than 2000 years of the Diaspora.

A century and a half ago, most people lived and worked in agrarian environments, and agriculture was the leading industry the world over. For countless centuries, however, Jews were deprived of the right to own and farm their own land in most countries they lived in. Consequently, they devoted their talents and skills to art, commerce, industry, sciences, and trade. But they yearned to return to agriculture.

Not surprisingly, therefore, the focus of early Jewish revolutionary thought was the yearning for agriculture. This hunger for healthy physical labor on their own farms was the catalyst for the incipient revolution.

In his autobiography, David Ben Gurion translated from German Dr. Leo Pinsker's speech at the First Zionist Congress. This landmark speech expressed Jewish feelings and views in 1897. Taking into account differences in translation, the speech stated:

"On the occasion of the one hundredth birthday of Sir Moses Montefiore, a man of outstanding achievement, we have assembled from various countries in order to perpetuate his name by establishing an institution that will be appropriate to our times, benefit the Jewish people, and be worthy of Montefiore.

Please permit me to present my views in a few words.

The situation of the Jews in countries where they are concentrated, and their severe suffering as a result, have led me to conclude it can be improved only by charting an entirely new course for our people.

It cannot be denied that during their two thousand years of exile, the Jews have been alienated from agriculture, often through no fault of their own. We should also pay heed to another fact, which explains perhaps more than any other the stilted development of their spiritual and material life, and caused them to lose prestige in the eyes of others.

The Jews have long since become the prototype of a merchant people. But what is considered quite acceptable in the case of other people is not so considered when it comes to Jews. Other people live in their own countries and must work their own lands. They are productive in the most direct sense of that term, and also indirectly through trade, the professions, science, and art. These other activities are certainly worthy, even if not essential or highly visible. The development of the spiritual and material resources of other peoples is, therefore, in balance: trade and the professions are legitimate vocations within the overall framework of society. The same thing, unfortunately, cannot be said of the Jews. They were removed, against their own will, from agriculture, and over the years have lost their feeling for it. The activities of the Jews have thus appeared to be unduly one-sided, and sometimes even harmful to their physical development.

In the past, when communications were poorly developed and most people lived in villages, the Jews served as a connecting link in the same way as the railway and the telegraph do today. They lived mainly in the cities and devoted themselves chiefly to commerce. Now the situation is different. As the urban population has grown denser and modern trade has developed, the Jews have become even more concentrated in the cities, and, as a result, have come into greater conflict with others, causing dangerous disturbances and anti-Semitism.

The commercial activities of the Jews have been considered unjustified in the eyes of the unfriendly nations, and frequently used against them. This indicates that we should take the masses of our people, rotting away in small-scale trade and crafts, and return them to their ancient, honorable, and natural calling of our forefathers, namely agriculture. The land loves to be exploited, and is more grateful for it than human beings, who exploit each other, but don't wish to be exploited in return, particularly if the exploiter is a Jew. We have already reached the point where our very existence is considered an act of exploitation.

We must, therefore, carefully analyze contemporary developments, however hard they are to comprehend, learning to adjust ourselves to prevailing economic conditions. This task becomes clearly imperative if we consider the social and economic revolution of recent years. It is still to be seen whether, justifiably or otherwise, war will be declared on capitalism, with an ensuing life-and-death struggle. But one thing is certain: the Jews are bound to be the victims, perhaps the only ones, of struggle, as they have been in its earlier stages.

As we find ourselves in danger of strangulation, we must seek air to breathe and an opportunity to exist. Until now, we have served as a link between men. Now, we must return to the soil, which blesses the hands that work it and judges people not according to their background, but their diligence. Just as we were once able to transform ourselves from farmers to merchants, so we should now go back to the plow.

We can depend more on the energy and adaptability of our people than the negative force of anti-Semitism; the Jews will understand the importance of the transformation and have the strength to undertake the difficult and unusual task of bringing it about. Jews, known for their ability to think, will quickly realize the goal cannot be achieved by hasty and unplanned action. A people cannot be transformed just by declaring a change is necessary. Moreover, we will be deceiving ourselves if we expect to see the fruits of our labor in our own generation. But what are a few generations to an eternal people? We will soon enough develop sufficient energy and wisdom to make the change. Fortunately, our task is made easier by the fact that Jews have already begun to sense the need for a transformation.

Henceforth, our slogan will be 'settlement.' Work has already begun.

With the aid of Russian Jews, who have an undeservedly bad reputation, settlements have been established, within the short space of two years, that demonstrate what our people can do, and justify our most fervent hopes. It is regrettable that our longings for the Holy Land have been greeted so antagonistically in various quarters. Montefiore himself has always shown great love and devotion to the Land.

> *Those assembled here have the great privilege of placing the holy task under the banner of a man who, during the hundred years of his life, has earned the gratitude of his people for his constant efforts on their behalf. By establishing an organization in Montefiore's name, to aid tillers of the soil, particularly in the Land of Israel, we will be paying him tribute in an appropriate and permanent manner, as well as blazing a new path that will lead our people to happiness and honorable labor."*

It should be noted that Dr. Leo Pinsker began to promote his ideas about a Jewish State as far back as 1884, thirteen years before the first meeting of the First Zionist Congress sponsored by Theodore Herzl.

The credit given Sir Moses Montefiore in Dr.Pinsker's speech was deserved, for he was the leading Jewish personality in the eighteenth century. He dared approach rulers such as Mohammed Ali, Viceroy of Egypt, Abed al Aziz, the Sultan of Turkey, and Nicholas I, the Emperor of Russia, to protest against anti-Semitism, and to rescind discriminatory rules against the Jews. He traveled extensively in behalf of his fellow Jews, and visited the Holy Land many times.

During Montefiore's first visit to the Old City of Jerusalem, so the story goes, he noticed garbage had been dumped in the vicinity of the Western Wall, and the garbage actually hid the Wall. He returned that night and dropped some gold coins. The next day someone found the coins and began digging through the garbage for more. To clear his way, the digger had to move the garbage elsewhere. Inevitably, the digger's activity drew attention. Soon hundreds of people were busily digging for gold coins, and also moving the garbage to the location designated by the original digger. Each night, Montefiore returned to drop more coins. Soon the plaza in front of the Western Wall was cleaned up, and the Wall was exposed in all its glory.

Dr. Pinsker's speech exhibited remarkable foresight, especially in his statement, "It is still to be seen whether, justifiably or otherwise, war will be declared on capitalism, with ensuing life-and-death struggle." He foresaw the growth of the socialist and communist doctrines, as well as the extreme left socialism in Europe. Similarly, his prediction that "... the Jews are bound to be the victims, perhaps the only ones..." regrettably also came true, not only with the horror of the Nazi Holocaust; but as recently as 1998 the Russians have blamed the Jews for the collapse of their newly established free market and economic reform system.

As these revolutionary thoughts developed, and persecution increased, so, too, did the desire for a Jewish Homeland. But what is a Homeland without agriculture and healthy physical labor? It was towards this vision -- Dr. Leo Pinsker, Theodore Herzl, Moses Hess and Dr. Chaim Weitzman, among many others -- directed revolutionary thought. Their carefully developed concept of agriculture, coupled with hard Jewish labor, would become the foundation of the future Jewish Homeland. The early Jewish pioneers who came to Palestine were physically responsible for putting the concept to work. Not surprisingly, those early Jewish pioneers came from East European countries like Poland and especially Russia, where "Jew-baiting" and other forms of Jewish persecution, was an ongoing sport for civilians and the military.

Those men of vision who convened at the First Zionist Congress fully understood it would take organized effort to make the dream of a Jewish Homeland a reality. Thus, in record time a foundation was in place, to administer, finance, and ensure continued solicitation, promoting Jewish immigration to Palestine from all over the world.

It is important to note here that most of those early pioneers arrived in Palestine with only the clothing on their backs. However, they more than compensated for their lack of money or material possessions by their willingness to work long hours to finally realize the dream they had all brought with them. They wished to live peacefully and with dignity in a Jewish Homeland, free from the senseless discrimination and persecution they and their forebears had been forced to endure for centuries. In pursuit of their dream, these early pioneers worked tirelessly from dawn to dusk, and often far into the night, so that they and their descendants could finally enjoy life in their own Jewish Homeland.

Only a few of the new arrivals came with funds they'd somehow managed to spirit out of their former homes before fleeing, which they gratefully spent to acquire their own land. The rest were fortunate in that Baron Edmond de Rothschild, of the French banking and wine dynasty, was a staunch Zionist and philanthropist. Not only was he the major financier for wine-making and other new industries, but also subsidized the new settlers' purchase of land and helped them build homes and settlements.

Those early pioneers led the growth of the labor movement in Palestine that ultimately led to the real revolution. Their sense of growing success, evidenced by continuous backbreaking labor in the desert and other areas as well as their word-of-mouth encouragement to potential new settlers, successfully brought many more Jewish men and women to settle and build their lives in Palestine.

This success, however, carried a high price tag.

Most of the land the pioneers were able to buy from local Arabs was marsh and swampland infested with malaria-carrying mosquitoes. Back in those days, before effective medicine to combat the resulting fever was available, many of those stoic pioneers suffered horribly before they died. Their survivors stubbornly persevered. Somehow, they not only managed to dry the marshes and swamps, they also built modest clay houses, plowed their fields with the help of oxen, and also grew vegetables and fruit. In time, more new pioneers arrived from Europe. These new settlers built villages and towns as well as farming communities and light industry.

The second wave of immigrants to Palestine is believed to have begun in 1903, when hundreds of young men arrived from Russia. However, the period from 1905 through 1914 is known as the Second Aliya, for it was during this period that whole families began arriving in Palestine on the heels of their adventurous younger members. Moreover, in this period, while an estimated half million Jewish refugees who had escaped the pogroms [deliberate massacre of Jews in Poland and Russia] emigrated to the United States, only a small percentage made their way to Palestine.

During the early twentieth century, the first political parties emerged in the Yishuv [general Jewish populace of Palestine] accompanied by their related institutions. Hashomer Association [The Watchman, which later became the basis of the Haganah] was founded to guard Jewish settlements against attack.

In 1908, the Zionist Congress opened its first office in Jaffa, headed by Dr. Arthur Ruppin who formed the Palestine Land Development Company, responsible for land acquisition. The Anglo-Palestine Bank, established by the Zionist Congress in London in 1902, began operating in Palestine. This bank, helped finance many new ventures in the Yishuv, and acted as the banker for Jewish settlers. [After the creation of the State of Israel, the Anglo-Palestine Bank's name was changed to Bank Leumi Le Israel.]

The first decade of the twentieth century saw the foundation of the Jewish Homeland laid with great growth and sustained immigration to Palestine. New social and political institutions, schools, and newspapers were established. The revival of the Hebrew language began to take place. In this same decade a major revolution erupted in the Ottoman Empire. The "Young Turks," as they were known, defeated the Sultan's forces, and established a parliamentary government which reinstituted the old Turkish Constitution and deposed the Sultan.

In 1903, the infamous Kishinev pogrom in Russia, during which more than a thousand Jews were murdered, along with political activity in Europe, motivated the Zionist Congress to take decisive action on the issue of immigration to Palestine. It began to forcefully lobby for the establishment of a permanent Jewish Homeland in Palestine. With some historic validity, it is believed the Kishinev pogrom also motivated the Second Aliya.

Educational institutions were developed with the establishment of Hebrew high schools, and the famous Bezalel Art School was founded in Jerusalem. New Hebrew newspapers, most affiliated with political parties, began publication. The foundation was laid for Ahuzat Bayit, which later became known as the City of Tel Aviv. The key to the ongoing defense of the Yishuv was the creation of Hashomer Association, which was the root of the Haganah.

The growth of Jewish settlements in Palestine triggered early Arab nationalism in the country. The Arab community in Palestine, mostly Muslim, lived in many small villages. There were few Arab cities. The most noted were Jaffa, Gaza, and Akko. The Old City of Jerusalem housed mostly Jewish residents.

The Jewish National Fund was established, its major focus collecting money for the acquisition of land in Palestine. The Fund's administrating officers helped the continuing settlement of Jewish immigrants in Palestine by providing newly arrived and impoverished immigrants with money to buy or lease their land and build their homes. The Fund also provided subsidies for farming and forestry equipment as well as labor.

Top priority, however, was the revival of the Hebrew language. After all, what is a Homeland without a national language? Hebrew, which had formerly been used only in prayer and the study of the Torah or the Talmud, increasingly became the country's major language. Scores of books written in Hebrew were published, causing the country's schools to include teaching Hebrew in their ongoing curricula. With the building of more institutions and schools, the Yishuv became increasingly acclimated and educated, and a clearer picture emerged.

In the Second Decade, World War I interrupted the development of the country and its institutions; the disastrous affects of the war were numerous and far-reaching, not only for the Land of Israel but the rest of the world as well. Initially, the Turks did not align themselves with either the Allies -- Great Britain, France and Russia -- or the Axis, Germany and Italy. Ultimately, however, Turkey aligned with the Germans.

Palestine was then under Turkish rule. Thus when Turkey declared war, they adopted a hard line regarding the multi-national Jewish immigrants to Palestine. Without regard to national origins, all new Jewish immigrants and settlers were targeted by the Turks for either deportation back to the European nations they'd emigrated from, or what was then known as "Ottomanization", a Turkish law requiring Arab and Jewish citizens of Palestine to become Turkish nationals and thereby aligned with Turkey against the Allies who had automatically become the enemies of Turkey and all its territories. This new Turkish edict did not sit well with the populace because it was too early in the war for anyone to predict when it would end. Moreover, most Palestinian Jews believed that British rule would prove more beneficial because it would assure the creation of a Jewish Homeland in Palestine. This belief was first fostered by Turkish rejection of all proposals for a Jewish Homeland in Palestine, and later strengthened by the devastating affects of the seemingly never-ending war. In order to provision the Turkish armies, and with no consideration for the inhabitants of Palestine, the Turkish government confiscated all farm equipment and farm animals as well as all available foodstuffs. Combined with the ravages of swarms of locusts that devoured crops down to the last visible green leaf, this left the Palestinians virtually starving.

Additionally, the Turks summarily deported everyone who refused to align themselves with Turkey. This caused families to be torn apart, and motivated the establishment of the first Jewish Underground. Known as Nili, the group, which also spied for the British, was ultimately exposed and its leaders hanged.

Another disastrous result of World War I for the people of Palestine was that all help from Europe came to a complete halt. However, Henry Morgenthau, the American Ambassador to Turkey before the United States joined the Allies against Germany and Turkey, was instrumental in the shipment of food and other supplies to the Yishuv, transported by American warships.

A significant event that took place during World War I was: the signing of the Sykes-Picot Treaty in 1916, by Great Britain, France and Russia, (though Russia held only a minor role). The treaty, which was actually an Agreement between the interested parties, effectively split "the booty" [lands parceled out as prizes to the victors at war's end], and clearly shows that Great Britain's master plan for the colonization of Palestine by the Jews after the war was the catalyst for the Balfour Declaration on November 2, 1917.

The facts are clear: Britain needed an ally because the Arabs were divided, with no specific aims. Britain's fear of Russian expansionism and the land route to India were strategic matters that weighed heavily on Britain's decision makers. Thus, despite the British army's initial refusal to accept Palestinian-Jewish volunteers, ultimately the British accepted the Jewish volunteers, who formed numerous brigades and fought shoulder-to-shoulder with the British against their common enemy. And, lastly, the Jews were willing to create their Homeland under British rule.

Through the ongoing efforts of Dr. Chaim Weitzman, the British issued the Balfour Declaration, which took the form of a letter and read as follows:

"Dear Lord Rothschild:

"I have much pleasure in conveying to you, on behalf of His Majesty's Government, the following declaration of sympathy with Jewish Zionist aspirations which has been submitted to and approved by the Cabinet.

"His Majesty's Government view with favor the establishment in Palestine a national home for the Jewish people, and will use its best endeavors to facilitate the achievement of this object, it being clearly understood that nothing shall be done which may prejudice the civil and religious rights of existing non-Jewish communities in Palestine, or the rights and political status enjoyed by Jews in any other country.

"I should be grateful if you would bring this declaration to the knowledge of the Zionist Federation.

Yours,
[Signed] Lord Arthur Balfour"

There was much jubilation in the Yishuv and Jewish communities world over. It was believed that at last the dream was nearing reality, and it was universally accepted that the future Jewish Homeland would be established under the auspices of British rule. In my own review of the Balfour Declaration, however, I find scant evidence of either genuine compassion or truthful resolve on the part of the British Government.

The statement "Nothing shall be done which may prejudice the civil and religious rights of existing non-Jewish communities ..." opens doors to potentially controversial issues, notably that of the civil rights of the Arab population. One must also question the date of the Declaration -- i.e. a full year prior to the end of World War I -- which leads to further questions as to precisely when this Declaration was actually conceived, and when it was actually planned to go into effect.

Despite French opposition, Great Britain managed to manipulate the ultimate outcome of the Sykes-Picot Treaty, which had been signed in 1916 and clearly indicates the British anticipated their involvement in the establishment of numerous Arab States. Thus, it appears Great Britain planned to simultaneously take over oil-producing countries while guarding territorial routes of commerce and communication.

In December of 1917, the British army captured Jerusalem, which was abandoned by the Turks. Nine months later, a few months short of the end of World War I in November, 1918, the rest of Palestine and Trans-Jordan were also conquered.

With the end of the war, immigration resumed, but in much smaller numbers, and most of the deportees returned. The Yishuv had to repair the ravages of war as well as the devastation caused by the Turkish confiscation of farm equipment and animals and rape of the Land's agricultural bounty. Farms and settlements had to be rebuilt, and the 5,000 men of Jewish battalions that fought with the British to wrest Palestine from the Turks were discharged, despite their expressed wishes to continue serving with the British army in Palestine.

The year 1919 was distinguished by the signing of an Agreement by Dr. Chaim Weitzman and Emir Faisal. This Agreement witnessed that the Arab movement recognized the Balfour Declaration, and indicated the Jewish entity would aid in the development of the Arab State. Predictably, nothing came of this Agreement.

Also in 1919, pressure was brought to bear on British authorities in Palestine, mainly military personnel, to permit people who had been exiled by the Turks to return home to Palestine. Thus, the first ship from Odessa [in the Russian Ukraine], which held hundreds of such exiles as well as numerous refugees claiming to be exiles, was allowed to land, and its human cargo permitted to disembark. This momentous event marked the beginning of the Third Aliya.

However, the Yishuv and leaders of the Zionist Organization learned that in an effort to maintain the demographic status quo, the British military authorities had banned immigration. Since the military were representatives of the British Government, who presumably controlled their actions, meaning the military were not a separate and autonomous entity, but were supposed to abide by the Balfour Declaration, it seemed natural to assume that the key statement in that Declaration: "His Majesty's Government view with favor the establishment of a national home for the Jewish people, and will use their best endeavors to facilitate the achievement of this object..." had been deliberately violated.

In point of fact, the British Government had set forth a Declaration which they failed to honor from Day One. As far back as 1916, the year of the Sykes-Picot Treaty, when they manipulated the terms of that Treaty to ensure their ultimate rule of Palestine and Trans-Jordan despite not knowing when the war would end or which lands would go to which Treaty participant, the British Government clearly intended that both Palestine and Trans-Jordan would be under British rule.

Nevertheless, despite British restrictions on Jewish immigration, thousands arrived. The Zionist Organization's continued lobbying of the British

Government met with no success, and the ongoing public debate in Palestine focused on whether or not future Jewish immigrants should immigrate to Palestine legally or illegally. Historically, the latter position won the debate, hands down.

The Second Decade of the twentieth century saw the changes wrought by the changeover in rule from the Ottoman Empire to the British Empire. The Italian-Turkish war in Libya had a distinctly negative affect upon Palestine's economy because the flow of funds from Europe came to a halt. The newly established Turkish Parliament debated the subject of Jewish immigration and settlement in Palestine for the first time. While Muslims in the Parliament opposed the Jewish influx, many delegates voted in favor of it. The obvious decline of the Turkish Empire strengthened local nationalism throughout the Empire.

Benefits to either side resulting from the debates in the Turkish Parliament were not immediately known. The Yishuv moved strongly ahead with the formation of various committees whose numerous conferences forcefully dealt with the issues of continuing Jewish immigration and settlement.

The decade following the disastrous wake of World War I was one of the most difficult periods in the tumultuous return to the Land of Israel. Despite the number of positive developments, the burdensome results of World War I were devastating to the country, for immigration to Palestine was only a trickle compared to that during the pre-war period of 1901 through 1914; the largest group of new arrivals were only a few thousand Yemenite Jews. Fortunately, however, this decade saw the birth of the Technion [which to date continues to be the leading technical university in Israel, equivalent to the Massachusetts Institute of Technology in the USA] and solid preparations for the establishment of the Hebrew University in Jerusalem.

In the third decade of the twentieth century, after Great Britain had been granted the mandate by the League of Nations, the first British High Commissioner for Palestine appointed Haj Amin el Husseini, the radical Muslim leader of the Arab body, known as the Mufti of Jerusalem. This venomous individual spread his poisonous anti-Jewish propaganda, and planted the seeds of hatred among the Arab community. The British did nothing to remove him until the beginning of World War II, when he was indisputably proven to be a Nazi collaborator, and then he was merely exiled from Palestine.

Not too surprisingly, Arab violence against the Jewish populace began with attacks against Jewish farm settlements, and later focused upon Jewish communities in the cities of Jaffa, Haifa and Jerusalem. British military simply watched the violence without taking any action against the Arab perpetrators. In fact, Ze'ev Jabotinsky, the Jewish commander of the defending forces together with many of his men, were all arrested by the British. Charged with what was termed "illegal" defense, Ze'ev Jabotinsky was summarily adjudged guilty of this non-crime and sentenced to fifteen years at hard labor in prison.

It became increasingly clear that the British Government had absolutely no intention of honoring the Balfour Declaration, and that the British were responsible for the developing chaos in Palestine. The powerful British army, which could easily have quelled any Arab attack or violence, did nothing. The poisonous Mufti should have been dismissed or exiled the moment he mouthed his villainous blasphemy against the Jews, but he was not. And the British military should have arrested the attacking Arabs instead of the defending Jews. The resulting Yishuv strike and numerous demonstrations against the British met with no appreciable success, and only the installation of the new High Commissioner for Palestine resulted in Jabotinsky being pardoned for his non-crime

The year 1920 saw decisive action taken by the National Council, the executive body for Jewish affairs in Palestine. In short order, the Council established the Histadrut, which was the Federation of Labor, and Keren Hayesod the financial organization charged with implementing Jewish aspirations in Palestine. The Jewish populace was becoming politically organized.

Haj Amin el Husseini's anti-Jewish propaganda, along with similar other manifestations of Arab hatred, motivated the Yishuv's decision that a strong defense was needed in event of Arab attack, and that such defense must be organized and managed. To this end, the strongest Jewish army in Palestine's history to date was created. Its name was Haganah.

The new army's seasoned veterans had firm roots in the earlier Hashomer [The Watchman] and all of its members, whether seasoned or new recruits, were devoted to the establishment of a Jewish Homeland in the Land of Israel. Haganah's sworn purpose was to immediately and effectively squash without compunction any Arab attack wherever it occurred, whether in the outlying farm settlements or in the cities, and to engage in whatever action necessary to ensure ongoing Jewish immigration to Palestine.

Thankfully, the period between 1922 through early August 1929 was peaceful. Despite numerous political events on both sides of the invisible line between Arabs and Jews in Palestine, there was no violence. The Arabs formed their own congress whose leaders demanded immediate curtailment of Jewish immigration coupled with the demand to stop the sale of land to Jews. Unfortunately, however, late August of 1929 saw the violent eruption of Arab attacks on Jewish settlements and towns throughout the country. Sixty Jews were massacred in Hebron, more than 130 Jews were killed or wounded in other cities, and the British military did little or nothing to stop the violence.

A surfeit of evidence indicated that the British military was at odds with British colonial policies. Superficially, British civil rule in Palestine indicated the authorities were trying to balance colonial policies between Arabs and Jews. But the British permitted the growth of military Arab organization, and secretly armed the Arabs. Haj Amin el Husseini, the violently radical Mufti, continually spewed his venomous anti-Jewish propaganda that incited the Arabs to attack the Jews while the increasing growth of the Jewish community and economy triggered ever more violent blasphemy against the Jews.

Despite all obstacles, and against all odds, however, Jewish immigration continued apace. No matter what legal immigration quotas were set by the British Government [the numbers changed yearly] they were met in full, while other immigrants made their way into Palestine by illegal routes mapped by the

Haganah.

If there was one-year that fully revealed the blatant confusion in British Government policies it had to be 1930. This was the year numerous Arab rioters and murderers were arrested by the British military and then, by virtue of some strange alchemy, these same lawbreakers were freed an equal number of times. An Arab mission to London pressed the British Government to halt Jewish immigration and acquisition of land in Palestine. This resulted in British officials and commissions appearing in Palestine to investigate the problems there, leading to the Government's official ban on immigration for six months. The resultant Jewish protests throughout the country focused upon the ban on immigration as well as growing Jewish unemployment in Palestine because Arabs, instead of Jews, were hired to fill jobs in the citrus industry.

Numerous protesters were arrested by the police, and the year ended with the British Government issuing their infamous White Paper, which made no mention whatsoever of the Balfour Declaration. The White Paper clearly stated that there was insufficient land in Palestine to accommodate additional Jewish settlement; that immigration must be restricted, and that a legislative council must be established to represent all inhabitants of Palestine. The White Paper infuriated Jewish leadership, and Dr. Chaim Weitzman, then President of the Zionist Organization, resigned in protest. Once again, strikes and demonstrations erupted throughout the country.

The stormiest session of the Zionist Congress was held in 1931, and the Revisionist party, led by Ze'ev Jabotinsky, submitted its proposal couched in the form of a demand that the Congress clearly define the final objective of the Jewish people with regard to the ultimate establishment of a Jewish State in Palestine. That proposal was defeated, but the scars of the violent debate remained, and the Revisionists, together with their supporters, continuously clashed with the Labor party. The clashes intensified to the point where the Yishuv feared the eruption of violent civil war.

The 1930's saw the rise of Nazi power in Germany and the resultant discrimination and restrictions against the Jews in that country. The rise of blatant persecution of German Jews led to increased illegal immigration by German as well as other European Jews; the Haganah planned, organized, and accomplished their successful exodus to Palestine. The early transfer of European Jewish assets into Palestinian banks resulted in a welcome economic upsurge benefiting both Arabs and Jews.

In this same decade, Europe, the United States, and virtually the entire world suffered the disastrous affects of the Great Depression, which resulted from the unexpected decline in the stock market. Despite the demoralizing affects of this far-reaching financial disaster, afterwards known as "the Crash of 1929," more than 45,000 Jews, with the help of the Haganah, made their way to Palestine in 1934, and an additional 65,000 arrived in 1935.

Vicious anti-Jewish propaganda spread by Haj Amin el Husseini in 1936 triggered major Arab attacks on Jews throughout Palestine. Daily attacks targeted Jewish public transport vehicles, farming settlements, and mixed neighborhoods in the cities. There were many deaths and grievous injuries.

Arson fires throughout the country resulted in costly damages.

Surprisingly enough, even British Government personnel suffered violent attacks, which stymied British authorities, unable to handle this unprecedented situation. British army field units from Egypt and as far away as Malta were called in to quell the Arab attacks. In retaliation, the Arabs mounted general strikes and work stoppages lasting several months.

These obviously premeditated anti-Jewish attacks by the Arabs activated the full strength of the Haganah. Along with defending outlying farm settlements as well as predominantly Jewish cities in Palestine, the Haganah mounted an offensive against a major Arab encampment in Samaria. Another result of the attacks against British Government personnel was the arrival of the Peel Commission, as it became known in Palestine, to study the cause and affects of "the Palestine problem" and report its findings back to the Government. The Arabs rejected the Commission out of hand, refused to participate in the Commission's study, and the British military did nothing to stop continuing daily Arab violence.

General strikes, plus the fact that the major seaport of Jaffa was no longer available to the Jewish community, motivated the British to permit the establishment of an alternative seaport in Tel Aviv. But despite Arab riots and other chaos throughout the country, more than 30,000 new Jewish immigrants arrived in Palestine. The combined affect of the riots and chaos in mixed Palestinian neighborhoods caused a tremendous Jewish refugee problem when about 10,000 local Jews fled their homes to remove themselves and their families from the path of the violence.

Heavy rioting against the French authorities erupted in Syria, and it was believed Arab leaders in Palestine and Syria were incited to riot by Nazi Germany, which supported the Arabs against British and French authorities. News reports of Nazi aggression in Europe further encouraged many of the Arabs.

Despite the bloodshed and chaos in Palestine, new Jewish settlements were established in various parts of the country. The national military organization, which was an arm of the Revisionist party, went into action independent of the Haganah and began offensive operations with a vengeance against the Arabs. This organization became known as the Etzel [short for Irgun Z'vai Leumi.]

Arab riots continued well into 1937, though they lessened during the six months of the Peel Commission's investigation. And toward the end of that year, the British authorities disbanded the Arab Commission and arrested and sentenced the majority of its leaders, but were unable to foil Haj Amin el Husseini's escape. Arab attacks intensified during the autumn. In retaliation, Etzel units attacked Arabs and demolished specific Arab targets.

The Peel Commission recommended the partition of Palestine, and offered the Jews roughly one quarter of the Land, leaving Jerusalem under British control. The Arabs totally rejected the Commission's recommendations. The Zionist Congress held in 1937 debated the Peel Commission's proposal, then rejected it because the proposed partition would leave only a very small territory, too small for the projected Jewish Homeland.

1938 was the worst year for Jewish casualties. For the first time, British military forces worked together with the Haganah to defend Jews and reduce Arab violence. The British recaptured Arab cities that had been taken by Arab militias. In this same year, numerous illegal ships carried similarly illegal Jewish immigrants, all of whom disembarked in Palestine without incident.

Early in 1939 the British attempted to hold a new conference in London to deal with the Palestine problem. This caused Arab demonstrations throughout the country, and the British authorities adopted a pro-Arab line. In consequence, for the first time, the Yishuv felt the British had turned its back on the Jews in Palestine, and the strengthening of Arab-British relations resulted in the sharp decline of Arab rioting and other violence.

In this year also, despite the continuing escalation of World War II in Europe and Africa, the British Government issued another White Paper, which baldly stated the British had fulfilled their obligations under the Balfour Declaration, that Palestine would not become a Jewish Homeland but should instead become an independent State with Arab-Jewish representation consistent with the size of their respective populations. This new White Paper also set the total number of permissible Jewish immigrants at only 75,000 over the next five years with any additional immigration requiring Arab approval.

With this new White Paper in 1939, the British Government halted the Arab revolt and the riots while at the same time signing its own death warrant insofar as the Jewish Yishuv was concerned. However, the Jewish leadership admirably restrained themselves from any retaliatory action because the British were fighting the Nazis, the acknowledged archenemy of all Jews everywhere, including Jews who lived in Palestine.

Nevertheless, the text of the new White Paper resulted in mass anti-British demonstrations in many cities. This led to the wholesale arrest of Etzel leadership whose members had mounted retaliatory attacks against selected British army installations, plus forty Haganah officers in training. And all of these arrests were made after the outbreak of World War II in Europe.

Meanwhile, curiously enough, the Yishuv was busily mobilizing young men who would help the British fight the Nazis, despite the indisputable fact that British authorities in Palestine were doing their level best to render the Jews in Palestine helpless against their Arab enemies.

The British appeared oblivious to Arab apathy regarding the war, evidenced by the fact that not a single Arab volunteered to help the British fight the Nazis. Doubtless, the British were unaware that many Arabs would have welcomed a Nazi victory. Yet, despite obvious Arab apathy to the British war effort compared to the equally obvious Jewish support of the British evidenced by Jewish volunteers willingly fighting with the British army against the Nazis, the peculiar dichotomy in the British Government's thinking concerning the Arab/Jewish dilemma in Palestine continued well into the 1940's.

As Nazi-instigated persecution and discrimination of German and European Jews intensified, so did the Jewish desire to get out of Europe via the most direct route possible. Regrettably, however, the gates leading to freedom in other countries suddenly closed, which resulted in the necessity for illegal transport to Palestine. This further led to more illegal ships than ever before sailing to Palestine at night and without lights to avoid the vigilant British navy. Those ships that were caught were ordered to return to Europe, without regard to the probable fate not only of the ships' captains, many of whom were Jewish, but of their helpless Jewish refugee passengers.

When news of such ships having been captured and callously ordered to return to Europe inevitably reached the Yishuv, the destructive dragon seeds of anti-British hatred were planted. The additional knowledge that Jewish volunteers were fighting with the British against the Nazi hordes in Africa while innocent Jews in Nazi Germany and elsewhere in Europe were forced to live in fear for their very lives, nurtured the Yishuv's fast-growing hatred of the British presence in Palestine.

The decade of the 1940's began with British troops searching Jewish settlements for weapons, and confiscating them wherever they were found, effectively reducing the settlements' defenses against Arab attack. As the war in Europe escalated, illegal immigration significantly increased, actively aided by the Haganah. British warships intercepted refugee ships, the detained Jewish immigrants were transported to the British island of Mauritius, located near the east coast of Africa. At the same time, the British authorities in Palestine dealt with those land issues described in the 1939 White Paper, resulting in anti-British demonstrations throughout the country.

Unprovoked action by Vichy French forces in Lebanon and Syria prompted a retaliatory invasion by the British army. Despite the Yishuv's hardened attitude to the British, caused by the new White Paper's implicit anti-Jewish directives, especially those that negatively affected Jewish immigration, young Jewish men began to be recruited into the British army because the Yishuv had promised to help the British fight the Nazis. A radical underground organization called Lehi was formed and immediately instituted terror activities against the British authorities in Palestine.

Assault troops, collectively called Palmach, were formed. While this group was separate from the Haganah, a fine line of communication existed between the two underground organizations, although superficially they appeared to be independent of each other.

German tanks invaded North Africa and headed for the Egyptian border. Italian aircraft bombarded Tel Aviv and Haifa, resulting in more than 100 dead and numerous wounded. Life grew extremely difficult in Palestine owing to mounting fear in the Jewish communities that the German armies might succeed in their efforts to capture the country from the British. Thankfully, however, a major counterattack by the British and volunteer Jewish brigades succeeded in pushing the Germans back. The American entry into the war, with the American army landing in North Africa, effectively ensured an Allied victory against all odds.

The three years preceding our hero Amnon's recruitment by the Haganah were chaotic indeed. Nazi underground forces were forced out of Lebanon, Syria and Iraq by the combined military strength of the British Army and its Jewish Volunteers, and, the Allies destroyed the German military machine in North Africa.

Regrettably, however, in the middle of the war, with no sense of when the war might end, the British High Command for Palestine announced the Government's ill-considered and ill-timed "Post-War Economic Plan." The plan, based on the 1939 White Paper and totally ignoring that thousands of Jewish volunteers were fighting with the Allies in North Africa, restricted Jewish immigration, banned the acquisition of land, and restricted Jews to Jewish quarters in Palestine. The Jewish Agency rejected the plan in any form, and the British Government's announcement absolutely infuriated the Jewish Yishuv.

October of 1943 saw two additional anti-Jewish incidents that further stoked the building fire of anti-British feeling. The first was a flag revolt caused when the British brass' arbitrarily rejected a request from one Jewish volunteer brigade fighting with the British army in Libya to show Palestine's blue and white flag alongside the Union Jack. The second was that Dr. Chaim Weitzman's personal bodyguard was sentenced by the British to seven years in jail for the non-crime of possessing a single rifle bullet. The increasingly obvious anti-Haganah and anti-Jewish attitude of the British was the daily focus of articles in all-Hebrew newspapers despite heavy censorship by the authorities.

All these events informed Amnon's decision to join the Haganah.

It was long past time for the agonies, persecutions, and terrors of the Diaspora to end. Amnon would willingly fight and die, if necessary, in the continuing struggle to ensure that all Jews should finally realize the 2000-year-old dream -- the irrevocable establishment of our Jewish Homeland in the Land of Israel.

BOOK TWO

CODE NAME: AMNON

Daniel Rosenfeld

Amnon

Today Amnon celebrated his 14th birthday, together with his acceptance into the Haganah, which alone made this a day to remember. He decided to keep a journal from then on so that someday, his children, were he to survive to have any, would read of their father's participation in the fight for a Jewish Homeland. Hopefully, they would be proud...

Tuesday, October 19, 1943

His code name was Amnon. His real name was ... well, it doesn't really matter. Very few people knew his real name, and most who did are no longer with us. In fact, two thirds of his classmates fell during the War of Independence. Several others were killed during the disturbances before May 15, 1948.

On that day, Amnon became a member of the Haganah. This happened as the result of an unexpected visit from Shmuel, his former Boy Scout master, who had come to his parents' apartment in Jerusalem the previous Wednesday for the express purpose of recruiting him.

It was not quite 4:30 in the afternoon. Amnon's mother was in the kitchen preparing dinner, when the doorbell rang. He hadn't seen Shmuel for quite a while, which he attributed to his Scout Master's activities as a member of the Haganah, a fact of which Shmuel made no secret. So Amnon was considerably surprised when he opened the door to see him standing there, tall and looking very tan and fit. His curly blonde hair, which had never really looked groomed, was short, and also lighter and sun-streaked. Those obvious changes, along with his very dark tan, led Amnon to conclude he must have been spending a lot of time in the sun.

Shmuel had never been aggressive. So, when he stepped inside without waiting for an invitation, Amnon suddenly found himself short of breath, as if in a premonition of the reason for his visit.

They sat at the dining room table, out of his mother's hearing, and in a low voice Shmuel advised him that his time had come to join the Haganah. Though sixteen was the more accepted age for membership, he would need to join on his 14th birthday, the following Tuesday, and he had come to ensure that Amnon did just that.

This came to Amnon as no real surprise, for several of his friends who were his age and a bit older had already been recruited, and he was actually just waiting his own turn. What did surprise him was that Shmuel had been sent to recruit him. Normally, much lower ranked officers in the Haganah were sent to recruit such youngsters as himself. Noting Amnon's surprise, he did not beat around the bush and immediately explained his presence.

"You," he told Amnon, "are very important to us, and that's why I'm here." Ignoring Amnon's surprised queries as to why he should be so important when he'd always considered himself just one of the guys, Shmuel continued, "There are two things that make you very important. One is that although you were born here and you're therefore a Sabra, through your father, you're also a British subject. The second is that though you're only 14 you're fluent in English, French and German compared to most of us Sabras of Russian or Polish heritage. None of us know the languages you do."

He forgot to note that Amnon also spoke Arabic, and, of course, Hebrew. Very likely his former master was unaware of his knowledge of Arabic, for he had begun studying Arabic only after his father had him transferred to St. George's School, the only British school in Jerusalem.

Shmuel was very curious exactly why his father had taken him out of the Hebrew Gymnasium in Jerusalem at the age of 11 and placed him into a British school. Amnon had no answer, for his father never explained his actions. He just gave orders.

He was elated that Shmuel had come to recruit him in person, for Amnon knew he was a big shot in the Haganah. But he was unaware of his rank until much later.

"You will need to continue your schooling during the day," he explained. "And you will also begin your training in the evenings, every evening from 6:00pm until at least 9:00. Do you have any problems with this, or with enlisting? ..."

Amnon didn't let him complete his question.

"Of course I have no problems," he assured Shmuel. "It has been my night-and-day dream to be active in the Haganah, and in the creation of the State of Israel," he declared.

Shmuel gave him an address in the Beit Israel quarter.

"You will report there, without fail, next Tuesday at 4:00pm. By the way, I have some questions regarding your father ..."

Just then Amnon's mother walked into the dining room. Immediately, the question became an abrupt apology for the having to leave for another appointment. He walked Shmuel to the door, who murmured, "I'll be in touch," before leaving.

As it turned out, Amnon's mother and father knew Shmuel's parents, and his mother remembered Shmuel from his Boy Scout days. Amnon's mother, may God rest her soul, was very astute and had the ability to see through people as if they were made of glass. He was nevertheless stunned virtually speechless when, no sooner had Shmuel left than she pounced.

"Ah hah! He came to recruit you into the Underground, didn't he?" Ignoring his startled reaction, she continued. "And I shall be the proudest mother in Palestine knowing my eldest son is fighting for the cause of a Jewish Homeland."

Having recovered his voice, he responded, "There will be danger."

"Naturally, there will be danger," she agreed, surprising him again. "Nothing worthwhile comes easy. And what, I ask you, could be more worthwhile than for you to enlist in the cause and fight for the creation of a Jewish Homeland all Jews may at last return to after the more than 2000 years of the Diaspora? Of course I'm well aware of the possible, if not inevitable, sacrifices. And I wouldn't be a caring mother if I didn't consider those sacrifices. But we're all obligated to participate in this God-sent opportunity. So be assured of my love and know that despite the danger and the possibility of sacrifice, I'll be the proudest mother in all of Palestine, if not the world, knowing my beloved eldest son has done his part."

Overwhelmed by his mother's empathetic understanding of her son's dearest wish, he could only kiss her cheek in appreciation of her unqualified support.

His father, a high-ranking official in the British Government's Ministry of the Interior in Palestine, presented an entirely different problem.

Always very British and proper, his father was extremely proud of his high-ranking government position. He also had a deep respect for British schooling. In the firm belief that nothing but a British education would do for his eldest son, together with the knowledge that his colleagues could not understand why the son of a British official was attending a Hebrew school, his father had him transfer to St. George's School in 1941.

It never occurred to Amnon that his father paid the slightest attention to the activities of the Haganah. Still it seemed prudent to cover his tracks in any event, and he pondered the consequences of his projected enlistment with his mother.

"What about Father? How will I explain having to return home after 10:00pm?" Amnon asked.

"We won't tell him anything," she counseled. "As for getting home after ten o'clock, simply explain you're taking a special course at the YMCA." In a loving reference to his then somewhat chubby appearance, she continued. "This will require you to use the swimming pool and the Health Club facilities to lose some weight. Your father, whom you know admires the 'Y,' will be greatly impressed with your initiative, and won't even raise an eyebrow over the time you come home."

Amnon had been ten years old when his father was transferred from Jaffa to Jerusalem; he hated the move and sorely missed the beaches. So he was both awed by his mother's simple solution to his problem, and delighted with the prospect of joining the YMCA, where, if and when time permitted, he could swim to his heart's content. Contentedly, he retired to his room to wrestle with math and other homework assignments.

The next day, with a 5-pound note from his mother in hand to cover the enrollment fee, Amnon went to the beautiful landmark building that housed the YMCA in Jerusalem. It had the city's only indoor swimming pool as well as a fully equipped Health Club with weights and exercise mats, all actively enjoyed by government personnel as well as British and some other civilians.

With the payment of the enrollment fee, Amnon not only had his membership card to show his father, he also had an indisputable right to return home around 10:00pm. He was so elated he celebrated by swimming laps in the pool until he was out of breath. Before leaving he quickly showered and dressed to walk slowly home.

World War II continued to rage in Europe and the Far East. But Amnon had no time to even think about it, although last month the Allied forces had landed in south Italy after defeating the German and Italian armies in North Africa.

In Palestine, staples like cooking oil, sugar, flour and meats were all rationed, and a cooked chicken was a major event. Fortunately, there was no shortage of vegetables, and many days their three meals consisted of various vegetable salads. Fruit was also available, from Arab peasants who brought their produce to the Mahne Yehuda market in large baskets carried on their heads. Shopping was time-consuming because of the necessity to wait in long lines for any special item that suddenly became available in the market.

Tuesday, the date of his crucial four o'clock appointment, he walked to the address Shmuel had given him. Beit Israel quarter, a small neighborhood of religious people, was situated next to Mea Shearim, a well-known quarter that housed a sect of ultra religious Orthodox Jews. The address Amnon needed was not too far from St. George's School in the Arab quarter of Sheikh Jarach.

He found the house easily enough, and knocked at the door. A moment later it was opened by a young woman wearing a scarf over her head, as all Orthodox women do. She asked for his name, and after he had given it, she ushered him into the living room, where a heavily tanned man in his late 50's met him. He did not provide his name.

He asked Amnon to sit down, and immediately asked if he knew what the Underground operations were all about. That struck Amnon as being a dumb question, for every child in Palestine knew the answer. He asked a lot of questions, which Amnon honestly answered to the best of his ability.

"How old are you?"

"Fourteen years old."

"Do you know why you are here?"

"I am being interviewed for recruitment by the Haganah."

"What is it that the Haganah underground does, according to your understanding?"

"The Haganah defends Jewish settlements and communities from Arab attacks. It is the major Jewish militia organized by the Jewish leadership in Palestine. It acts as the undercover or clandestine army for any emergency that may arise in our communities. It also helps smuggle Jews into Palestine."

"What political party would you join when you become eligible to vote?"

"I will vote for the Labor Party."

"Why is it so important that we have a Jewish Homeland?"

"Because we Jews were dispersed to live in almost every country in the world for over 2000 years. In most of those countries, we were forced to live in ghettoes, we were hated and mistreated for being strangers, we suffered all kinds of discrimination and persecution, and we fled those countries to avoid being massacred in bloody pogroms ordered by the host country's emperor or king who made us the convenient scapegoat for all the country's major problems."

"How do you know so much about Jewish suffering?"

"My mother's family came from Russia. They actually fled Russia to avoid being massacred in the big pogrom in 1890. My mother told me the history of our people's suffering."

"Do you feel that we, the Jewish people in Palestine, need a change?"

"Absolutely."

"Why is that?"

"Because we need to continue the work of our early pioneers, who left Russia and came here to settle. We must continue to strive for and build our own Homeland, so that we may realize the two thousand year old dream of all Jews, to finally return home."

"Do you see yourself as fully committed to our cause?"

"Absolutely, yes. And, to achieve my objective and fulfill my commitment, I need to become a member of the Haganah."

"Do you consider yourself obedient, and can you obey orders without question?"

"I have no doubt about that, for I am disciplined by nature. I will follow all rules and instructions to the letter."

"Won't you be afraid of all that's entailed with being a soldier?"

"I don't think so."

"As you probably know, we are very secretive about who we are, and what we do. Can you keep your mouth shut about everything you might do or hear or see, at all times, even to your closest family?"

"No question about that – I'm fully aware of the need for strict confidence. You can trust me. I'm disciplined, loyal, and devoted most particularly to our cause."

That was the initial recruitment process. The questions then shifted to subjects related to his father's position in the British Government in Palestine, and Amnon immediately sensed the latent hostility coupled with a certain suspicion as to his own trustworthiness. Instantly, Amnon took the defensive initiative.

"I suspect you have some doubts regarding my trustworthiness because my father is a British official," Amnon forthrightly began. "But I hope you're aware there are a number of Jewish officials in the British Government, here in Palestine as well as in Parliament in London. Most, whether in Palestine or in London, are united in their aspirations to help establish a Jewish Homeland."

His interrogator said nothing, and Amnon worked up a fine head of impassioned steam as he plowed ahead with determination. "Instead of being suspicious of my father, the Haganah should try to recruit him! He has access to valuable information because he was enlisted by the British Government just like a lot of other Jews to make sure the British Government continued in compliance with the Balfour Declaration and the White Papers published in the early 1920's."

Looking back, this was not one of the most pleasant meetings in which Amnon was a participant over the years. He didn't think the statements relating to his father sat too well with his interrogator. [Even Amnon knew the British Government was becoming increasingly pro-Arab.] Years later, Amnon learned that not only had his father been approached by the Haganah and the Jewish Agency, but also that he'd provided a variety of information and help at great personal risk until the final departure of the British in May, 1948. Indeed, his father's decision to quit the government and stay in the newly established State of Israel was a great surprise to him.

What bothered Amnon about that crucial meeting was the way it was conducted, as well as the type and tone of the questions, all of which raised his hackles.

"Very possibly, you have not been told I am a Sabra who was born right here in Palestine," Amnon enlightened his stone-faced interrogator. "So no doubt you are not aware that despite my youth, I'm totally dedicated to the cause of the Jewish people's right to their own Homeland."

His interrogator's continuing silence tipped Amnon into rage, and he railed, "You have no right whatsoever to deny my participation! And, if I am not accepted into the Haganah, I shall simply go and join the Irgun, even though their ideologies are not in line with my own!"

When he heard this, especially that Amnon's ideologies were not in line with those of the Irgun, a much more radical group than the Haganah, his interrogator finally spoke.

"And exactly what, young fire-eater, are these ideologies of yours?"

"I do not believe the Biblical 'Land of Israel' of over 2000 years ago should be the focus of the present generation's aspirations and objectives," he boldly stated. "In fact, if we are so fortunate as to retrieve for ourselves even half of the land of Palestine, we should be grateful unto God for His benevolence in bringing us back home."

At that, his interrogator finally seemed to relax, and actually smiled.

Amnon was surprised at himself, for this marked the first time in his life he had stood up for his beliefs, and spoken out with real chutzpah. His interrogator/interviewer apparently liked that, for thereafter his questions took an entirely different direction and tone.

"*Am I really only 14 years old? Or, am I actually a 34 year old in a 14 year old's body?*" Amnon thought. He did not know where he'd gotten the sheer gall to challenge a seasoned member of the Haganah who was old enough to be his father. He was utterly amazed at his own temerity, for surely it was his threat to enlist in the Irgun if he was not accepted into the Haganah that had finally cracked the man's stone face, and he paid close attention as the interviewer fully corroborated Shmuel's summation of his importance to the Haganah.

"You are fluent in several languages, which is most unusual in a young man only fourteen years old, and we are very impressed," he assured him. "Most of us Sabras speak Russian or Polish, plus Yiddish or Hebrew. And, in a pinch, we might possibly speak broken English."

[In fact, the Yishuv, as the general Jewish population of Palestine was then known, was suffering a national language crisis. In the push to speak only Hebrew, feelings regarding the revival of the Hebrew language were so strong that those new immigrants who were heard speaking other languages on the streets were subjected to shouted derogatory insults and called traitors.]

Soon after, and not entirely to Amnon's surprise, his interrogation and interview ended without either detailed explanation of his projected duties or the slightest hint of possible future responsibilities. There was only the terse instruction;

"You will appear in the offices of the Jewish Agency in Rehaviah tomorrow, where you will receive further instructions from the receptionist." His interrogator then executed a military about-face and left the room. Minutes later, the young woman returned to show Amnon out.

Wednesday, October 20, 1943, when he arrived at the Jewish Agency building, the receptionist directed Amnon to a basement room where he was first introduced to his future commanding officer, a tall very tanned young man who looked in his late twenties, as well as to two dozen young boys about his age plus some a few years older.

One by one, they were called to the desk at the far end of the room and given their code names. From that moment on, he was to be known only as "Amnon", no last name. From now on, his real name would never be used at any time, for any reason, in the course of his military experiences while in the Haganah.

When this was over with, they were directed to another room and seated. The speaker, standing before them in front of the room introduced himself:

"My name is Nechemia. I will be your commanding officer. You will attend numerous lecture sessions and go through extensive military and commando training over the course of the next 12 months. The site of your training will constantly shift from one location to another, and the majority of your training will be at night, with the exception of specific school and religious holidays as well as some weekends. This is necessary because British military and civilian police constantly search for hidden Jewish weapons. Just a few days ago, Kibbutz Hulda was searched, thankfully without incident.

"Some of your early training will include sessions devoted to the history of Jewish immigration to Palestine. You will also be provided with a complete and intimate knowledge of every kibbutz, moshav or town.

Since most of our operations are conducted at night, you will be taught night warfare, house-to-house combat and commando techniques as well as topography so that you'll become familiar with all possible routes leading to and from all locations in the dark of night."

When the commanding officer completed his informative speech, they were taken to yet another room with a large desk in front, behind and slightly to the right of which stood Palestine's own blue and white flag. The air filled with an immediate indescribable, almost electrical, tension, and suddenly there was a lump in his throat, which he suspected was the case with the other recruits. When the commanding officer walked in front of the desk and stood facing them, he didn't need to call them to attention, for all of them were already in that military stance.

There followed a brief, but very moving, swearing-in during which they all stood erect and tall with a deep commitment to their avowed cause. And when the ceremony ended, for Amnon at least, there was a strong feeling of connection with an almost overwhelming great strength. In fact, Amnon felt he had enough strength and ability to move mountains, if he tried hard enough, and he knew he would surely try!

They were given the location of their next meeting, scheduled for 6:00pm the next day, and formally dismissed. So, as of Tuesday, October 19th, Amnon's relatively peaceful life underwent a drastic change.

In order to report for training at 6:00pm, Amnon had to rush home from St. George's School (which was about two miles from his home). He never took the bus, he always walked to save the bus fare for pocket money and the cinema. That meant he had to run all the way home since he had to complete his homework in the two hours he normally gave himself for this chore. Then, a piece of bread or fruit in hand, he took off running to report for training at 6:00pm.

It was not at all easy. But then, he'd never really expected it would be. St. George's School always gave endless work and Amnon suffered, particularly in math, which was always difficult for him. Exciting thoughts of his upcoming training and possible early activity with the Haganah outshined his less exciting schoolwork, and his studies suffered. It became increasingly difficult for him to concentrate simultaneously on two goals. Predictably, Amnon decided his full focus should be on his Haganah training; it was more important to kick the British out of Palestine, bring in as many new immigrants as possible, and one day finally create their own State. Amnon did whatever he could to maintain passing grades at school, but what would be would be. The dreams and national aims of the Jewish people had to come first.

Lectures during the first phase of their training focused first upon the history of the Jews. They then moved on to the development of the Zionist movement and the early pioneers' dedicated efforts to build a Jewish homeland, beginning in the latter part of the 19th century. And, finally, through occasional special guest lecturers, they learned everything they needed to know about Palestine, including British policy and activities, especially as these related to Haganah activities.

Amnon and his mates learned about the early settlements, and how the kibbutz [collective farm] became the principal vehicle of the pioneering growth of Palestine. All those early kibbutzim were built in desolate areas, either in the mountainous regions of the Galilee or in the malaria infested marshlands and swamps of the Jesrael Valley. Additionally, they learned the Zionist Congress in Basle, Switzerland, in 1903 voiced the urgent need for a Jewish Homeland, and at that Congress Theodore Herzl supported the concept of a temporary homeland in British Uganda, Africa. The resulting fierce debate nearly split that Congress, but the Palestine faction won, and the resulting first wave of Russian Jewish immigrants eventually became known as the Second Aliya.

During the early 20th Century, the Zionist organization opened an office in Jaffa, responsible for the acquisition of land and settlement of new immigrants. Another important development -- the introduction and use of the Hebrew language -- also took place during those early years. Thus the organization had to master the art of communication within Palestine's Hebrew and Arab city communities and outlying territories.

Because the majority of Haganah activity took place at night, they had to learn to read maps in the field, especially at night, to gain first-hand night experience. So first they were introduced to maps of the country so they'd become familiar with every route, path, road, and highway. Then they were taken to various locations at night and taught to find their way from one location to another in the dark with the help of their maps. Only when their instructor was convinced they could successfully accomplish this did he permit them to move on to the next phase of their training -- the study of weapons.

Amnon was shocked when he saw the incredible array of guns, revolvers and rifles; he doubted there was a single make or model of firearm the world had ever produced not in the display. And he was expected to learn how to use each one of them. The Haganah bought or stole weapons however it could, and from every source around the world.

Bluntly, their weapons instructor advised:

"You never know what arms you'll need to use, because our arms caches are scattered all over Palestine. When you go out on a mission, you will receive arms from the closest location. Therefore, you've got to be ready and able to use whatever arms might come your way."

Amnon recalled that earlier in the year the Palmach, the commando division of the Haganah, ceased its cooperation with the British army. That resulted in a search for arms at kibbutz Mishmar Haemek, where the British confiscated everything they found. Days later the Palmach successfully raided a British arms base near Haifa and their booty included two-dozen machine guns, plus hundreds of rifles and plenty of ammunition for all.

Those early days of his involvement in the Haganah movement meant more to him than anything else in his life up to that point. He was filled with spirit and enthusiasm, and always walked with his head held high as the result of unquenchable hope and great pride.

Unfortunately, the news from Europe was less than encouraging. The revolt in the Warsaw Ghetto was ruthlessly crushed by the Nazis, and only God knew the number of innocent men, women and children those soulless monsters had killed there.

The urgent necessity for the creation of a Jewish Homeland where Jews could live peacefully without hate and constant persecution assumed top priority in his mind and heart. Something else that increased his determination and strengthened his commitment was the continuing deterioration of conditions set forth in the British Mandate for Palestine.

When the Nazis were closing in on the Egyptian borders, thousands of Jewish men and women enlisted in the special Jewish Brigades that fought shoulder-to-shoulder with the British armies to successfully repulse the Nazis. Later, when Italy was invaded, several thousand more Jewish volunteers accomplished the same result. It was unconscionable that despite obvious Arab indifference to the war -- not one Arab volunteered his services to the war effort the way the Jews did -- Britain found it necessary to reduce the strength of Jewish defenses by searching for and confiscating defense weapons whilst simultaneously inciting the Arabs against the Jews.

Thoroughly incensed, and determined to expedite his training so as to become an active soldier as soon as possible, Amnon attacked his studies with vengeance. Not only did he have to be first in his group, he also had to be a leader. He absorbed all the information and lectures like a sponge absorbs water, and his thirst had no end. Speedily, he mastered every weapon he was shown, which was easy because the Haganah's arsenal contained every weapon then known. Unfortunately, the supplies were appallingly insufficient for the job at hand.

Tuesday, November 30, 1943

Amnon's first week in the Haganah was over, and it was truly a personal triumph for him. He was on his way to becoming a fighter for the cause.

Continuing bad news from Europe disclosed that the Nazis daily murdered hundreds of innocent Jews in their concentration/death camps, while the rest of the world not only displayed little or no interest, but also didn't seem to care. Indeed, very little was said or done about the Nazis' murder of innocent Jews, and there appeared to be an international conspiracy to keep the Nazis' systematic annihilation of Jews hidden under a cloud of deliberate denial.

Amnon was away from home daily, leaving the house at 5:30pm to dash off to his assigned training location. His group never met in the same place more than once a week. His original group, having expanded to about thirty young men, was separated into ten groups with only three men in each to permit more concentrated study in specific subjects. When one subject had been completely covered by all groups, they switched to another subject as well as another location. This ensured that studies, training, and location continually changed. They arrived at and left their training locations one by one, and never walked in groups at any time. Neither did they carry textbooks or notebooks or anything else that might possibly tweak the suspicions of the British military or civilian police seen everywhere, patrolling the streets in armored cars the moment the sun set. If they were stopped and questioned, they were just returning home from having visited a relative or friend, and they quickly became adept at dodging the authorities.

Since Amnon didn't have school on Saturdays or Sundays, he was assigned to work in the agricultural girls' school near Jerusalem every Sunday. When the rest of his group members were attending Hebrew schools, he was learning to plow farm fields behind two oxen. He was justifiably proud of himself when he mastered the handling of a plow, and could plow a whole field in one day. At age fourteen, he was a hard-working man doing a man's job. All the Jewish men of Palestine were either in the army or working the farms, kibbutzim and moshavim.

That month would be forever engraved in his memory for the many searches conducted by the British to find the hidden weapons caches of the Haganah. One such search erupted into a full-scale confrontation when members of kibbutz Ramat Hakovesh resisted the search and the British fired into the crowd, leaving one Jew dead and many others wounded.

Most Hebrew newspapers, having first refused to publish a whitewashed news release provided by the British authorities, published detailed reports of the incident at kibbutz Ramat Hakovesh without going through British censorship channels. That caused the British authorities to suspend publication of two major Hebrew newspapers, which so outraged all other Hebrew newspapers in Palestine that they also stopped the presses to display solidarity. Two weeks later, the British rescinded the original two suspensions.

Saturdays were always very pleasant, for early in the morning Amnon's group was bussed to different mountain and hill areas of the country where they learned the terrain. Pretending they were merely having a group picnic followed by wild flower identification and collection, they were in fact training and being lectured on commando operations and techniques as well as house-to-house combat. On some occasions they were driven to one kibbutz or another, where they received first-hand training with newly received weapons. They were also trained to use grenades, which required wide-open spaces.

The evenings of the last two weeks were taken up with actual military exercises in and around the area west of Jerusalem, which left Amnon covered with dirt and mud from head to toe, and he had to sneak into his home to streak for the shower. Not too surprisingly, all the plowing and other exercises rid him of nearly all of what his mother called "baby fat", and he not only became taller, but also satisfyingly more lean.

Their Saturday outings were absolutely wonderful. Enroute to their destination in the bus, they sang their hearts out, and the entire group performed so well he was certain they would make a superlative choir. On two occasions, their bus was flagged down by British military police and searched. However, their driver was a most resourceful chap who had worked out a foolproof evasion procedure for such stop-and-search operations. When the police asked where he was driving, his response always referred to the closest recreational area, and he always drove the bus off in that direction to substantiate his response and assure the police didn't follow them or radio another police car. Since all of them were in their teens, and looked like school children, there was nothing the police could do but let them go on their way, and they joyfully sang their elation at having successfully foiled them.

Though he said nothing to Amnon, he suspected his father's suspicions were aroused by his continuing absence from home in the evenings. Before his recruitment Amnon was always somewhere in the apartment when he returned from work. In fact, there was very little traffic after dark and most people stayed home. From time-to-time, the British imposed a nightly curfew from 8:00pm until dawn because of ongoing daily attacks by either the Irgun or more radical Lehi group upon some British installation or the police. The predictable result of those attacks was that anti-Jewish feeling among the civilian police and military was building like boiling mercury.

The British Government appeared to be stymied. The Jewish Agency continually declared its opposition to the radical groups, and openly criticized their activities. Amnon thought they were secretly pleased knowing that a combination of terror plus the skyrocketing maintenance expenses would weaken the Palestinian economy to a point that would finally force the British to leave Palestine. Regrettably, however, that was not likely to be soon. British policy in the Middle East focused on preserving Britain's ownership of land routes to India as well as control of the Suez Canal and the vast oil empire developed after World War I.

Recently, a newly created terror group formed by a splinter of the Irgun was trying to unite all underground forces into one cohesive unit. The Haganah not only forbade any of its members to join the group, they managed to disband it.

Friday, December 17, 1943

That day was a sad day. Seven members of Kibbutz Hulda were found guilty of the non-crime of possessing defense weapons, and sentenced to two to six years in prison.

"Are we not permitted to defend ourselves?" Amnon asked himself. *"Aren't we supposed to be prepared to defend ourselves when attacked?"*
All too obviously, the British not only didn't agree with that concept they didn't seem to care.

Accordingly, their evening sorties had intensified in effort and material. Amnon's group training had also been stepped up and accelerated to include specifically planned night combat situations. Nechemia, their commander, had become more aggressive.

Very bluntly he announced, "Tomorrow, your next combat exercise will include the use of live ammunition. You will not be permitted to return home tomorrow night, and your return to your homes is scheduled for late Sunday afternoon. You will, therefore, tell your parents you're spending tomorrow night at a friend's house. That is an order."
Amnon went straight to his mother with what he considered to be the inevitable problem.

"What shall I tell Father?" He chewed worriedly at his lip.

"Don't worry. I'll take care of it. And stop worrying your lip," his mother responded.

But it was not to be that easy, for his father flatly refused to permit him to stay at any friend's house. Despite all his pleadings, Amnon's father was adamant in denying his request, and he went to bed knowing he would not return home the following night, and also knowing he could no longer hide from his father the fact of his membership in the Haganah.

Though unhappy with his father's intransigence, he nevertheless slept like a log and dreamed of the argument he knew would ensue Sunday afternoon when he returned home from the combat exercise. In his dream, his father told Amnon he loved him and didn't want anything bad to happen to him. Then Amnon saw himself assuring his father of his love and promising he would take good care of himself and would be perfectly okay.

Amnon

The dream argument ended when his mental alarm woke him at 5:00am and he immediately sprang into his disciplined army mode, under total self-control, everything else wiped from his mind, to quickly shower, dress and brush his teeth. Then, with a light breakfast of orange juice and a couple of biscuits under his belt, he left a brief explanatory note for his mother that the class was going on an outing to the Beit Vegan hills, and she should expect him when she saw him. Amnon felt she would understand the subterfuge, and would accordingly show the note to his father.

Beit Vegan was a newly created Jewish housing community northwest of Rehavia. Behind it you could see the Judean mountains as they seemingly descend toward the coast. Amnon had heard it said that on a clear day you could see the legendary blue waters of the Mediterranean Sea. But since that never happened for him, he chalked it up to heresy and decided the teller of this tale had very likely seen some sort of a mirage.

That Saturday he walked directly to their encampment at the lower end of Gaza Street in Rehavia. Every member of his group was there by 6:00am, and they immediately took off in a single file through a hilly path that led westward. As usual, they sang with gusto as they briskly strode along for the next two hours, passing three mountaintops on their way until they finally walked downhill into a lush green valley. The summer-scorched ground was still damp from the first heavy rains of autumn, and blooming wild flowers poked their heads out of the thick vegetation.

Amnon loved all the beauties and the smell of nature, especially the way it glorified the surrounding landscape and his view of it.

The moment they arrived at their destination, a large rock next to where they were sitting seemed to move. The rock's bizarre movement was immediately followed by the unexpected appearance of a huge opening in the hill facing them. Two men emerged from the opening and walked up to the group commander. Minutes later, they were given weapons with live ammunition as well as a carefully drawn battle plan.

Nechemia, their commander, had them split into three commando platoons. Each platoon had its own commanding officer. He then tersely issued his instructions.

"Your orders are to capture the simulated British station you will find behind the next hill that is not immediately visible to you. Two groups will flank the left and right sides. And," pointing at Amnon, he continued, "your group will head straight for the target. There will be a man who will fire over your heads to ensure the appearance of a real battle and give you the feeling of being involved in real combat. Your attack will commence at exactly 1:00pm. It is now 11:00am. Synchronize your watches, return to your starting positions, and be ready to move at 1:00pm."

Amnon promptly chose Ari to act as a scout, and gave him explicit instructions. "You will quickly and carefully explore the area, then return without delay and within the hour."

Since all scouts and platoon officers were to meet at the starting point at noon, on the dot, Amnon suggested to the other two platoon officers they do exactly as he had done, well before that time.

Pretending this would be a real battle instead of just an exercise, he went to their group commander and asked, "How secure is this place from the British?"

"Our scouts have assured us there isn't a British police officer or soldier within several kilometers of here," Nechemia responded.

Then, after a few minutes during which he appeared to be sizing him up, Nechemia advised, "You will serve as platoon chief for this exercise."

Amnon was pleasantly surprised, for determined to be the best at whatever he did, including his studies and his Haganah training, he had poured everything he had in him to achieve his goals. To be chosen to serve as platoon chief meant the commander thought highly of him and his capabilities, and he declared, "I'll give it everything I have, Sir," with a proud salute before executing a military retreat.

Returning to his group, his thoughts were of his younger years and his life at home under the rule of his strict disciplinarian father. Though honor and strict discipline were as much a part of his father and his life as his stiff backbone, he was ever the true gentleman. He was the benevolent despot who expected his orders to be instantly obeyed without argument or even the slightest dissent. Yet, more often than not, he allowed his mother's strong love and devotion to him and their children, combined with her inimitable common sense, to gently sway his decisions in some matters, thereby successfully maintaining a certain balance in their home.

Amnon concluded that his father's, strict discipline, together with his mother's loving and empathetic understanding, had successfully molded a barely 14-year old youth into the disciplined young man whom his commander obviously believed to be capable and strong enough to shoulder and discharge the responsibility he had been given after only one month of training. Amnon was extremely proud of his new responsibility knowing that, despite his father's initial reservations in the matter, he and his mother would surely also be proud of him. However, Amnon couldn't spend more time on his thoughts. Time was short; the latest more than slightly skewed interpretation of the Balfour Declaration and succeeding White Papers made it obvious the Haganah needed to build its ranks and strength as fast as possible.

A quick glance at his watch interrupted his wandering thoughts and brought them back into soldier mode, his attention directed to the terrain in front of them.

Not much different from where he was standing, it was hilly and scattered with small and large rocks. All sorts of weeds, some very prickly, seemed glued to the rocks, and there were yellow and pink wildflowers nodding everywhere. The next hill looked not more than 500 or 600 yards away, a distance he was certain could be covered in fifteen minutes or less, and probably there was a similar hill just beyond that. He wondered just how many miles the valley stretched between the two hills, and on the heels of that thought came his sensible decision to wait for the scout's report before even contemplating his next move.

All of them watched as the scouts approached the top of the hill, then dropped to the ground to crawl the rest of the way before disappearing from their sight. Though Amnon knew this was merely an exercise rather than actual combat, he was anxious and excited, barely able to wait for the scouts' return. Time seemed to move very slowly as they waited, eyes focused and watching for the slightest movement on the hill; they almost became hypnotized. Then, suddenly, they could see only two scouts crawling back over the peak.

"*But where the devil is Ari, my scout?*" he wondered.

As soon as the two scouts had jumped over the peak, they ran downhill towards their companions waiting in the center. Both were out of breath, but one managed to advise Amnon that Ari seemed to have good terrain cover, so he'd decided to keep crawling toward the target structure to scout further. Waiting for Ari's return, he became increasingly edgy as the hands on his watch face moved inexorably closer to noon.

"*Where is Ari? Has he been caught, and is he now being 'held prisoner' until the end of this combat exercise?*" Amnon thought.

He could feel his blood pressure rocketing as he impatiently scanned the area through his binoculars. Knowing they were moving closer by the minute to their scheduled attack time, he was nervously trying to check his watch while at the same time peering through his binoculars when his peripheral vision caught something moving. Noting it was five past twelve, he feverishly focused his binoculars on what he could see was a crawling object; when his binoculars zeroed in closer and higher, he could clearly see Ari's face. Suddenly, Ari jumped to his feet and took off like a gazelle as he ran the rest of the way downhill.

Before Amnon could open his mouth to reprimand Ari for not obeying his orders to return the moment he had scouted the area, Ari rattled off the location of the target house, that it was built low to the ground, that there were only five soldiers inside, all facing front through small windows, and that there were no windows on either the left or right hand side of the structure.

"What about the terrain? Are there any differences compared to where we're standing right now?" Amnon asked.

"There are only minor differences. Small ravines, some higher rocks, some isolated trees, mostly old olive trees," Ari responded.

Of course, he didn't follow through on his intention to reprimand Ari, for his detailed report gave him other things to focus on.

Turning to the other two platoon commanders, Amnon suggested, "I think the best plan is to have your two platoons slowly crawl toward the building from the two flanks. Every now and then, they should allow themselves to be seen for a few seconds. Then my platoon will slowly move forward, making every effort to remain invisible. With any luck, the soldiers in the building will focus on the two platoons they can see moving from the left and right flanks and decide the attack on the building is coming from those two flanks. This will permit my platoon to scurry as close as possible and hurl our fake grenades through the windows. Your two platoons should attack the house with live fire, firing into the upper wall to ensure they won't hurt anyone inside."

43

The other two platoon commanders agreed with his plan, and they synchronized their watches while they waited the few moments to 1:00pm. Then they began to move.

At 1:15pm, having reached the peak, they dropped to the ground and started to crawl. At exactly 1:35pm, Amnon's platoon hurled the fake grenades while the two flanking platoons began to fire. By 1:40pm, they had successfully captured the target, at which time they all jumped for joy and belted out the Hatikvah, their national anthem. This made perfect sense because of the words, "Od Lo Avda Tikvatenu" [translation: We have not yet lost hope.] After that they danced for joy.

Nechemia joined them and congratulated them on a job well done, and Amnon was so proud of the others and himself, he was about to burst with joy. Then the commander reminded them that real battles are not so easily won.

"Your dearest friends may be wounded or killed during an assault attack such as this," he soberly stated. But they didn't want to hear such words, for they were much too elated with their victory.

In a more quiet moment, Amnon asked his commander if he could speak with the soldiers inside the target structure to get their view of the attack. When he explained that he wanted to assess the psychological value of his battle strategy, the commander gave his permission. Five minutes later, they all squatted on the ground in a circle, and Amnon took the floor.

"Tell me what you saw, beginning with 1:00pm," he opened.

"At first, we didn't see anything," the lead soldier responded. "Then we began seeing movement on the right hand side followed minutes later by movement on the left hand side."

"Did you see anything coming toward the building from the center," he pursued.

"No, nothing at all," a second soldier answered.

"What did you assume was the attackers' plan?" was Amnon's next question.

"We figured we were about to be attacked from the right and left flanks, and prepared ourselves accordingly," was the answer.

"Exactly when did you focus your attention on the right and left flanks?" he asked.

"When we realized the only movement we saw came from there."

"Did you focus on the center at all? And, if not, why not?" Amnon kept at it.

"Not really, just occasionally, for our attention was on the right and left flanks, because we were convinced the attack was coming from the sides," they insisted.

"Thank you very much," Amnon told the soldiers.

At that point, Nechemia, asked Amnon, "Are you sure you're only fourteen years old?"

"You have my sworn word," Amnon assured him with a smile.

After a few more comments, and the return of all weapons and ammunition to their assigned keepers, they were ordered to form a single line, and permitted to start walking back.

At about 3:30pm they arrived at the Hurva, a deserted monastery just 500 yards from the edge of Rehavia, the more affluent quarter of Jerusalem. There they found their history lecturer waiting for them with snacks, which they ate sitting in a circle with the lecturer in the middle.

Minutes later, he began his lecture.

In order for them to fully understand their cause, it was important for them to learn the history of the Zionist movement in Palestine. For that reason, they were taught about the early pioneers, who came to Palestine from Russia in the 1880's, and the growth and development of the Yishuv. They were taught about the political development following the end of the First World War, when the Ottoman Empire literally collapsed, and they learned of the creation of the British and French Mandates in the Middle East that resulted from their signing the famous Versailles Treaty in 1916.

While Amnon listened to the history lecture, he realized the Haganah as well as the Jewish Agency knew that to inspire the youngsters to give everything they had to the cause, they had to ensure they understood and fully appreciated every single one of the numerous historical events that had led all of them in Palestine to these turbulent times.

As far as Amnon was concerned, they were doing everything right.

Friday, December 31, 1943

It was the last day of the year, and what a year it was! Amnon couldn't just move on to the next year without first reviewing not only all that had happened to him, but also what the entire Yishuv had experienced in the year ending at midnight.

To Amnon's great satisfaction, he was well on his way to becoming an important cog in the Haganah machinery. The Haganah consisted of four main bodies. There was the Palmach [better known as the commando outfit], the rank and file regulars that included the core of military operations, the intelligence services, and the administrative body, which was also in charge of procurement. The Jewish Agency and its numerous fund-raising organizations called upon world Jewry for financial support, and were surprised that the response included a large number of non-Jews, all of whom very generously contributed to the Jewish cause.

A number of noteworthy events took place during that year.

Approximately 700 orphans, known as the Teheran Children, who had miraculously survived the Nazi Holocaust and were smuggled into Iran, finally arrived in Palestine. Brigadier Frederick Kisch, a Jewish engineer serving with the British army, was killed by a land mine. A German submarine sank a ship with 400 Yishuv soldiers aboard, and all of the soldiers drowned. The Allies successfully captured North Africa from the Germans. Twenty members of Lehi, the most radical of all the Jewish underground groups, who had been jailed by the British, escaped through a tunnel, and resumed their attacks and acts of sabotage. And, shortly thereafter, Menachem Begin became the head of Etzel [short name for Irgun Z'vai Leumi].

That year also went down in history as the year of the searches. British military and civilian police searched all Jewish quarters and kibbutzim as well as Jewish Agency buildings and offices for hidden Jewish weapons. That resulted in many Jews being jailed and sentenced to years in prison for the non-crime of possession of defensive weapons.

November saw the meeting in Teheran of United States President Franklin Roosevelt, Britain's Prime Minister, Winston Churchill, and Russia's Premier Josef Stalin. On their Agenda was the weighty subject of how to carve up Europe after the war. Despite everything else that was going on all around them and in Europe, that was the sole subject on which they focused.

While the three world leaders discussed the eventual spoils of war, in Palestine, they went through their days not knowing what the next day would bring. The Nazis expanded and accelerated their extermination of Europe's Jews and totally obliterated the Warsaw Ghetto, leaving thousands dead and tens of thousands railroaded to Nazi concentration/death camps.

Neither by word nor the slightest gesture did these three men evidence any interest in the desperate plight of Europe's Jews. What was most infuriating was the British attitude toward the ongoing Jewish quest for a Homeland in Palestine. Amnon could fully understand the extremists' acts of sabotage against the British, but he believed such sabotage should have ceased until the war in Europe was over. One thing was absolutely clear to him. The British had to be ejected from Palestine so that the Palestinian Jews could more directly and forcefully deal with the Arabs.

Friday, January 14, 1944

Amnon's platoon was sent to kibbutz Motza, located just a few miles west of Jerusalem on the road to Tel Aviv. There, members of the kibbutz taught them how to use mules for transportation. At first none of them were terribly excited by the project, which they later learned was of vital importance. Virtually all of the weapons and ammunition used by the Haganah was smuggled into Palestine, very often piece by piece. To avoid the inevitable penalties if such smuggled arms were ever found in a surprise British search, the weapons had to be rushed to specified locations over mountain roads at night to ensure they reached their designated locations. Over time, Haganah experts had learned "the hard way" that the best mode of night transport over any sort of dangerous terrain, like curved and/or hidden if not non-existent mountain roads, were the silent and sure-footed mules.

To his surprise, Amnon soon learned that the mule was a friendly animal. Being a city boy, he had only limited knowledge of animals. So this was a brand new experience during which he learned the mule's vision was better than that of a human, and, more importantly for their purposes, the mule had an incredible capacity to carry heavy loads weighing as much as 500 pounds. When necessary, the mule could also carry a passenger on its back.

All day long they rode mules loaded with all manner of heavy cargo up and down mountainous terrain. He was impressed with the mule's native ability to judge the terrain ahead, and to simply forge its way forward. So long as they were headed in the right direction, the mule was the undisputed king of the road.

Amnon's small unit began transporting arms at night from Motza or Ma'ale Hachamisha to Jerusalem, which meant a trip to Jerusalem one night and the next night back. They also had to transport arms to hideout locations around the western perimeter of Jerusalem. Each person was responsible for one mule even though they traveled in caravan formation.

For the next month or so, as instructed, Amnon bought a ticket on the last bus to Tel Aviv or Jaffa so as not to arouse suspicion, and got off at the appropriate stop to walk to his assigned kibbutz. There, in the dark of night, he loaded his mule and made ready for the trip. The next morning he reported directly to school with virtually no sleep at all, and if he had to travel to a different location than the city, the next day he didn't attend school at all.

Predictably, slowly but surely his grades declined because he had very little time for assigned reading or homework. That infuriated his father, who by then knew of his Haganah involvement. Somehow, though Amnon could not be sure when or where, he finally found sufficient chutzpah to firmly tell his father of his recruitment by the Haganah, and of his unswerving desire to be a part of the fight for a Jewish Homeland.

Being a British Jew and a high-ranking British Government official, together with the new fact that his eldest son was working with the Haganah, forced his father to make a most difficult decision. He simply elected to play a dual role. To his British friends and work colleagues who knew him only as a loyal, stiff-upper-lip British subject, he never displayed his heart-felt Zionist sympathies. At home, in the bosom of his loving family, who never knew he was an ardent Zionist, he displayed only a minor interest in Haganah activities.

Amnon's father's closely guarded secret was revealed only years later, when Amnon finally learned of the real risks his father had braved on many occasions in order to provide the Haganah with the valuable information to which he alone had access by virtue of his British Government position.

Horrible news headlines and articles focused on the arrival of three Holocaust survivors who detailed the atrocities inflicted upon Jews in Europe and in Nazi concentration/death camps. General strikes by the Yishuv protested the Allies' failure to save Europe's Jews.

Sunday, February 26, 1944

Miraculously, Amnon had no idea how he came to be so lucky -- he had the day off. Perhaps his commanding officer needed the day. He had been absent before, and the brass always managed to find a temporary replacement for him. Something had to be going on, though he could not imagine what.

"*Can it possibly have some connection with the mounting daily attacks and acts of sabotage of the Etzel and/or Lehi? Or maybe, it has something to do with the numerous problems facing Mapai, the leading Labor Party,*" Amnon thought.

Whatever the cause, to celebrate his first day off in far too long, he slept in for the entire morning. Because of all the turmoil within the country, there were numerous meetings within the British Government in Palestine, and Amnon's father was away attending some such meeting or other.

This happy circumstance provided the first opportunity in far too long for his mother and him to converse at their ease, and they took full advantage of it. Amnon's mother, who he most passionately loved, was the most important person in his life at that time. Extremely intelligent, clear thinking and astute, she possessed a heart of gold and an unbounded love for her family and for her country. Her abiding hopes and dreams were focused upon the creation and irrevocable establishment of a Jewish Homeland where her own family and all of her descendants, as well as all Jews everywhere could finally and forever be assured of a free and independent life. With the irrevocable establishment of a Jewish Homeland, the Diaspora that had continued for nearly 2000 years would end, and Jews could finally return home from all corners of the world, to live in dignity and peace in their own Jewish Homeland in the Land of Israel.

That was his mother's ongoing hope and prayer. And Amnon silently vowed to God, to his mother, and himself that he would do whatever necessary, even if that included fighting to the death, to ensure his mother would see the realization of her dream in her own lifetime.

She had prepared an eggplant salad and a hard cheese sandwich she knew was Amnon's favorite, and they shared a meal while discussing a wide range of topics. They talked for hours. Curious about his activities in the Haganah, she asked him the nature of his responsibilities and how he viewed the future.

Avoiding full disclosure of his involvement in the Haganah, Amnon kept his responses to a bare minimum, and he couldn't give his view of the future because he lacked sufficient information on which to base an intelligent and logical assessment. Amnon's group's accelerated and intensified training, in the field, on the move, and on the job, left no time for any of them to read the newspapers or talk to anyone outside of their group. Usually, after one of their training sessions, all they wanted to do was to catch up on their sleep.

At that point in 1944, all that anyone could hope for was that the Allies would speedily emerge victorious from the war. Hopefully, an Allied victory would destroy the Nazis' killing machine, and thus end their soulless persecution and slaughter of Europe's Jews.

They prayerfully placed their faith in God's hands.

Sunday, March 19, 1944

Back to commando training, only this time at night, which was very difficult because it was hard if not impossible to see, especially when the sky was clouded. When the moon was out, it was a different story, and more dangerous, and extra care had to be taken to avoid being seen.

The most crucial phase of their training was house-to-house night combat. Night after night, they trained out in the hills, plains, or desert stretches. Many times they were taken to an area near the Dead Sea, and had to climb the Massada at 3:00am when the temperature was lowest. Those exercises were made on very limited food rations and little or no water. This was essential because they had to be able to do a lot without much to eat or drink. They learned to fight, hike, trail and attack.

At school, Amnon fell asleep at his desk. When he was caught napping, his excuse was that he must have some kind of virus. That prompted his being sent to the school's matron who checked his temperature but could find nothing wrong. He told her he was nauseous and felt weak. That lie got him sent home sometimes with a note suggesting his parents should have him see a doctor. The truth was he was neither nauseous nor weak, merely in need of a few hours of uninterrupted sleep. According to his mother, his father seemed to have started being more understanding. Amnon remained dubious. Usually in a world of his own, his father seldom spoke to or spent time with his children. In fact, Amnon could not recall a time when his father sat down to read a book with him, helped him with his homework, or played with him. And his sensitive mother silently suffered from his seeming lack of parental interest in his two sons. But, in that earlier era, women accepted that their men lacked time and patience for their children. So his mother found the time to do all those things for her sons for which his father never had time.

Though his father often assured Amnon of his love, he never made him believe or feel it. Without saying a word, however, he taught Amnon to be honorable, to be strong, to be honest and fair, and to stand up for his rights. By his example, Amnon learned to always be a gentleman no matter what the circumstances, and for that he would ever remain grateful.

Amnon's brother's eighth birthday was last week. He was always a picky eater, so the food rationing didn't bother him at all. Amnon's father didn't like hyperactive children, which explained why he had virtually no patience and little time for his always-hyperactive young son. In fact, though he distanced himself more from his brother, he wasn't very close to Amnon either.

Within the past month, the Etzel and Lehi attacked dozens of British installations and Government offices throughout Palestine with extensive damage to the Immigration Offices and CID [Criminal Investigations Department.] Incidents of sabotage were stepped up with killings and destruction of property on a hitherto unknown scale, all of which created a major rift in Mapai, the leading Jewish political party. A crisis, seemingly motivated by ideological differences, developed between the moderates and the radical left. However, the accelerated attacks and sabotage by Etzel and Lehi were probably the real reason for the rift.

The British authorities declared a full curfew, starting at 8:00 every evening and ending at 6:00 the next morning. And to enforce this curfew, British armored vehicles patrolled the streets at night driven by civilian or military police with orders to shoot any pedestrian who could not speedily identify himself.

That curfew created a new headache for the Haganah, and a new problem for Amnon. How was he, or any other member of his group, supposed to return home from training during curfew hours? They needed to sneak into the city, which meant much more walking, running, ducking, and otherwise endangering themselves at night.

Special permits were issued to doctors and government personnel.

Eventually, no doubt using some trumped-up excuse or other, Amnon's father arranged for him to have such a permit. Thereafter he always carried his British Passport as well as his new Identity Card, but he made no mention to his commanders that he had such documents. It seemed prudent to avoid his seeming to have unwarranted privileges. But, the documents did save his life on two occasions.

Friday, May 12, 1944

Today marked the Palmach's third birthday, and the occasion was celebrated at their nightly training session. Wine was poured into small cups, which they raised in the toast, "L'Chaim!" [Long live our main fighting arm!] and sang the Hatikvah.

Amnon told his commander he'd be on a week's vacation from school during the Easter Holiday. Nechemia arranged for him to attend day training in a kibbutz in the Galil.

At school, Amnon began to feel extremely awkward, for most of his classmates were sons of British officials, other children of elite Arab and few Jewish families. They all knew Amnon was Jewish, and he could sense the growing hostility. Only one English boy remained friendly with him throughout that period. Unfortunately, the boy's father was transferred to Egypt, and he left the school.

When Amnon arrived at the kibbutz in the Galil on the first day of his Easter vacation, he was taken to an underground cellar and introduced to Moshe. Moshe explained he had numerous documents and letters written in French, all of which needed to be translated into Hebrew. For the duration of his stay there, he was the translation expert. Regrettably, he did not train as he had hoped to.

The kibbutz was near the Lebanese border, and various Arabs who worked for the Haganah were infiltrating, usually after midnight, delivering all kinds of reports. Most of those reports were written in French, which was the main language used in Lebanon and parts of Syria. Amnon was fascinated by some of the reports he translated, and impressed with the network of Haganah agents in the north. On occasion, Haganah members dressed as Arabs also crossed the border.

Some pockets of Arabs that supported Germany remained in Lebanon, and a few were also in Syria. Most, however, were found in Iraq and Turkey. It became imperative to spy on those groups, which they did most effectively. Even more surprising was the continuing acquisition of arms in the Arab countries, and their smuggling into Palestine.

During April, 1944, the Jewish Agency and other community organizations declared all high school graduates must enlist in the Jewish battalions within the British Army, the auxiliary police service, or the Palmach. Eventually, they would fight with the Allies in their determined efforts to liberate Europe, or they would do community service for the Yishuv. Jewish parachutists were dropped into Yugoslavia, Romania and Hungary to find and free Jewish people and smuggle them into Palestine.

The Yishuv's frustration first mounted against Etzel and Lehi, and then expanded to include the Allies.

Palestine's Jews saw the familiar British as the major force in the Allies, and the peculiarly skewed British view caused endless demonstrations against them because they did nothing to save Jewish lives from Nazi atrocities in Europe. Etzel and Lehi, on the other hand, having mounted an unceasing war against the British in Palestine in the form of daily sabotage and attacks on British installations and offices, frustrated the Yishuv because their actions were responsible for the burdensome new curfew, as well as the fact that the timing was wrong.

Monday, June 5, 1944

This day Amnon's group was instructed to make note of all Etzel and Lehi locations known to the Haganah; they were to spy on their operations. Amnon felt something was wrong. He could identify with the dilemma. The question was, how could they stop the radical organizations from operating against the British? At that point they were not told much about their mission except that they needed to keep an eye on their operations, and identify any unusual movements. This was not a pleasant job. They were given different locations throughout the city, and were split into small units of two. Etzel and Lehi's operations were then under observation 24 hours a day.

Tuesday, June 6, 1944

The greatest news since the beginning of the Second World War! Allied forces invaded France by landing in Normandy. According to news broadcasts, massive forces landed and the battle was fierce. The Germans were putting up a very tough defense and casualties were high. Continuous Allied bombings of German industrial centers and major cities all but wiped the Germans out.

"Is it possible that an end to the war may actually be in sight? What about the Jews in Nazi Germany's numerous concentration/death camps in most of the East European countries? Would the Nazis' killing machine be accelerated to annihilate all those helpless innocent Jews who were in their clutches?" Those questions haunted Amnon.

Every day one or more Jews somehow managed to smuggle themselves across the Turkish border and arrived in Palestine to tell horror stories of unbelievable atrocities. Amnon's thoughts deviled his waking hours, and made it impossible for him to sleep without nightmares. He found it mind-boggling that human beings could ruthlessly aim their rifles or machine guns and in cold blood massacre innocent men, women, and children whose only non-crime was that they lived their lives in compliance with the tenets of Judaism, the Jewish religion.

But, then, the Nazis were not human.

They were inhuman, and thus, soulless monsters that enjoyed watching human beings of all ages die of starvation and brutal torture. They could walk innocent women and children into their poisonous gas chambers and watch them die through glass windows, then boil their victims' remains in huge pots filled with lye to make soap for use by themselves and the rest of the German people.

The news that reached Palestine was too unbelievably horrible, and it spurred their determined efforts to do all in their power to create a Jewish Homeland in the Land of Israel for all Jews, but especially for those suffering innocent victims who might survive the Nazis continuing efforts to annihilate them.

Rallies and demonstrations were held throughout Palestine demanding action to save Europe's Jews. All shops and entertainment facilities were closed for the day. Amnon didn't believe any of this would accomplish anything constructive. The British military and civilian police in Palestine had more than sufficient reason to thoroughly despise the Jews. Police stations and military installation were attacked daily, and scores of casualties were killed or wounded, with no end in sight.

Mapai split into two political parties, and Amnon lost patience with all this political nonsense.

"How is it possible to find time to make an issue of ideological differences, when Jewish men and boys are daily enlisting in the British Army to fight in Europe? How and where can our politicians possibly find time to engage in political disputes, when Jewish boys are destroying British property, and in the process killing British personnel? Germany remained undefeated, and thousands of innocent Jews were daily murdered by Hitler's soulless hordes, and yet our politicians somehow find time for trivia," Amnon pondered. The entire concept was unacceptable to him.

"What a peculiar people we must be," he thought to himself.

Friday, June 30, 1944

Amnon's school year came to an end.

"Will I return in September? Only God knows the answer to that question," he thought.

Again, Amnon and two of his group buddies were sent to the girls' agricultural school to spend the summer doing a man's work. Having been ordered to do all the heavy fieldwork the girls were unable to do, they plowed and cultivated the fields. They also planted vegetables and fruit and collected ripe produce that they boxed and sent to selected Haganah locations. The girl students received no vacations, but a lucky few got two or three days off now and again throughout the summer.

Up every day at 5:00am, Amnon and his buddies worked until 7:00am when they stopped for a fifteen-minute break during which they quickly ate a light breakfast. Then they headed back out to the fields and worked until 1:00pm when they stopped, and were served a light hot meal. After they ate, they immediately returned to the fields to work until 4:00pm when they were ready to collapse from fatigue and just fell into bed. They didn't always make it to dinner, for sometimes they slept straight through until the next morning.

And so it went until the first week in September when school resumed.

Encouraging news from Europe indicated the Allies were slowly but steadily moving toward Germany, with the Russians successfully pushing the German armies back, too. It seemed possible the war in Europe might end soon, and that was when their war would begin.

Amnon could not keep from wondering how it would develop.

"*When and where will it start?*" He doubted the British would easily decide to leave Palestine, for the Suez Canal was very important to them, and so were their friendly relations with the Arabs. "*But only time will tell,*" he thought.

Tuesday, August 22, 1944

Amnon had managed to visit his parents the night before. His parents had no telephone; in those days a telephone was a luxury very few people could afford, so he'd been unable to call and let them know he planned to come home for a visit. Although surprised, they were very happy to see him. Not having seen him for six weeks, they barely recognized him. He was taller and more lean, and his deep tan from spending so much time in the sun made him look almost black. His mother couldn't seem to stop kissing and hugging him close, and his father kept shaking his head over the changes in him.

There was really no way to communicate with loved ones except by mail, but Amnon couldn't find the time to write. If he did have some time for himself, he used it to catch up with the news, reading headlines or listening to news broadcasts. When he returned from his work in the fields, he always listened to the American Hit Parade, and Bing Crosby was his favorite crooner.

All news broadcasts were censored by the British Government, which controlled the radio broadcasting system. The Yishuv couldn't accept everything they heard as the truth. Music broadcasts came through without any trouble, and there were always rousing war songs and martial music. Hebrew publications were also censored, but they managed to smuggle in a few uncensored news items from time to time.

Terrible news from the Black Sea reached them. The Germans had sunk a vessel carrying 400 Jewish immigrants who had somehow managed to escape from Europe, and only five people survived that disaster.

"*Was there to be no end to the senseless deaths? And what a horrible world we live in, that so many innocent people must die for no reason other than that a satanic megalomaniac ordered their deaths.*"

Wednesday, September 20, 1944

School started on Monday, September 4th, and Amnon was in no mood either for school or to face the few remaining English students left in Jerusalem. He'd learned that most of his British classmates had been sent to Egypt and some to Trans-Jordan. His French teacher, who was Egyptian by birth, remained very friendly, doubtless because Amnon loved reading French, a very melodious language, and also because his reading of French poetry, which is both melodious and very touching, won him first prize and two valuable books were dedicated to him. Of course, it could also be the French teacher knew that some of Amnon's mother's family lived in Egypt, and particularly his Uncle Sam, chief supplier of silks to the royal house of King Farouk.

"*But what am I to do?*" Amnon kept asking himself.

Certainly Amnon knew it was important he get an education, but he found it very difficult to concentrate upon his studies. Amnon's obligation and responsibility to the Haganah grew daily, and it would soon be one year since he'd become a member.

"I've come a long way in the service," he reflected. *"My initial fear I'd be distrusted has disappeared. I've been respected, and what's more, my commander counted on me to do a top-rate job, and I fully justified his confidence in me. I not only excelled in my training and all military exercises, I was always dependable and punctual. And when volunteers were requested, I never failed to volunteer my services. My personal objective was to never disappoint anyone."*

Though his dedication to the Jewish cause was unwavering, he grew thoroughly disenchanted with the existing political system, especially when suddenly there sprung up three labor parties.

"Why in God's name do we need three labor parties? Why do we need any parties at all? In Europe, the Nazis are annihilating our Jewish brethren. Here in Palestine our main priority is the ongoing struggle to solidly and establish a Jewish Homeland in the Land of Israel so that all Jews can at last return home, finally safe from the mindless persecution they suffered during the nearly 2000 years of the Diaspora," were his thoughts.

Given the grave nature of those two realities, it was unconscionable that the politicians and the underground organizations' leaders wasted precious time on ego-based territorial squabbles. Even the Resistance movement had three different organizations directing the activities.

What was urgently needed was one cohesive fighting team, fighting and working together to achieve their common objective -- the irrevocable establishment of a Jewish Homeland in the Land of Israel.

Etzel continued its attacks on British police stations throughout the country, and the British Government announced the formation of a new Jewish Brigade, which would consist of three battalions to be stationed in Egypt. Amnon was wondering whether the British deliberately recruited young Jewish men to reduce the number of fighters in the terrorist organizations. The Jewish Agency issued endless denunciations of Etzel and Lehi.

Friday, October 19, 1944

Today was Amnon's 15th birthday. There was no birthday cake or congratulations from anyone, and he celebrated his day in his own heart. He knew his mother was thinking of him.

The Haganah was being prepared for some kind of action against Etzel and Lehi, Amnon wasn't clear yet what. The commanding officer of the Haganah met with the chief officer of Etzel and demanded all action against the British stop until the war was over. Menachem Begin refused, and like a petulant child who prefers not to share his toys, walked out of the meeting.

Meanwhile, the British exiled over 250 captured members of Etzel and Lehi to Eritrea, Sudan, and Kenya. Amnon was told the Haganah was preparing to block future operations of those organizations, but he didn't believe for a moment the Haganah knew all their bases of operation. And what bothered him most was that Jewish blood might well be spilled as a result of this unnecessary in fighting between the leaders of the three Resistance organizations.

"Why can't they see just how much damage they're inflicting on our country and each other when they refuse to work together as a team?" That questioned nagged him continuously.

Monday, November 6, 1944

That Monday two Lehi members, who were afterwards caught, assassinated Lord Moyne, the British Minister of State in Cairo.

"Inevitably they'll be tried by an Egyptian Court and probably sentenced to death," Amnon thought.

The Yishuv was paralyzed with dismay. The Jewish Agency denounced this horrible act, and called for decisive action to eradicate the terrorist group. Doubtless, the shock waves were reverberating throughout the British authorities in Palestine and the British Government in London.

Sunday, December 31, 1944

Here they were at the end of another year of violence and uncertainty. There had been one successful assassination and one attempted assassination. Jewish political parties and politicians in Palestine were in turmoil owing to elections and in-fighting, but Mapai remained the leading party by a slim margin. More Jewish parachutists were dropped into the Balkans. Hana Senesh was executed in a Hungarian jail. Lord Gort became the new British High Commissioner for Palestine. Menachem Begin finally instructed his soldiers not to resist arrest by the Haganah, which was determined to stop attacks and acts of sabotage against the British while the Second World War continued. Lehi complied with the request to halt acts of violence. Etzel followed suit a little later, and stopped operations. The Allies, with the help of the Jewish Palestinian Brigades, successfully fought their way through Italy.

Fortunately, Amnon was not involved in any action against either Lehi or Etzel. He believed that he and his group were considered too young to deal with that particular issue. They did a lot of spying, and reported daily on the movement of Lehi and Etzel to their Haganah superiors, but that was the extent of their participation. Interestingly enough, during that period of sleuthing, Amnon did not work too hard, and for the first time in a year, he did not suffer from exhaustion. Owing to the endless curfew imposed by the authorities, movement in the streets after dark was difficult. But with the help of the special permit with Identity Card his father managed to get him, he could get to the YMCA to swim a few laps every now and then.

The continuing war effort brought them an indefinite live-in guest, to whom Amnon's family had to give up their living room. Surprisingly, he was his mother's English cousin, whose family lived in Newcastle-On-Tyne, England. He was a British Medical Officer whose father and Amnon mother's father were brothers. In 1890, one brother migrated from Odessa, Russia to England, and the other migrated to France.

Thursday, January 6, 1945

They stepped into the New Year without any fanfare. There was no time to waste on the usual celebrations when so many obstacles lay ahead of them. Most of their evening sessions were devoted to long discussions focused on the development of an uneasy truce between the Haganah and the other two fighting organizations, Etzel and Lehi.

As a Jewish youth, Amnon had naturally attended Hebrew school where the curriculum included the obligatory study of the Bible. This study included the interpretation of statements and events together with the writing of essays, and memorization of endless passages from the Bible, which was the most difficult part of all his Hebrew school studies.

In his view, the core of the problem facing Palestine these days was the strong differences in aspirations regarding the creation of a Jewish Homeland. Two groups would fight to the death for their belief that a Jewish Homeland must be established on the site of ancient Israel, as defined in the early days of the Kings of Israel. This included all of what was known as Palestine -- the Galilee, Samaria, Judea, Negev, the coastal plains, and the entire eastern part of the area bounded by the Jordan River, then known as Trans-Jordan.

Earlier mainstream Zionists wanted whatever they could get on the western side of the Jordan River, even if that meant the partition of Palestine between the Jews and the Arabs. They would have happily settled a Jewish Homeland even if established under the aegis of a major foreign power.

Development and growth of the Zionist Organization was quite complicated since numerous obstacles continually hampered its inception in the last half of the 19th century. Jews in every country in Europe dreamed of someday living in a Jewish Homeland in the Land of Israel. As they suffered under all kinds of persecution, and Jewish lives were lost in the Russian and Polish pogroms, the Jewish dream flourished and grew stronger with every passing day.

"Next year in Jerusalem!" was a cry from the heart during the Passover reading of the Hagadah.

Bringing together the mainstream of Jews and the revolutionary Jewish thinkers of the day was a task for Hercules. But finally the continual whips of persecution and the threat of death at the whim of a Russian Czar, or Austro-Hungarian Emperor, some other European despot bit too deep and at last became intolerable. The long-held dream resurfaced with new force, and this time the dreamers were determined to make it come true for them and their descendants. In whatever ways possible, they somehow managed to struggle home to Palestine. Here, despite innumerable problems and frustrating obstacles, they settled in and stubbornly carved out homes for themselves.

Russian Jews were the earliest pioneers to reach Palestine in the 1880's. The Zionist Organization had barely begun its operation when the first few hundred Jewish immigrants streamed into Palestine. Avoiding the cities, they headed straight for the most difficult terrain in the country, the malaria-infested marshlands and swamps and the arid desert, where they immediately built modest homes for themselves and, despite disease and the continual threat of starvation, they stubbornly farmed the land. For this was Palestine, the ancient Land of Israel, and they would fight to the death to stay here.

Those early pioneers provided a study in perseverance and strength against all odds, coupled with commitment, idealism and loyalty to a dream that defied all description.

There was, as well, the ongoing need to somehow deal with the military representatives of the Ottoman [Turkish] Empire, the foreign entity that ruled the Palestine of those very early years. Most early pioneers were Jews from Russia, a country despised and also feared by the Turkish military that thus regarded the pioneers as their natural enemies. This enmity blocked the pioneers' efforts to settle and farm the land in Palestine.

Some of those early pioneers in the Zionist Organization had to have been thoughtful men who were gifted with compassion for the plight of European Jewry throughout the Diaspora up to that time. They also had to have complete understanding of Palestine's history, and enough vision to plot a course through the complex, obstacle-laden, but necessary diplomatic relations with all interested governmental officials and local politicians of the day. Truly, it was an immense job, rivaling the labor of Hercules facing down and ultimately defeating the triple headed Hydra.

During Amnon's days of action, more than sixty years after the arrival of the first wave of pioneers from Russia, some Palestinian Jews unfortunately cherished dreams that ignored the realities. Although war raged on in Europe, where Hitler's minions continued to slaughter millions of innocent Jewish brethren, too many Palestinian Jews cherished their unrealistic dream of a Jewish Homeland established on the site of the ancient Israel of more than 2000 years ago. To attain this unrealistic objective, they vowed to fight to the death.

Although only 15 years old, Amnon hoped he was intelligent enough to know what was right and also what was wrong for Palestine.

Certainly, tens of thousands of Jews had lived in Palestine throughout the history of the country. But the same was true of at least an equal number of Palestinian Arabs.

"Shouldn't there be some level of understanding, some compromise on both sides?" Amnon mused. *"Why can't today's hard-core Zionists soften their attitude to conform with the earlier Zionists who would happily have settled for only a portion of that ancient Land of Israel if it meant they could live in peaceful coexistence with their Arab neighbors?"*

This solution seemed only logical, and might even have lowered the level of hostility between the two factions. Unfortunately, his youth made his views negligible; he had no real say in the matter, and could only hope that sane and logical older minds would prevail.

It took a monumental effort to convince Etzel and Lehi to suspend sabotage and other hostile acts against the British until the end of the war in Europe. They were told countless times this was not the time to fight the British, but to help them win the war along with the rest of the Allies, finally stopping the murder of innocent European Jews. It was pointed out to their leaders that the continuing attacks and sabotage would only further stiffen the already hostile

British anti-Jewish attitude, a decided mistake. In fact, the outcome of this verbal confrontation proved the Jewish Agency was absolutely correct.

Wednesday, April 4, 1945

The Jewish brigades fighting alongside the Allies were nearing northern Italy. The Allies forces that landed in France were closing in on Germany.

"*Maybe the war will be over soon. God knows it is high time,*" was a constant thought that haunted Amnon.

He shuddered to think of the staggering number of Jews who were killed by the Nazis in Europe. Lacking the actual count or sufficient details, they had only the horror stories that filtered in from various sources to fuel their worst nightmares.

Amnon was out of school for the two week Easter holidays, and had reassembled with his group for full days' work. They now trained in the open in various parts of the country. Most of the time, however, they were in the Galilee area. Military training started at dawn and continued until dusk. They were taught to face and fight any type of warfare. The British military and civilian police continued to search everywhere for hidden arms, and the previous month five Palmach members had been caught and sentenced to seven years in prison. The two Lehi members who assassinated Lord Moyne in Cairo were condemned to death by an Egyptian Court and immediately executed.

The Jewish Agency and the heads of the Haganah were planning rescue missions to begin as soon as the war in Europe was over.

'But with the latest British restrictions on Jewish immigration to Palestine, what was to become of European Jewry, especially the survivors of Hitler's atrocities?' That was the question of the day. The only place in the world for those survivors was Palestine. At that time it seemed they'd be waging the upcoming struggle on two fronts -- one would be the resumption of terrorist activities against the British by the radical underground, and the other the battle to bring in (illegal) Jewish refugees.

Amnon was confident they would win both battles.

Thankfully, the Jewish authorities were well ahead of the game, and the latest training sessions focused upon diversionary tactics. They were told the Haganah's arm operating in Italy was beginning to assemble a veritable fleet of boats to carry refugees to Palestinian shores. Their objective would be to divert the British military and police away from the projected landing sites. All landings would necessarily take place at night, and preferably in isolated places. Sometimes this would mean traveling through Arab villages, or walking for miles along the beaches.

Henrietta Szold, the founder of Hadassah, died at the age of 85. She was also the leader of the National Council and was heavily involved in Youth Aliyah. Ms. Szold was probably the greatest Jewish woman to live and work for the future Jewish Homeland.

Tuesday, May 8, 1945

The great day had at last arrived! The Allies had defeated the German armies and this was officially declared "Victory in Europe Day", otherwise known as "VE-Day."

At last, the time had come, for themselves, and for Palestine. Amnon's thoughts kept jumping from subject to subject.

"How will the Etzel and Lehi react? What will the Arabs do? What is the Haganah, now planning?"

Tens of thousands of Jews were reported to be on the move. The resources of the Yishuv were stretched to the limit. There were so many unknowns, and yet so much to be done. Amnon wished he were older, but at his level in the Haganah, all he could do was obey orders.

"And that I shall do to the utmost level of my ability and beyond," he declared to himself.

What frightened him most, however, was the internal struggle between the warring factions in Palestine.

"We're all striving for the same objective, so why in God's name can't we be one united front? Why must we be divided and working against each other?" Those questions nagged at him day and night, and he was thoroughly frustrated because he had no answers.

That evening his group was bussed to the western outskirts of Rishon le Zion where they walked a short way to the beach. It was dark, but the moon was out. The night sky was cloudless, and the waves rolled gently in, barely kissing the shore. Nechemia, their commander, stood facing them just a few feet from the water, his back to the sea.

"This is one location where the refugee boats will be landing, usually after midnight. They have to stay away from land during the day so they won't be seen from the coast. But as soon as it gets dark they'll start moving toward the coast. Contact is made by radio. The boats will anchor about 300 feet from the shore, or farther, depending on conditions, and the refugees will be taken ashore in whatever small craft are available. We'll have to direct the refugees to small trucks hidden alongside the dunes or side roads. Each vehicle will be driven to a different kibbutz where the refugees will change clothes to look like local farm workers. It sounds simple, but the greatest risk is encountering British personnel. If the refugees are arrested, they'll be taken to the British barracks at Atlit and later deported. If you are arrested, you will be sentenced by British courts and jailed.

Your orders are to create whatever diversions are necessary to draw British military and civilian police to locations other than the projected landing areas." He paused and barked out, "Am I clear so far?"

"Yes, Sir," they promptly responded, and were then dismissed to return to the bus that took them back to their encampment.

During the following two weeks they concentrated their efforts on endless details of diversionary tactics, continuously moving up and down the coast at lightening speed. They synchronized their watches and timed every move; split second timing would be crucial to avoid any risk of being caught.

They made mental notes of the boat landings sites, and memorized the access and escape routes. Nothing was ever committed to even the smallest piece of paper, so they also committed to memory all the side roads, trees, hills, caves and any possible spot that might be used as a hiding place, as well as the distances between points of embarkation and ultimate destinations. Needing to be ready for anything that might crop up, they worked through the night and slept during the day. In the afternoons they were briefed on other developments in the country.

At that point, Amnon began missing days at school, as did other group members. There was no time for study; their focus was saving Jewish lives, and bringing Holocaust survivors into Palestine in defiance of the British edict that there was to be no Jewish immigration into Palestine.

"If not Palestine, where are the survivors to go?"
With their homes and possessions throughout Europe lost and gone forever, how could even the British expect the survivors to consider returning to countries that had betrayed them, tortured and murdered them, orphaned them, deliberately starved them to death and delivered them to the Nazis? If the survivors actually did consider such a course, any competent psychiatrist would declare them insane!

Thus, the only sensible destination for those people was Palestine, which was at the time under British control, but which they hoped and prayed would ultimately end up as a Homeland for all Jews.

"To this cause I am committed, to this cause I shall devote myself, and for this cause if necessary, I shall fight to the death!" Amnon vowed.

Thursday, May 10, 1945
The night before, Amnon's group had engaged in their first diversionary exercise. They had to create a real diversion even though there was no boat of refugees to unload. Driven to their target area a few kilometers north of the city of Ashdod, they were told they had to operate under real conditions.

At 11:00 pm they arrived at the target area. It was a cool night with only a few clouds in a star-studded sky, and a slight breeze blowing in from the sea. The plan was to launch a dummy boat to a distance of about half a kilometer, and make sufficient noise to attract the attention of a British patrol. As soon as the scout informed them of an approaching vehicle, they were to scatter and hide in the vicinity. Once the British left the half-truck, which was the type of vehicle usually driven by the British military or civilian police, one of Amnon's group, disguised in a British uniform, would jump into the vehicle and quickly drive off. Without a vehicle, this patrol would be hours away from help and unable to inflict any damage.

The habits and ways of the British military and civilian police were an open book to the Haganah's intelligence arm. Their first exercise went off without a hitch.

"This was only a trial run, so don't get cocky," Nechemia beamed at them. "Don't think every diversionary action will be as simple as this one. The patrol may leave a man behind in their truck while others run to the beach. If that happens you'll have to disable him without making any noise or letting him do so, and only then can you drive off." Moreover, he warned, "After a few such incidents, the British will undoubtedly arrive in two or three vehicles and with plenty of armed supporting manpower."

"What if they open fire?" someone asked.

"You will return fire, and attempt to capture their trucks," the commander responded tersely. "Remember, this is war, not a game. And it is a war we mean to win. Clear?"

"Yes, Sir!"

"Good! Now, go home, all of you."

As of that night, they were out every single night running through similar but different maneuvers that included diverse possibilities the commander suggested in order to be prepared for any contingency. Just as their commander had warned, nothing was ever as simple as their first maneuver.

When their commander felt reasonably certain that they could acquit themselves well under fire, they learned that acts of terror against the British would begin again. Additionally, they heard rumors that the three resistance organizations would be united under one command to fight the British.

"Well, it's about time," Amnon rejoiced. He was thoroughly disappointed when time proved this was not the case at all. While many of their actions were unified, each fighting organization had its separate commander-in-chief.

It would have been more sensible for them to establish what the Russians call a troika -- a three-horse team harnessed to each other to pull one cart. Only in this case, it would be three chief commanding officers working as a team to direct the activities of one unified organization for the ultimate benefit of the country they served, and their country's sworn cause.

Great news! Members of the Jewish Brigades in Europe were directing Holocaust survivors toward Palestine. A special unit of the Haganah was engaged in organizing a fleet of illegal boats to transport the refugees to Palestine.

Unfortunately, it seemed a concerted effort by the British was also underway to block any and all Jewish immigration to Palestine. The Labor Party, which had won the elections in England, had made no effort to change the law governing Jewish immigration to Palestine. In fact, the situation had considerably worsened. In Palestine, the British military and civilian police had intensified their surprise searches to locate caches of hidden Jewish defensive weapons. British warships, free from wartime naval activity, were blockading the shores of Palestine. Additionally, British patrol boats stopped and searched all boats moving within the territorial waterways of Palestine to make sure no illegal immigrants set foot on the ground in Palestine.

British military and civilian police arrested everyone they deemed suspect, and ship them to countries as distant as Eritrea. In furious retaliation, Etzel mounted attacks against targeted police and railroad stations as well as oil pipelines. This resulted in a strict curfew imposed in many cities throughout Palestine. This curfew, in turn, hampered everybody's movements so that the Haganah fighters were forced to use hidden dirt roads and other difficult terrain for their various operations.

Not too surprisingly, and not very long after they learned of the intensified anti-Jewish immigration activities, Amnon's group received their orders to engage in their first sabotage mission, to destroy a bridge used by the British military. Amnon could barely manage to sleep in his mounting excitement, and his thoughts went flying off in all directions.

"Would the bridge be guarded? Would they need to kill any guards?" Not having had to shoot anyone to date, he wondered how he would feel if faced with the necessity of killing or wounding someone.

"I'm not at all sure I'm quite ready to deprive someone of his life just because he's a minor cog in a political machine run by distant politicians who make life and death decisions, and whose destiny is thus decided for him without his permission," thought Amnon. *"Such a man might have a loving family back home in England, and be utterly innocent of any wrong perpetrated action against us or our cause, aside from having to be where he is and obey his superiors' commands."*

This difficult decision didn't seem fair. But he couldn't avoid it, for what had to be done had to be done, whether by him or someone else.

"After all, what of our millions of kinsmen, whose only crime was being Jewish, and who were murdered in cold blood? Did even one minor cog in the Nazis killing machine waste one second's consideration before taking yet another Jewish life? And, what of the anguish those innocent victims endured and continue to endure as they strive to reach Palestine, their only hope for a future?" These were his thoughts of the day.

In the face of all that, Amnon gritted his teeth and bit down hard on the thought that he would have to do whatever might be necessary to ensure the success of their mission.

All of their night combat training dictated complete silence, for even the slightest noise carried over a great distance, and posed serious risk for all of them. For that reason, they were taught to speak in whispers when engaged in a mission and only when absolutely necessary. They committed their training to memory to assure they never forgot it, and carried it with them into all their combat missions.

The next night was designated by all of them as "M1-Night." They met at their assigned rendezvous point and silently headed for the bridge that crossed a road frequently used by the British military. This road connected the Atlit military barracks with the Arab sector of the West Bank. Swiftly and silently, they walked a few yards off the road to avoid being seen by any traffic.

Two men carrying explosives managed to get to the bridge undetected. A military command car was parked at the head of the bridge, a few soldiers standing there chatting and smoking cigarettes. The rest of the group crawled noiselessly through the underbrush toward the bridge. When they neared the bridge, they fired a few shots at the command car, which immediately focused the soldiers' attention on the road in front of them, and Amnon's group was then able to rise and sprint to the bridge. Within minutes, explosives with timers were laid and set, and the men sprinted off under cover of their sporadic shots.

Unable to see any of them, the British blindly shot right and left, and within minutes the bridge blew up. The soldiers immediately jumped into their command car and sped away in the direction of Atlit. But they never made it.

The saboteurs were extremely careful not to damage the command car, which they triumphantly drove back to their base.

Throughout the night, dozens of other bridges were destroyed in various parts of the country.

Friday, May 11, 1945

They barely rested after the previous night's action. The following morning they took a public bus to Nahariah. This small and lovely coastal town in the far north of Palestine, about ten kilometers from the Lebanese border, was settled by the first wave of German Jewish immigrants.

When they arrived, they were directed to a safe house where they immediately collapsed onto some mats that had been laid out on the floors.

Amnon slept for several hours, and it was close to 6:00 when he was awakened with the others to eat the meal waiting for them. A platter of rice and beans in tomato sauce followed the mixed salad with fresh pita bread. For dessert, each got an apple.

When darkness had fallen, they were joined by Uri and Akivah, two Haganah members Amnon had not seen before. They distributed rifles with ammunition and about a dozen grenades from the trunk of their dilapidated car. Minutes later, walking swiftly but carefully so as not to get any sand in their rifles, they set off for the beach where they settled into the bushes.

Rendezvous with the refugee boat they were told was enroute from Turkey was set for 1:00am, and they had a long wait. With time on his hands, naturally Amnon's ever-active thoughts jumped to the refugees.

"Who are these people, and where were they during the war? Did they lose any loved ones? Will there be women and children as well as men, and how old are they?"

Just then, one of their scouts came running up to advise that a British patrol car with four soldiers was driving in their direction. Well hidden in the bushes a few feet from the road, they remained silent, ready for whatever would happen next in the quiet night around them. Soldiers jumped out of the car as it stopped, and one headed toward the water with his binoculars in hand, where he stood scanning the sea. He must have seen something, for the rest of the soldiers suddenly took up positions along the beach with their rifles at the ready.

Aware the boat needed at least two hours to reach the shore, the rescuers sent their scout back to his position on the road to see if any other British patrol cars were around. The report was negative, and since the British patrol car was small and carried only the four soldiers, they followed their planned strategy.

The British patrol, which had been in the general area, had no doubt been told about the incoming boat, and that the boat was small and carried only 30 or so refugees. Therefore they must have decided no reinforcements would be needed until all the illegal refugees were on shore. The soldiers focused their attention on the water with no thought or notice of anyone crawling behind them. Around three in the morning, when the boat was just 100 meters from the shore, Amnon's group put their plan into action. The British soldiers were completely surprised when they were jumped.

"Turn around! Drop your weapons!" They complied. Then it was the group's turn to be surprised. Not one of the British soldiers could have been more than eighteen or nineteen years of age.

They were marched to the closest tree, stripped of their uniforms and boots, and carefully tied up. Their mouths were taped so as to prevent any immediate outcry. Their weapons were collected and put in the car for transport to Amnon's base. By that time, a few small dinghies had neared the shallow shoreline and quickly pulled up onto the sand. Their occupants jumped into the water and ran up to the beach.

Amnon's scouts reported no movement had been seen or heard on the main road, and Amnon felt he could safely proceed with the rest of his plan.

The Turkish fishing boat's captain and his assistant came ashore, shook Amnon's hands and wished him well before taking one of the dinghies and returning to their boat full speed. All the other dinghies were pulled onto the sandy beach and smashed to unrecognizable bits while the fishing boat quickly disappeared over the horizon.

The touching encounter with this first batch of refugees, would forever live in his memory, for its emotional impact was overwhelming. Amnon actually cried seeing the refugees' obvious relief at having finally reached the shores of Palestine, and he suspected others in his group also had tears in their eyes.

Tearfully, the refugees hugged and kissed Amnon and his men before nearly all of them dropped to their knees to kiss the ground. But time was passing, and Amnon had to quickly move into the next phase of the operation.

None of the refugees carried luggage, having only the clothes on their backs. And despite their having survived a five-day trip in a cramped fishing boat, as well as all the horrors of their recent past, they laughed and cried with happiness and excitement as they constantly tried to touch their rescuers. Regretfully and carefully Amnon explained the need for haste to avoid being caught by the British police, who would take them away to a British barracks for next day deportation back to their port of embarkation. It could not have been easy for them to hear this, but they cooperated splendidly as they were rushed up the beach to waiting transport.

Having loaded as many refugees as possible into the British command car, most of the remaining refugees were loaded into their own old car, leaving the youngest and strongest to walk alongside them to the safe house in Naharia. But, before leaving, Amnon carefully checked the British soldiers to make sure they wouldn't cause them any immediate problems. Amnon quietly told them they were lucky his group wasn't with the Etzel or Lehi, and he thought he saw gratitude in their eyes that they were left alive, even though left in their underwear. Certain they couldn't raise a rumpus for several hours, Amnon raced back to join his comrades and the remaining refugees. The walk to Naharia was long and difficult, but they managed to make it to the safe house just before dawn. Once inside the house with curtains covering the windows and only dim light, they finally had time to see the new arrivals to Palestine. Even though many of them could barely talk, they were anxious to express their great happiness and gratitude, so again they jumped at their rescuers to smother them with grateful hugs and kisses. All were crying through their happy tears, undoubtedly with grief that many of their loved ones had not survived to see this day.

First, Amnon explained they needed to shed their clothing and put on new clothing similar to that worn by native Palestinians, to avoid arousing the suspicions of the local British authorities. Then he gave each of them soap and a towel, directing them to the bathroom for a quick shower before donning the new clothing. Their own clothes would be washed for further use or destroyed, depending upon condition and looks. When they were all washed and wearing clean clothing, they were given steaming cups of coffee and some biscuits.

Finally, they all sat, mostly on the floor for they only had few chairs and one old sofa in the house. Nobody appeared to mind, and all seemed comfortable as Amnon momentarily stood at ease and let his eyes travel from one to another until he had inspected them all.

Most of the men appeared to be no younger than 50, and a couple seemed much older than that. The six women and four youngsters had drawn faces with deep circles under their eyes. His guess was that the cumulative result of the refugees' ordeal, first in Europe, more recently their cramped journey, made all of them look older than their actual ages.

Two of the youngsters were related to one of the men, a widower. The rest were widows, widowers, and orphans, and all their faces combined grief for lost loved ones with happiness at the successful outcome of their journey to Palestine. The discomforts they had endured in the cramped quarters of the Turkish fishing vessel that sailed under cover of darkest nights, through unfriendly waters, with patrol boats waiting to block their voyage, were well worth their safe arrival and anticipated new life in Palestine.

Their palpable happiness could be seen in their eyes, and Amnon could almost read their thoughts, as he silently looked them over in that quiet room, feeling at least as overwhelmed as they were. The silence continued for several more minutes until someone at last began to talk in a language neither he nor his Haganah comrades could easily understand.

But thank God for Yiddish! This polyglot language, combining virtually all the languages of the countries Jews had lived in throughout the Diaspora, was the key that unlocked the silence. Fortunately, though Amnon never spoke Yiddish at home, he had become sufficiently fluent through applying his knowledge of German to the Yiddish he heard on the streets, and this made it possible for him to haltingly converse with the refugees.

He quickly learned and translated for his Haganah comrades, that the refugees never again wanted to see a German, Pole, or Russian. Germans and Poles were the majority of the guards in the concentration/death camps, some of whom were brutal killers and torturers. The refugees were overjoyed to be in Palestine, to live at last among Jews. They hoped to build new lives, and would work hard to achieve that goal. And all of them swore they would rather die than ever again live in Europe.

Much as Amnon wanted to continue talking with them, he had to make arrangements for their earliest possible transfer to temporary or permanent housing. It was anyone's guess as to when the British military would find their lost soldiers, and then they would almost certainly start searching for the perpetrators as well as the illegal immigrants.

Time was running out, and Amnon could not afford to waste another minute. He asked the refugees if any of them had relatives in Palestine, and made notes of the names and addresses they gave him, checking off those that would need to be contacted. Those with no immediate relatives would need to be transported to whichever kibbutzim had room, and were prepared to accept the arrivals right now. But they had to be very careful to avoid the British.

Transporting the refugees from the safe house in Naharia to their kibbutzim destinations was the responsibility of others. And soon enough an elderly couple arrived to take inventory of the new arrivals and make plans for their transportation. Knowing they would proceed elsewhere the next night, Amnon bid the refugees farewell and wished them good luck in their new lives in Palestine.

At that point, Amnon and his group went into the next room and quietly collapsed onto the bunk beds. Amnon could not have been asleep very long when he suddenly awoke because he felt someone gently stroking his face and murmuring.

"Mein zin, mein zin," (my son) she was saying.

Carefully slitting one eye open, Amnon recognized one of the refugee women. Tears running down her cheeks, she kneeled by his bunk, repeatedly murmuring what sounded like a name. Instantly wide-awake, Amnon opened his eyes. Seeing his eyes were open, the woman leaned over and kissed his forehead.

"I had a son just like you," she said in Yiddish. "They took him away from me four years ago, and I never saw him again. You must be fifteen or sixteen, just the age he would be now." She tearfully stroked his hair, her eyes filled with love for her lost son.

Unable to find appropriate words of sympathy, which he couldn't have spoken over the lump in his throat anyway, Amnon sat up on his bunk and impulsively reached over to hug her. In response, she again kissed his cheek and forehead.

Tearfully, she asked, "What is your name?"

"Amnon."

"Please forgive me, but you remind me so much of my beloved son. I couldn't help myself. I believe he is dead, like all the other children the Nazis took away and killed. As for my husband, I don't know whether he's alive or dead, for the Nazis also took him away. I don't know anything, and I'm alone in this world," she sobbed uncontrollably.

Never before in his life had Amnon witnessed such intense grief. Not knowing what else to do, he simply held her and let her cry it all out. Doubtless, this was pent-up grief over the death of her husband and child as well as the probable deaths of other family she might have had. Knowing he had to say something to her, Amnon mentally gathered sufficient broken Yiddish to assure her, "You're safe now. You have arrived in Palestine, where you'll soon have a new home and new friends. And perhaps," he said, leading her back to the room where the other refugees were waiting for transport to their assigned kibbutzim, "One day, when all your grief over your husband and son has healed, perhaps God will give you another family to love."

Silently, she hugged him before rejoining the others, and Amnon returned to his bunk.

Sleep was not possible. He turned and twisted, pounded the hard pillow, counted sheep jumping over a gate into a meadow, and even tried to hypnotize himself. Nothing worked, for his mind would not release the nagging memory of the refugee woman.

"How could a wife and mother survive the pain of not knowing the fate of her husband and young son? And, how could she have survived all the other horrors she must have been forced to endure?" he kept pondering.

Amnon thought of his own mother, knowing how she always worried about his brother and him. Immediately, he resolved to make every effort to send her more messages so that she and his father would always know he was all right, and there was no need to worry about him.

"In fact, I'll send a message off to them first thing in the morning." On that comforting note, he finally slept.

His internal clock having awakened him, he washed and went to the kitchen where he found a hot breakfast awaiting him. Most of the refugees were on their way to their kibbutzim, and the few who were left soon joined him and his group at the table. The first shock appeared to be over, for their accumulated anxiety had dissipated and they looked more relaxed.

Amnon's group's instructions were to take the 6:30 bus to Hedera and meet at one of the Haganah's safe houses there. They wished the refugees well in their new life before leaving, one at a time, for the bus terminal.

Not wishing to attract attention, they sat separately, one of them carrying a duffle bag containing four guns and ammunition. That bag was placed underneath the last seat, and, if British soldiers stopped and searched the bus, they would make no effort to reclaim the bag.

Upon arrival in Hedera at 8:10, they again took different routes to eventually reunite at the assigned safe house. Guns and ammunition placed in the cache, they sat first at the coffee table and then on the floor to chat while awaiting their commander. The focus of their conversation was last night's refugees. Although Amnon was sad at not having had an opportunity to wish every single one of them well, he was certain they understood he was very tired and needed to get some sleep. Night missions had become routine, and sleeping during the day was not always possible. So when they had an opportunity to catch some sleep, they jumped at it.

On that consoling thought, Amnon and the others continued their interrupted chat on several topics until their commander showed up.

Immediately he declared, "In a few days, war will officially be declared against the British forces in Palestine. British military facilities, police stations, and various joint barracks are targeted for attack. The objective is to break down British interest in Palestine, take as much military hardware as possible, and to create sufficient panic to permit several clandestine ships carrying immigrants from Italy to safely reach our shores. British resistance to Jewish immigration into Palestine must be cracked. And now we have the United States on our side. Heavy pressure is being brought to bear on the British Government to let tens of thousands of Jewish refugees now stranded in numerous European seaports to complete their journey to Palestine."

During the next ten days Amnon's group experienced the most strenuous level of training to date.

Taken to a special camp just outside of Hedera, they were issued Arab style clothing and ordered to strip and put on the clothes provided. This transformation would permit them to move freely despite watchful British eyes, for the British rarely thought to look for Jewish resistance men who might be wearing Arab clothing in Arab territory. Thus they crossed the bridge that led into an Arab village situated in an enormous valley.

During every aspect of their military training from that day on, not only did they train under live fire, their weapons used live ammunition and they threw live grenades. They did not, however, learn the use of explosives. That was the function of a special unit entirely separate from their own group.

Ten days later, they received their newest assignment in their commander's usual terse style.

"You will take your positions on the marked section of the highway between Rehovot and Be'er Sheva, where you will disrupt British military vehicular movement. You will destroy as many of their vehicles as possible without unnecessarily killing any military personnel. If you are fired upon, you will return fire, making every effort to wound rather than kill. But if you do kill, remember, wounds and death go along with war. Additionally," -- here the commander paused for a moment to scan their faces, and zeroed in on Amnon before delivering his last very deliberate instructions -- "If there are too many vehicles for you to destroy all of them, you will take out only the first few vehicles, which will block the highway to further traffic. As soon as you complete that maneuver, you will immediately move off to a different location where you will repeat the action. Clear?"

"Yes, Sir!"

The operation went off as planned, and soon they found themselves in what amounted to a game of hide-and-seek. They hit, ran, and hid. The British then had to search for them. Fortunately, they won the game without casualties to their side that day, and were jubilant with what they considered a roaring success. Similarly, other Haganah units played and won the same game with the British military in numerous other parts of Palestine.

Friday, June 22, 1945

The Etzel and Lehi joined the party. Scores of police stations throughout Palestine were attacked. They went so far as to cut telephone lines, and also bombed the oil pipeline.

Meanwhile, Amnon's group was informed numerous clandestine shipping vessels from Italy carrying thousands of European refugees were expected to arrive soon. That meant they would be busy diverting British attention away from the landing sites over the course of who knew how many nights in the immediate future.

It became clear that the continuing battle to permit Jewish immigrants to finally set foot on the soil of Palestine as the first step in their new lives has assumed new parameters, and would doubtless grow more harrowing with every day that passed.

Eliyahu Golomb, the Head of the Haganah, died of natural causes, a sad day for all of them, for he was greatly admired by all Haganah personnel. His death was a great loss and left a gap that could not be immediately filled. They had no idea who could or would replace him.

Wednesday, July 18, 1945.

That Wednesday morning, Amnon's group scouts apprised them of a massive and slow moving British operation riding about one kilometer behind what appeared to be a small convoy of patrol cars. The scouts also reported that the slow movement was slower than usual, which indicated something was wrong. Immediately, the group split into three units stationed about one quarter of a kilometer apart from one another. Their commander's instructions were concise and clear. "Only the unit stationed at the northern point will open fire on the first convoy to disable it, and intermittent firing will commence. The other two units will stay hidden and wait until the second convoy has arrived to help the first. At that point the convoy will have entered the ambush zone. Once they are inside the ambush zone, begin the attack from the rear." His eyes met Amnon's and held; "You will command the middle unit."

Amnon promptly chose six men to accompany him, and they sprinted into the sand dunes no more than one hundred meters from the road. There they hid and waited, in total silence and without stirring, in the 90 degree heat of the blazing sun until the first convoy of cars appeared in the distance. The second convoy could be seen moving no more than half a kilometer behind the first.

The moment the lead convoy came within 100 meters of the first unit, shots were fired at their tires; and at the same time, the thin wire that released the firing pins were pulled detonating the numerous grenades buried in the side of the road. The first vehicle in line, with its armored steel top, was immediately disabled, and tires of the other vehicles were shot to shreds. At that point, the first unit ceased firing. British soldiers jumped out of the cars of the first convoy to hide behind their vehicles and began firing in all directions. Amnon's unit, being very well camouflaged, could not be seen, and the British soldiers couldn't pinpoint its location.

Now the second convoy of armored cars sped up, and as it neared the first convoy, began firing two heavy machine guns as well as one two-pounder cannon aimed in the general direction of the first unit. It passed Amnon's hiding place; about thirty soldiers jumped out to begin a frontal attack, advancing in the general direction of the first unit. It was then that Amnon and his men moved out of hiding and opened fire from the rear killing two soldiers and wounding many. The surprise attack immobilized the British soldiers when they realized they were surrounded.

The third unit then crossed the highway to guard the other side. Within seconds, that entire British movement ceased firing, and a white flag appeared on a raised bayonet. Two of the Haganah front units ordered the British soldiers to lay their weapons down on the sand, and retreat about fifty meters toward their cars. Their medics were instructed to care for their wounded, and they instantly obeyed. As soon as the scouts told the three units the highway in the direction the convoys had come from was clear, Amnon had the soldiers place their wounded in one of their trucks, with the rest piled onto three other vehicles, and ordered them to drive back to their barracks.

Amnon took down their names as they mounted their vehicles, and warned them if they were caught again, they would most likely be killed. He also told them that their quarrel was not with them, but with their government, which didn't care about the suffering of the Holocaust survivors and had refused them entry into Palestine where they hoped to start new lives. The soldiers said nothing, but Amnon could see they were grateful not to have been killed, and they appeared to understand the reason for the battle with their government.

Thankfully, Amnon's group suffered no casualties.

Seizing all operational vehicles and weapons, Amnon's unit and the other two swiftly drove to the nearest well-hidden base in the desert. In high good humor, the base commander and his deputies accepted the captured booty -- two heavy machine guns, three dozen rifles, one two-ponder cannon and loads of ammunition plus, of course, the vehicles. They were congratulated and toasted for a job well done with some wine and biscuits, before being allowed to take a much-needed rest.

But sleep eluded Amnon. He couldn't stop thinking of the two British soldiers who had died. They were young, their whole lives ahead of them.

"*Why did they have to die, and who had they left behind? Parents, for sure, but who else? Had they been single or married, and if married, might they have started families? What was it about the British cause, which was to keep Jewish immigrants from setting foot in Palestine, that was so important that these young men had to fight and die in defense of it?*" He could understand and sympathize with the need to fight and die to protect homeland and family from ruthless invaders. But that these young men had died to keep innocent men and women from even the chance of building new lives after years of untold anguish and torture and the daily threat of a hideous death was simply unacceptable. They had used six-shooters, and Amnon hoped and prayed his hadn't been the bullets that had killed those two men.

That was Amnon's first major battle, and it was not pleasant because he felt fear for the first time in his young life.

Before this, he had been ignorant of the workings of fear, for he had never experienced it. He had never before felt his stomach clench, nor his blood rushing to his head in terror. He didn't like knowing he had feared the very real bullets of the very real "bad guys" in a game that was not a game, and that those real bullets were meant to really kill his comrades and himself.

"*War games are fun,*" he thought. "*Real war is deadly and no fun at all.*"

But the very real inner strength, of which Amnon had also been ignorant of until the moment of battle, overcame his fear and wiped everything else out of his mind. From that moment on, Amnon had focused his thoughts only upon what had to be done to win that first battle. Later, when they had inventoried the captured-booty, he was very proud of his own contribution to that first victory, and resolved that from that day forward, he would always be strong. Never again would he let himself feel even one second of fear, for fear numbs the mind and slows its reflexes. When engaged in a vital mission, whatever its nature or objective, he would be an actor on a stage, playing the role of an invincible man totally without fear.

Two days later, Amnon was promoted to the rank of deputy commander and he believed that he was the youngest of all his counterparts.

The latest news reported that the British Allies were the first to enter the Bergen-Belsen concentration camp in Germany, and were horrified at what they found there. They were closely followed by Americans whose medics literally threw up at the sight of the pitiful living remains of the victims of the Nazis' merciless "medical" experiments on helpless human beings. No doubt it was the United States they had to thank, for their fearless journalists made sure the entire world knew what had been found at Bergen-Belsen, most likely motivating the great British gesture that also made headlines in the world press -- Britain would permit 5000 Jewish immigrants per month to enter Palestine.

"Big deal!" Amnon thought. *"Boy, the British Government is really humane! But how dare they? A mere five thousand of the more than two-hundred-thousand victims who miraculously survived the horrors of the Nazis' concentration/death camps in Germany, Czechoslovakia, Poland and most of the Balkan countries, even in Russia. The exact number of survivors was not yet known. But of one thing we can all be certain, not one of those men, women and children want anything to do with any European country. If they do, it's only because their brains must have been scrambled by the untold horrors they were forced to endure.*

How can the British Government, which at one time wrote the Balfour Declaration declaring its sympathy for the Jewish cause in Palestine, be so heartless as to favor its own political position in Palestine over the right of human beings to enjoy life, liberty and the pursuit of happiness in dignity and peace in their own homeland? Why can't they show they truly do have sympathy with the Jewish cause in Palestine -- not the Palestine of the Balfour Declaration, but today's Palestine -- by relaxing their inflexible position in the matter of Jewish immigration to Palestine? And why must men continue to die, as surely they will, because the British Government wants to hang on by its teeth to guard its selfish interests in Palestine?

Survivors of the Holocaust want to come to Palestine, to rebuild their lives. This has been their birthright since the time of the Bible, and the world, including Britain, should bend over backward to help them create a permanent Jewish Homeland here. Instead, Britain has deliberately blockaded the coastline of Palestine, and deprives Palestinian Jews of the right to defend themselves against the Arabs, their sworn enemies."

How were the British even able to sleep at night?" On that note, thankfully, his thoughts shut down and sleep took over. He slept like a rock until shortly before dawn, when one of his men awakened him. Somewhat groggily, he heard him say they needed to move to another location because British soldiers were searching the area. Instantly, Amnon was fully awake and on his feet, ready to spring into action.

Their own military hardware, as well as their booty, was buried in the sand in huge crates well outside the moshav where they'd spent the night. The captured vehicles had been driven away, for when he awoke, they were gone. Outside the building in which they'd slept; a dilapidated old truck with all sorts of farming equipment in its back awaited them. They jumped onto the truck, each holding a rake or shovels or hoes as they drove off.

They arrived safely at kibbutz Give'at Brenner, and spent the day working around the kibbutz. There was always plenty that needed to be done in any kibbutz, so they were warmly welcomed and invited to stay for a while.

During their brief respite at the kibbutz over the next few days, Amnon managed to swim in the pool a few times. Just splashing in the water, something he hadn't done for what seemed like ages, was a treat. It felt like the war had come to an end. What a wonderful feeling that was! Looking at his friends, then down at himself, he was struck with how rugged they looked. All of them were lean and fit, with deep bronze tans from so much time spent in the blazing sun. Amnon wished he could stay there for the rest of his life.

Wednesday, August 1, 1945

August 1st was his father's birthday, but Amnon couldn't telephone him; his parents didn't have a telephone at home. But the kibbutz's office manager let Amnon make a long distance call to his father's office. His father was very happy to hear from him.

"Mother is okay, but misses you terribly, and so do I. Are you all right?" he asked.

Amnon assured him he was, and that he was working in a kibbutz for the summer. His father knew better than to ask which kibbutz.

Elections had been held in England a few days ago, and the Labor Party won. Only time would tell if they would be any better for Palestine than the Conservative Party. Amnon found that democracy works in strange ways, some of which were really amazing. The war in Europe was barely over, the war in the Far East raged on, and in England, Winston Churchill, who headed the entire British war effort, was soundly defeated in the country's elections.

All of that happened during the world leaders' meeting held in Potsdam. Clement Atlee, the newly elected British Prime Minister, replaced Winston Churchill; with United States President Franklin Roosevelt dead, his Vice President Harry Truman replaced him at the conference, and Russia's Premier Josef Stalin was the third member of the triumvirate. The participants didn't reach any world-shaking decisions, and no one made even the slightest mention of the misery of the Jews then traveling freely in Europe.

News reports indicated tens of thousands of Jews were moving out of Eastern Europe and Russia and heading for Italy, where they hoped to get transport to Palestine. Members of the Jewish Brigades in Europe, and a special unit of the Haganah, were helping direct these refugees.

Another news report indicated that the first Jewish Congress since the beginning of the war was meeting in London beginning that day. Topping their Agenda was a demand that 100,000 Jewish refugees be permitted to enter Palestine; U.S. President Harry Truman urged the British Government to approve the request to permit immigration immediately.

Monday, August 20, 1945

Amnon's group received a new assignment, and even though it meant leaving the kibbutz, which all of them had enjoyed despite the hard labor, they looked forward to it.

As it happened, they were needed to replace the men who had enlisted in the Jewish Brigades from this kibbutz. In fact, most of the men who enlisted in the Jewish Brigades came from various kibbutzim throughout Palestine. In consequence, young men like Amnon came from all over Palestine to work in kibbutzim to fill the manpower shortage. The kibbutzim provided most produce, fruit, and dairy products, as well as some beef and poultry to the people of Palestine. A number of kibbutzim had begun to breed carp in fishponds they developed for that purpose. Fishing had also been developed in Lake Kineret by neighboring kibbutzim.

Amnon was told that numerous vessels, traveling by night, had left Italy with hundreds of refugees, and the British Navy had prepared a blockade in the Mediterranean Sea off the coast of Palestine. It wasn't easy to break that blockade, but try they must. That was why they were being readied for a great deal of night action.

Knowing the British were already aware of the Haganah's diversionary tactics and were prepared to deal with them, a wide variety of tactics were discussed. Diversionary action along the coastline was one thing; "But how do we divert British attention when they are in warships on the high seas?" That was the great dilemma of the day.

For the first time since his promotion to deputy commander, Amnon was invited to participate in a planning session, because he was told, Nechemia, his commander, gave him very high marks for strategic analysis, and his superiors had thus learned of Amnon's potential.

After a thorough examination of the map, which clearly showed the 42-kilometer stretch of coastline between Jaffa and Ashdod, Amnon felt prepared to suggest his plan.

"We need to create a double diversion, first in an area as close as possible to Jaffa, then shift to a center point somewhere southeast of Rehovot, about half way between Jaffa and Ashdod. This diversionary tactic will be repeated an hour later when the vessels have passed the blockade line. Let these vessels first travel in the direction of Ashdod, then as they reach two kilometers off the coast, change their direction toward Jaffa.

First, the British warships can't navigate too close to the coastline, since the waters are shallow and unable to accommodate them. Second, having assumed that we deliberately want to engage them in the north, leaving the south clear, they will direct their attention to the south. The British will assume the vessels will discharge their passengers in the south, and send forces to meet the refugees, whom they plan to later deport through Atlit. But in reality the refugees will be delivered to the north."

The Haganah command center liked Amnon's plan, and accepted it in full. He told his group that eight fishing vessels were expected to arrive in a few days, and that they should be prepared for some heavy night action.

Thursday, August 30, 1945

This was the heaviest night of activity Amnon could record. He was then in command of a 20-man unit, all his age, or slightly older. His orders were to block the road going south at the southern mouth of Bat Yam, a fairly new suburb of Tel Aviv located just south of Jaffa. That meant that they had to divert Jewish traffic to alternate routes while completely stopping British military and civilian police vehicles. Other units did the same at 15-kilometer intervals.

This operation began at 10:00pm.

At the same time, other units attacked police stations from Jaffa to Rehovot simply by firing at them and generally creating havoc. Fires were also started in various locations. Numerous old cars were set afire to create the impression of continuous fighting. The Haganah was sure the police stations would call for help, and they were set to block the passage of any convoy heading into that area.

That game was played for about an hour when an armored convoy was sighted coming from the Sarafand barracks, and getting closer. The 2-pounder the Haganah had captured just a few weeks ago was ready for firing, and Amnon waited until the first armored car was less than 10 meters away to give the firing order. Within seconds the first car was out of commission and on fire. A minute later it exploded with everything in it, and debris from the explosion hit two of his men, leaving them with minor wounds.

The convoy stopped, and soldiers jumped out to take positions behind the cars. In rapid succession, Amnon's men fired off the second and third rounds while the rest of his men covered the British soldiers with constant gunfire. The next two cars exploded within seconds of each other, and Amnon instructed his men on the other side of the road to keep silent while one of the men crawled close to the British from behind, and threw a couple of grenades, then immediately returned to his unit.

The convoy was pinned down and surrounded. However, Amnon's men kept their distance. Every so often they fired a few shots just to let the British soldiers know they were still there, and they constantly kept moving to the left and right of their original location to confuse the enemy and make them believe they were far greater in number.

The unit further south of Amnon's encountered only one patrol car, which it too pinned down, and the third unit farthest to the south stopped help coming from that direction. Their orders were to sporadically fire at the British soldiers to keep them aware of their presence, and though the British could have called in additional troops, it was doubtful they would do so at night. They knew all too well the Jewish resistance forces were expert night fighters.

Soon after midnight they got word that the first Italian vessel had signaled its position, which Amnon thought was too early; he had estimated their arrival time to be nearer to 2:00am. Later, however, he learned the Haganah officer on board had decided to send one of the smaller vessels to test the waters. Being small, it navigated very close to the coast, and passed through without incident. Then all the others followed suit and arrived soon after.

Upon notification that the vessels were arriving, they launched a barrage against the British convoys. At the same time, the units attacking police stations also stepped up their activity.

During the next hour, those refugees who could, jumped into the water and swam ashore while those who couldn't were taken ashore in a variety of small sailing crafts. In less than two hours, all of the refugees had been whisked inland and were on their way to Tel Aviv. Though Amnon very much wanted to see those new arrivals, his duties and responsibilities made that impossible. So, again, he simply blocked all other considerations from his mind and concentrated on the job at hand.

When the welcomed word was received that all refugees were safe and away from the beaches, Amnon's men gradually reduced their firing at the British, and quickly disappeared into the night.

Amnon's unit was picked up and driven to a safe house in the Arab quarter of Jaffa where they spent the rest of the night and the next day, for Jaffa was the last place the British would look for Jewish night fighters. Other units were taken to different locations to assure the British wouldn't find any of them.

News broadcasts the next day reported heavy fighting with Haganah forces in numerous locations south of Jaffa, making no mention of British losses or fatalities. Amnon and his men laughed heartily, but didn't dare leave the house for any reason, and waited for a Haganah courier to bring further instructions.

Haganah safe houses generally had no telephones, and the only method of communication was by Haganah couriers. Somewhat impatiently they waited for the courier. Late in the afternoon, an old Arab couple knocked their special signal on the door, and as they walked into the house, they threw off their Arab clothing to reveal two elderly Haganah couriers.

Instructions were for two men at a time to leave the house at 5-minute intervals beginning at 11:00pm. They were told to regroup in one of the houses near the main bus station in Tel Aviv. At just past 2:00am, Amnon was the last to leave. Walking carefully through the deserted streets, he kept alert for the sound of any moving vehicle or the sight of car lights, and quickly hid when his ears or peripheral vision picked up anything.

Fortunately, he encountered no one, and within the hour safely arrived at his destination.

Monday, September 3, 1945

Late the night before, Amnon had arrived in Jerusalem, and went home where his parents greeted him as if they hadn't seen him in years instead of only a couple of months.

His mother understood when he wouldn't answer any of their questions about where he'd been and what he had been doing. She accepted his brief reply that he'd been working in a kibbutz for the summer to replace the men who had enlisted in the Jewish Brigade.

His father felt insulted by what he believed was Amnon's lack of trust in him. He knew he was involved in something, but stopped pressuring him in the face of Amnon's stubborn refusal to answer any of his searching questions.

Instructions from GHQ, through Amnon's commander, were that he should return to school, which was starting that day, to divert suspicion from the ongoing refugee operation. So, though he didn't particularly want to, he returned to school where he was promptly called on the carpet in the Headmaster's office to explain his numerous absences of the previous year. Amnon told the Headmaster he had suffered a serious sinusitis infection coupled with migraine headaches; he was instructed to bring a note from his doctor, which was easily accomplished. The Haganah doctor issued a certificate verifying his illness. That effectively solved the whole problem.

A week later, Amnon learned that top Haganah officials were negotiating with officers of the Etzel and Lehi to create a unified force under one command to fight and resist the British. Amnon liked that a lot. He could never understand why there were three separate organizations, each one doing the same thing but with different perspectives in terms of timing and degree of radicalism. In recent weeks, the Etzel and Lehi had commenced their newest enterprise-- robbing British banks. Amnon didn't envy the job of the British authorities.

"When will the British Government give up Palestine? Surely they're aware of the hundreds of thousands of Jewish refugee survivors of the Holocaust, as well as those from Russian Siberia, flooding Italian seaports and those of other countries with their frantic efforts to obtain transport to Palestine because they have nowhere else to go..." Amnon's restless mind was at work.

The Haganah's clandestine radio station's nightly broadcasts kept the Jewish population of Palestine informed about the illegal arrivals of refugees. It also reported about the vessels caught by the British authorities whose passenger refugees had been taken to the detention camp in Atlit.

It became impossible for Amnon to concentrate on his schoolwork or studies because of the daily news reports announcing British searches, arrests, and deportations. Most of the time, those arrested were people who just looked suspicious to the arresting officer, and many were sentenced to three to seven years in prison.

Another curfew was announced, all public transportation was being searched, and British soldiers or civilian police were posted at every corner. The British still believed that only Palestine could guard their vital Suez Canal, and there was still talk of a land route to India, as well as fear of Russian expansionism, including Russian Jews.

"What's wrong with them? Don't they know all Jews hated Russia for their cruel pogroms in which Jews were hunted down and massacred? Aren't they aware those devastating Russian pogroms motivated the entire pioneer

movement to Palestine? Couldn't the British understand that just as thousands of Jewish men formed military brigades to fight alongside British soldiers against the Germans, the same Jewish men and many thousands more would join them in any war with Russia?" Such questions haunted Amnon.

He had difficulty finding answers to those questions. He wondered whether the answers could be found in political issues, but it became increasingly obvious to him the real issue was OIL. That issue not only concerned the British authorities in Palestine, but also was an issue of grave importance to the British Government in London.

The Arab countries had untold deposits of oil, with new discoveries announced frequently. Britain and virtually all of Europe depended upon Middle East oil to fuel industries and utilities valued at countless billions of dollars.

"By comparison, of what value is human life, especially if it's Jewish?" he reflected. *"To protect their oil interests in Arab countries, and keep the Arab leaders happy, the British have to display their solidarity with the Arabs, and they accomplished that by their continued restrictions against Jewish immigration to Palestine."*

Great news was announced from the Pacific -- Japan had surrendered! That meant the war in the Far East was over, which also meant that World War II had finally come to an end, wonderful for the rest of the world. But the war in Palestine raged on with no end in sight.

"So what should I do? Or, rather, what can I do? I can't just go back to school and ignore everything that is going on around me, when I am heart-and-soul involved with the continuing refugee operation. We must have a Jewish Homeland, an irrevocable Jewish State where the world's Jews, especially the Holocaust survivors, can finally find their salvation after so many years of cruel persecution," Amnon reflected.

Sunday, October 20, 1945

The British Government announced it would soon give India its independence.

Hip Hip Hooray!

"But what about Palestine?" Amnon asked.

British resistance to Jewish immigration continued in force. In retaliation, a major commando attack on the Atlit refugee detention camp released two hundred detainees into freedom. British pride was hit, which motivated the military to surround a section of Tel Aviv and conduct numerous searches for hidden Jewish defense weapons, as well as the freed refugees.

"Do they really believe we're that stupid?" Amnon mused.

British soldiers met citizen resistance in many locations, and anti-British feeling was growing by the day. The very air was heavy with a sense of impending explosion. People went to work and life went on, with difficult decisions that had to be made accompanied by many serious uncertainties.

"Where do I fit in this huge puzzle?" Amnon wondered.

Amnon received instructions to prepare for a new assignment. Two days later he was instructed to carefully study every rail link in Palestine, especially military and civilian police movements, along with their method of guarding train stations.

His main assignment was to cover the only railroad station in Jerusalem, located just south of the city, and his shift was from 7:00pm to midnight. The next shift worked and slept in their hiding place; the shifts rotated every midnight. They took notes on the number of guards and their shifts, as well as all other military movement. Trains departing from that station went to Tel Aviv with connections to Egypt through Gaza in the south, and to Haifa and Lebanon in the north.

Toward the end of the month, Amnon was instructed to report to a meeting of commanders, where he came face-to-face with men from the Etzel and Lehi. It soon became clear the meeting had been called to discuss the details of a massive attack planned against major railroad stations in the country's railroad system. The main focus of the meeting was the attack planned for the Jerusalem station, and all the railroad tracks leading west. This would be the opening attack in that operation, with the target date set for the night of November 1st.

Similar meetings were held throughout Palestine, for the plan was to put the entire railroad system out of commission. This would disrupt virtually all British and military life indefinitely.

Friday, November 2, 1945

Operation Rail began throughout the country last night. All railroad stations; rail links and crossings were severely damaged by a joint operation of the Resistance forces. The target of Amnon's unit was the main Jerusalem station.

At precisely 9:00pm Amnon and his men descended on the target. The guards, completely taken by surprise, didn't know what had hit them, even though there turned out to be more guards than they had reported earlier.

The attackers fired heavily from three directions, and threw grenades as they stormed the main entrance. Next, they shot out all of the light fixtures, causing total darkness that sent the British policemen into panic; they started shooting blindly in all directions without hitting anything. A few soldiers came rushing out wildly firing, but a few seconds later they lay dead or wounded.

As the firing subsided, the demolition experts laid their timed explosives along the rails, which were blown up within minutes. Sirens wailed in the distance, which meant someone had called for help. Amnon ordered two of his men to proceed straight ahead on the main road and ambush whatever help arrived. It wasn't long before a half-truck carrying a few men was ambushed and the men held at bay while the truck was destroyed. Minutes later, they blended into the night and made their way to a safe house where they hid their guns and ammunition before returning home under cover of darkness.

This wasn't easy, however, for many police cars had begun to patrol the streets using heavy-duty searchlights aimed in every direction. Amnon hid behind trees and bushes before deciding on the best route. He hurdled several fences in the backyards of the houses along his way until he reached his home. There was no hot water, but he took a shower anyway. The freezing cold water was such a shock he practically hit the ceiling. He dried off quickly and got into his pajamas.

Amnon's mother had heard him come in and prepared a hot glass of tea with some biscuits that he swallowed down standing in the kitchen.

"What were those explosions I heard?" she asked.

"We blew up the railroad station and some tracks south of the city. And other forces did the same throughout the country," Amnon confessed.

"Thank God, you're safe!" She hugged and kissed him before slipping back to her bedroom. Amnon quickly rinsed his glass and turned out the light to avoid anyone noticing it at that hour, then collapsed into bed where he slept like a rock until morning.

An interesting news bulletin reported that the British High Commissioner had announced his resignation owing to poor health, and a General Cunningham was appointed to replace him.

The Jewish leadership understood that the appointment of a general to the position of High Commissioner meant the British were planning military action against the Jewish resistance forces for the near future. Amnon wondered how long it would be before they moved into action, and exactly what form that action would take.

Again Amnon and his men went to the beaches, even though no vessels were expected. The plan was to frustrate the military and civilian police and keep them hopping. To this end, they shot over the tops of passing British vehicles, set up roadblocks to block traffic in crucial locations, cut telephone lines, threw Molotov cocktails at police cars parked outside police stations and generally did everything they could to drive the British crazy and out of Palestine. The main objective, however, was to draw the world's attention to the British Government's heartless indifference to the plight of the refugees. This was reflected in their inflexible restrictions against Jewish immigration to Palestine, coupled with the urgent need for an irrevocable Jewish Homeland.

Thursday, November 15, 1945

Ernest Bevin, the British Foreign Secretary, announced the Labor government would permit 1500 refugees per month to enter Palestine. This quota sparked violent demonstrations and protests throughout the country that drew live fire from the military and civilian police, leaving many of the protesters dead or wounded. The British army then mounted a major campaign of searches and arrests at numerous kibbutzim which met with violent resistance and left many casualties on both sides. In retaliation, British soldiers shot people without cause as they were entering Jewish settlements, which in turn caused chaos throughout the country. The war General Cunningham brought on would last for a long time.

At that point, there seemed to be some similarity between the British and the Nazis...

Tuesday, November 27, 1945

Last night, having received his new assignment, Amnon and his unit were on their way to Tel Aviv and points north. Haganah intelligence discovered that the British army had installed two maritime tracking systems designed to follow incoming refugee vessels. One such system was in the new British complex near Herzeliah, a peaceful little community a few kilometers north of Tel Aviv, and the other was north of Hedera, halfway between Tel Aviv and Haifa.

At the stroke of midnight, Amnon's unit attacked the British complex in Herzeliah while another unit attacked the other.

Having split his unit into four groups of four men each, they crawled nearly half a kilometer in the flat fields for about an hour and a half before reaching the starting point of attack. Amnon's plan called for each group to fire off intermittent salvos to make the British think they numbered in the hundreds. Firing from different directions began and stopped every few seconds. Each time a group stopped firing they advanced a few meters until all four groups were about 20 meters away from the complex. By the time they reached their destination, Amnon had a pretty good idea as to what forces were inside and outside the complex.

Since the complex backed almost into the Mediterranean Sea, there were only three sides to attack. The British had built two bunkers to the left and right of the main entrance, each about 20 meters apart. Amnon instructed the two groups to the left and right to attack from the front while the other two groups fired heavily, covering the bunkers and any other target shooting at them. A fierce battle ensued.

The two groups attacking from the north and south didn't need to shoot their way through because the British soldiers concentrated their fire on the center, creating the semblance of an attack. Soon grenades were hurled into the bunkers, and instantly there was silence. A number of British soldiers walked out of the main entrance to the complex with their arms raised in surrender. They were herded to one side and held at gunpoint. Two of Amnon's demolition experts entered the complex, and minutes later emerged, mission accomplished. Another few minutes and the complex was flattened.

Amnon made sure all the guns, rifles and ammunition they could find were put into the two armored vehicles parked outside the complex, then walked over to the group of British soldiers and told them exactly why the Jewish resistance forces were fighting their government. They said nothing, but as Amnon and his men drove off in the two captured vehicles some of the soldiers actually waved at them, which was quite a sight. It was close to dawn when they finally headed for base. Amnon's feeling of success was heightened back at base when he learned that the other tracking system had also been destroyed.

British retaliation mounted a far-reaching campaign of searches to catch the perpetrators. Though they interrogated hundreds of residents in many kibbutzim throughout the country, they met strong resistance and got precisely nowhere. Frustrated, they arrested hundreds of people, in various kibbutzim, who eventually had to be released because none were in any way involved, not just Amnon's operation, nor did they know anything of value.

Amnon

Monday, December 31, 1945

Every night they engaged in rescuing illegal vessels carrying Jewish immigrants, mainly from Italy and Greece, where they had waited weeks or months for transport to Palestine. The Haganah had numerous small crafts operating in the waters near the Palestinian coast, and all were actively engaged in either guiding incoming vessels or distracting the British. Unfortunately, those small craft could carry no more than 30 people, but on occasion they carried twice their normal load, making the operation more difficult and dangerous.

Men, women, and children comprised the nightly passenger load of refugees. All knew the trip would be dangerous. But since nothing could possibly be worse than the Nazi cruelty they had experienced, they willingly braved the trip to Palestine with nothing more than the clothes on their backs. They were hungry and thirsty, and many were weak and sick.

When the small craft unloaded its passengers as close to the shore as possible, those who were unable to jump into the water and swim or walk ashore had to be carried. Some of the craft got beached in the sand, and had to be forcibly pushed back into the water so the crews could take them back out to sea.

It was a horrendous operation, for British patrol boats searched and fired in all directions. Despite the known hazards, they fought for their cause and their assignment, and willingly continued their nightly diversionary tactics and rejoiced at their success in drawing British attention away from the illicit activities.

Occasionally they suffered a failed mission that resulted in the immigrants' capture by the British and transport to the Atlit detention camp. Though Amnon agonized over their probable deportation, he and his comrades forced their focus on the continuing necessity to ensure the safe arrival of other refugees.

Usually there was no time to speak with the refugees, for they could not waste even a second on anything but the normal courtesies. But once the refugees had been transported to various safe houses throughout the area, they could take the time to converse with and observe their refugee charges. Having willingly left everything else behind them, they had only the clothes they wore, which they were told would be promptly replaced with native Palestinian garb so as to avoid British notice. They were so happy and relieved to have at last arrived in Palestine that they laughed and cried, and couldn't seem to stop showing their gratitude by hugging and kissing Amnon and his men over and over.

One night they had a problem with a group of refugee arrivals when a boatload of women got beached on the sand. Either its captain had incorrectly calculated the distance to shore, or was so emotionally touched by his passengers that he hadn't concentrated on the job at hand. In any case, about 50 women between the ages of 50 and 70, haggard, very frail and also very likely ill, simply could not jump off the small craft. Owing to a shortage of help, Amnon's unit helped the women to reach shore, by both helping them into the water and hand-walking them to shore, and by carrying them to dry land. Some of the women were obviously terrified; some were simply awestruck that they were on land in Palestine.

The moment they'd gotten the last of the women to shore, the captain ran off; they tried to stop him. For some reason he started to scream in a language Amnon didn't recognize but thought might be Greek. Afraid to attract the attention of any nearby British patrol boats, Amnon instructed one of his men to shoot the captain in the leg. He fell to the ground and was instantly knocked out to stop his screaming. With all those women depending upon them for their safety, they didn't need an unexpected fight with the British. When the medic had tended to the captain's wound and also tranquilized him, they turned their attention to their refugee charges. They had bunched together on the beach, and some of them bent down to kiss the sand under their feet. Others appeared to be in a trance. In his broken Yiddish, Amnon explained the need to be absolutely quiet as they rushed them off the beach and started walking them towards the nearest safe house. With intermittent stops along the way the women caught their breath and gathered the strength to go on. It took about two hours to reach their destination.

Inside the house they had only a few chairs, the sofa, and the floor, upon which the women literally collapsed before revived with hot tea and some biscuits. Then, with the drapes drawn against the light outside, Amnon could clearly see their faces, but he could not speak over the lump in his throat. His eyes were filled with tears, that despite all their suffering including their dangerous voyage to Palestine, they could still manage to smile through their tears at him and his men. Amnon felt moved to assure them in his broken Yiddish that he and his men were proud and happy to be of some assistance to them.

As usual, the questions that haunted him surfaced once more.

"*Where had they come from? Which of the numerous concentration camps had they survived? Where were their families?*"

Amnon was sure the ravages of their previous experiences made them look much older than their actual ages; many were undoubtedly younger than they appeared. "*With good food and rest coupled with healthy exercise in a safe environment, in time their bodies and minds will heal,*" Amnon hoped.

Suddenly, he realized his feet, socks and boots were soaking wet, and that sand had gotten into his clothing. He decided he was not only wet to the skin, but also filthy and should take a shower. But he was too tired to do more than close his eyes for a much-needed nap. Not more than a quarter of an hour later he came awake and looked around.

Most of the women had fallen asleep where they were. In another room, piled almost on top of each other, his men were also asleep. He very much needed and wanted a shower, but figured there was no point; he had no clean clothing to change into. So he sat down on the floor with his back against the wall, not too far from one of the women, closed his eyes, and was dead asleep within minutes.

At some point, he was suddenly awake and listening to a woman who seemed to be talking to him in a very low and tired voice. Since Amnon could distinguish between numerous languages, he decided she was speaking to him in Polish, but he couldn't understand a word she said. In his broken Yiddish, he asked her, "Do you speak Yiddish?"

Grinning, she nodded; "Yes. So, where am I, and what's going to happen to me, and the others? Were there any men among the passengers that came in last night?" Taking her questions in turn, Amnon responded, "You are in what we call a safe house, and no, there were no men on the boat that brought you in or any other boat which arrived last night. At the moment, I have no idea whether there were any other boats, but the one that brought you carried only women."

She sounded so weak she could barely talk, but she obviously had lots of questions and wanted to. So Amnon got up and walked over to the kitchen where he found some biscuits in a cupboard and brought them back to her with a glass of water; there was nothing else in the kitchen except tea, and he, too, was very tired.

Watching her eating the biscuits and drinking the water, Amnon couldn't for the life of him determine her age, for she looked older than she may have been. Unable to control his natural curiosity, he asked where she'd been during the war, and shuddered when she said Dachau. He had read newspaper articles that described what the Allies found as they liberated each of the concentration camps, and he knew that Dachau was one of the worst. Her husband and two children had disappeared two years ago, she told him, and she doubted they were alive or that she would ever see them again.

As if she felt she had said too much, she stopped talking and closed her eyes. Perhaps, she felt a little better with the biscuits and water calming her stomach. Or, perhaps, her closed eyes and silence meant she was too tired of life just then. Too tired himself to conjecture further, Amnon closed his own eyes and was out cold within minutes.

When he awoke, the light shining through the curtains indicated bright sunlight outside, and the usual morning noises in the house assured him everyone else was also awake. Soon a horse-driven cart with food and clothing for their charges arrived. They gave the women bread and cheese with tomatoes while one of the guys brewed coffee in the kitchen. There was neither milk nor sugar, but nobody complained.

After everyone had eaten, Amnon gave each of their charges clean clothing and a clean towel and directed them to the only bathroom the house boasted. In his broken Yiddish he carefully instructed them to place their old clothing in the hamper inside the bathroom before showering, and put on the clothing he'd issued them. He explained they needed to wear clothing similar to that worn in the kibbutzim so as to avoid British attention. And, he went on to explain, they'd be taken to different kibbutzim where they'd live while they became familiar with life in Palestine before going to relatives, if they had any, or if they chose, could stay on in the kibbutz.

Questions came at him from every direction. A number of the refugees had relatives living in Palestine or they'd been given the names and addresses of friends of relatives. Amnon explained his unit had been assigned only to assure they arrived safely in Palestine, and others would arrange transporting them to their assigned kibbutzim and contacting their relatives.

Most of the day was gone before the refugees were on their way to their new temporary homes in kibbutzim scattered throughout the country. They were grateful, of course, but most of them appeared to still be in shock. Given their past experiences, including loss of loved ones, their dangerous voyage to Palestine, having to be rescued on the beach to avoid capture by the British, and now facing a new life in a new land, they were not likely to return to any semblance of normality for some time.

Amnon checked on his unit. Most were still sleeping, either on the floor or in cots, and since he could use some more rest, he went into a bedroom to sleep on the floor until he was awakened close to 8:00pm. Feeling hungry, he went into the kitchen where he quickly devoured a meal his considerate men had left for him.

Within the hour, instructions for their next assignment arrived by courier, together with the information that British civilian police were planning to conduct a door-to-door search of all homes, villages, and farming communities along the coast, meaning there would be new arrests. British military and civilian police were continually searching for illegal arrivals, or for hidden caches of Jewish resistance weapons. His unit's assignment was to stop any police vehicles heading toward the beach.

Amnon was still carrying his British passport, but his clothing made him look too much like the soldier he was. So he decided to mail his passport to his mother, which he did the next day.

Amnon and his men left the house after dark and swiftly walked toward the beach, stopping only when they reached their assigned destination near one of the many dirt side roads leading to the beach. Quickly, they dug large trenches in the sand and hid.

The entire refugee operation was enormous, and one that required many men, and many units similar to Amnon's were engaged in diversionary tactics along the beach to mislead the British. As always, Amnon made certain he had two scouts behind them to provide advance warning of any approaching British vehicles while they guarded the road after the boats landed. That night he followed the same procedure, and his two scouts were stationed at least two hundred meters behind them.

Around 3:00am, one of his men raced up from the beach to announce the arrival of some three-dozen refugees. Within minutes, while his unit was on its way to the beach, one of his rear scouts raced up to him to report a British patrol car was heading their way. Quickly he had two men place land mines in the road, covered them with dirt and connected a thin metal wire, which would detonate the mines the moment anything touched it. Next he sent his scout back to the beach to warn the shore unit of the approaching British patrol car.

Standard operating procedure was to hide wherever they could, availing themselves of the local topography. In this case, it meant lots of sand.

Within minutes, the patrol car neared their location, its huge searchlights circling the area left to right in search of illegal immigrants. An explosion suddenly split the night – the mines had done their job. Tires blew and screams ripped the air; one or more policemen had been wounded. Amnon's men were instructed to do nothing, but wait for his command. In the following silence, nothing and nobody moved. Then a few policemen finally jumped out of the vehicle, probably thinking they'd hit a mine and nothing more. But the moment they stepped onto the road, Amnon's battery-operated high beamed flashlight hit them square in the eyes, and over his loudspeaker he commanded: "DROP YOUR WEAPONS! RAISE ARMS OVER YOUR HEADS!"

There were five policemen, and the one wounded in the explosion couldn't be moved. Their arms, ammunition, and some other materials were taken. Then, since Amnon was the only one of his unit fluent in English, it was his pleasure to talk with the British policemen. Very soon, he not only learned they were raw recruits from Ireland, but that they also hated the British. Amnon told them that anyone who hated the British was their friends, and assured them they meant them no further harm, but would need to keep them until dawn when they would be free to go. Amnon sent his medic to tend to the wounded policeman.

The young Irish recruits knew nothing about the Jewish struggle with the British in Palestine, nor any knowledge of the Jewish aspirations; they had been told only that the Jews were ruthless terrorists who were shielding enemies of the British Empire. They were all young men who were ignorant of the true situation in Palestine, and they hated the British for the suffering they caused the Irish in Ireland.

"How very ironic I should meet up with others who hate the British," Amnon thought.

He sent one man to the unit on the beach assigned to the refugees instructing them to make a detour to avoid the captured policemen seeing any movement. Next, he consulted with his medic about the condition of the wounded policeman. For the next hour, Amnon educated his Irish prisoners as to the true nature of their ongoing struggle with the British in Palestine.

As they were preparing to leave, one of the young Irishmen asked to speak with Amnon privately, and when they were a short distance away from the others, he offered Amnon his name and address and suggested he could help the Jewish cause. Amnon told him that was not his responsibility, however, since the Haganah normally took the identity cards of captured British police or military to be passed on to their intelligence service, Amnon assured the young Irishman that he would see to it his information was passed along to the appropriate office. Before they left, Amnon instructed them to stay in their immobilized vehicle until help arrived, and he seriously doubted they moved an inch.

The next day, Amnon's unit was ordered all the way south to Ashdod so none of them would be recognized by anybody anywhere near the previous operation. Amnon immediately reported his entire conversation with the young Irishman to his superiors.

1945 came to an end with very little sign of progress in the direction of a Jewish Homeland. There was, however, significant political activity. A British-American Commission was organized by Britain to analyze the European Jewish refugee problem. With Britain's encouragement, neighboring Arab countries established the Arab League, which denounced Jewish immigration to Palestine and boycotted all Jewish products. There was no sign that the British were easing their inflexible stand on Jewish immigration. Confirming that, the sometimes brutal search for hidden Jewish defense weapons continued throughout Palestine. All three Resistance organizations had stepped up their activities against the British, who retaliated with daily arrests and deportations of those arrested to distant countries.

The Jewish population of Palestine remained strong, however, and vowed to continue the struggle. And, in the end, they believed they would win.

Thursday, January 3, 1946

Amnon was summoned to a special operational meeting in Haifa headquarters, and Avi was appointed to take his place on the beach.

Arriving in Haifa a little before 5:00pm and knowing the meeting was set to start at 7:30pm, Amnon decided to visit his Uncle Mordechai, his father's eldest brother, Mordechai's wife, aunt Tamara, and their family, daughter Rachel and son Dror, both still living at home. Amnon loved Uncle Mordechai, a very warm-hearted and sentimental man, and he always looked forward to seeing him and his family again.

During his summer vacations in elementary school, he had often visited Uncle Mordechai. Amnon loved these visits, for they were always very warm and affectionate to him. And despite the nearly ten year age difference between Amnon and his cousins, they always made sure to keep him entertained during his visits.

They all welcomed Amnon with hugs and kisses as if he were the Prodigal Son, until he protested he couldn't breathe, and then Aunt Tamara started stuffing him with food as if she believed he'd just come off a severe hunger strike. And then, everyone talking at once, the questions started;

"Look at you, so tan you're almost black. And, I can't believe how tall you've grown, and how skinny. Where have you been? And what have you been doing?"

"Please don't ask," Amnon begged them. "Believe me, it's better you know nothing. All I will tell you is I've been very busy working in a kibbutz near Jerusalem."

"And how are your parents?" asked Uncle Mordechai.

Unable to respond because he hadn't seen his parents for quite some time, he could only hope they were both well. Amnon fudged the question by telling them he needed to leave but would return soon. After more hugs and kisses all around, he was able to pry himself away.

He hurried to a private home on Mount Carmel where the meeting was being held, and arrived just before the scheduled time.

Elishav, one of the Northern Haganah commanders, greeted Amnon and began the meeting by congratulating him on a job well done. He then went on, "You are the youngest commander here, and you have been invited to join this meeting because I was told you possess an outstanding analytical mind together with excellent judgment of tactics." Amnon started to say how very much he appreciated his comments, but Elishav waved his hand: "Enough of that. We have more important matters to discuss here."

Spreading a large map of Galilee on the dining room table, Elishav pointed to a location just outside of Nazareth. The six commanders in the room, none of whom Amnon had met before, leaned forward to examine the map. Looking straight at Amnon, Elishav soberly enumerated all aspects of the reason for this meeting.

"The city of Nazareth and its surroundings is a major Arab area, and we have reason to believe the British military is building a special headquarters outside Nazareth. We think this large structure will be delivered to the Arabs when the British finally leave Palestine. Similar activity has been noticed in other areas throughout the country.

We must not allow the British to hide behind Arab lines. Therefore, we must not only destroy this structure, we must also destroy other such structures being built by the British now or in the future. And we will destroy them one by one. But it won't be easy because we have reliable intelligence that hundreds of soldiers guard each of these installations."

The terrain was familiar to Amnon, because he had been there many times in the past. Just then, Elishav's wife called from the kitchen to say that refreshments were ready, and Elishav directed his visitors to the kitchen for tall glasses of fresh grapefruit juice and biscuits. Then he led them back into the living room where they seated themselves on the sofa and some chairs. Amnon sat down on a hard chair, which he always preferred.

He was totally surprised when Elishav turned to him, and said, "All right, you've heard the problem. How would you destroy this facility?"

Totally stunned that Elishav had asked him, the youngest in the room (the rest were all in their mid-twenties or older and therefore Amnon's seniors not only in age but experience) he had trouble believing Elishav was soliciting his opinion. Elishav had sensed Amnon's thoughts, for he assured him, "I have deliberately chosen to ask you, the youngest man here, for your opinion, because this is my way of testing your tactical and judgmental military abilities."

When Amnon thought about it later, what really shocked him was that no sooner had Elishav requested his strategy, than without further thought he forthwith presented his plan.

"I'd plan the operation for 5:00am Saturday morning when the Arab peasants from the surrounding villages flock to the Nazareth market with their produce. They usually arrive by donkey and on foot accompanied by Arab women carrying big baskets of produce on their heads.

We should form a unit of twenty-four men dressed in British army uniforms that will march in the direction of the installation, and meet up with the peasants just as they reach the fork in the road that leads to Nazareth. One man, fluent in Arabic, will tell the peasants that the unit is there to guard them because they'd heard of a possible Jewish resistance attack. The Arabs will be delighted.

A runner will tell the guards at the front of the installation that a replacement unit is on its way. When the peasants are a few meters from the entrance, they will be steered through the entrance rather than straight down the road. Our fake British military unit will follow them, in full British style, into the complex. The guards will be perplexed.

While the peasants are walking with their produce toward Nazareth, two dozen or so Haganah men dressed as Arab peasants, and leading donkeys loaded with boxes of what will look like fruit and vegetables, will be waiting hidden behind the big rocks at the side of the road.

Before the authentic peasants reach the British complex, our false Arabs will join and follow behind the real group. The guards will be bewildered by the entry of Arabs carrying all that produce. But knowing they're supposed to be friendly to the Arabs, they'll do nothing to stop them. Then they'll see a British military contingency marching into the complex behind the Arab peasants. This will confuse them even more, but still won't raise suspicion.

With my best British accent, I shall advise the guards that all is okay, and we are their reinforcements since we had learned the Jewish Resistance was planning an attack. In the ensuing confusion, we will prod the Arabs into a state of panic, which will be relatively easy since they panic at the drop of a hat, and they will start running in all directions at the first shot fired.

Meanwhile, our men, who are already inside the complex, will take positions and block every doorway. Demolition experts will lay their timed plastics, and we will retreat under heavy fire cover. Two machine guns will be placed about two hundred meters from the front of the installation to block any British soldiers' attempts to pursue our retreat. Within minutes, the explosives will go off and the building will be demolished, bringing our mission to a happy conclusion.

I also suggest that fifteen minutes before this attack begins, a number of police stations in the vicinity be fired upon to create the impression they're the targets for the day.

Our trucks will be waiting for us just one half of one kilometer down the road, and will take us to various kibbutzim in the area, but not to Migdal Haemek. From these the men will take the early morning buses leaving for different locations. One truck will await our fake British soldiers up the road and drop them off in Nazareth where they will take public transportation to Haifa using the Arab bus company, as if going on leave."

Haifa was the major port city for Palestine, and British soldiers and sailors spent their leave time in the city's bars and cabarets located along the downtown highway.

The commander-in-chief, seeming confounded, looked at Amnon in silence. No one said a word, and all were staring at him. Amnon suspected he must have blushed at his own totally unexpected audacity, but it wasn't noticeable because of his deep tan.

After some moments of deep reflection, Elishav, the commander-in-chief, came over and fiercely hugged Amnon.

"You have a great future in the service," he assured him. Turning to the other commanders, he asked, "Any comments or questions?"

There were none. Amnon's plan was accepted without a single change.

The Haganah already had plenty of British uniforms and gear. Donkeys were quickly assembled from nearby kibbutzim, and Arab clothing was available anywhere. With only one day to prepare this entire operation, before leaving, the commanders quickly decided on manpower, arms, vehicles, some of which must be British, and all other requisite gear. The commander appointed Ariel to procure the necessary materiel.

Kibbutz Migdal Haemek was to be the starting point of the operation. The next day, Friday, was the one day they had to complete all their preparations; the operation was set to begin Saturday morning at 5:00am. This meant all involved units had to be at the starting point at 3:00am in order to be ready to move out at 5:00am, the official start time.

And so it was.

Precisely at 3:00am Saturday morning, Amnon's unit got into their vehicles, the fake British soldiers in one large transport truck, the rest of them in smaller cars. Their phony Arab peasants with their donkeys and cargo had left shortly after midnight, as they had to take mountain paths in order to avoid public roads.

With only their parking lights on, the vehicles moved slowly towards their destination and stopped about half a kilometer from the intersection the authentic peasants would be arriving from. The fake British military unit was ready to march as soon as they got the word from their front scout. The Haganah unit disguised as Arab peasants was already in place and waiting. As usual at that hour there was no traffic.

Following their usual habit, the Arab peasants moved along their regular routes with their produce for market, the women carrying vegetables and fruit in large baskets on their heads. The fake military unit came in from the rear and followed them. Amnon sent over one of his men who was fluent in Arabic and with a beautiful Arabic/English accent he explained to them the unit was there to help them in case the rumored attack by the Jewish resistance forces took place. Of course, the authentic Arab peasants were enchanted, and even offered fruit to the fake British soldiers, which was politely declined. And, without their notice, the fake Arab peasants followed suit.

As this procession approached the main entrance to the complex, Amnon's men made some noise in the rear and prodded them inside. They went in like sheep, followed by the fake British unit. Amnon ran to the front guards and told them that a replacement unit was coming in. When the guards asked what the Arabs were doing there, Amnon told them there was a rumor of a Jewish resistance attack, to which response they heartily laughed.

In the still of night, no movement could be seen or heard until Amnon rejoined his unit and ordered the first shots fired to create the necessary chaos. With the unexpected sound of gunfire, the real Arab peasants started running in all directions, dropping their baskets as they ran. At that point, heavy firing was directed toward all windows and doors in the complex, while the fake Arabs dropped grenades into the few bunkers surrounding the building. Just as Amnon had predicted, none of the British soldiers fired at either the real or the fake Arabs. In fact, they hardly shot at all.

With the bunkers taken out of action, heavy fire continued to be directed at all windows and doors. Then, each movement preceded by grenades, Amnon's front unit entered the building, and the other units secured the rear and sides without encountering much resistance. As they advanced further into the building, the demolition experts laid their explosives, and the moment they had finished, Amnon's men quickly exited the building under cover of heavy machine gun fire. Less than two minutes later, the entire structure was leveled to the ground, but they did not stop to look back as they rapidly moved out of the area. They did, however, notice the screaming Arab peasants, some of them were still running around in shock.

Once they were out on the road, the disguised British unit ran to the truck parked further down, jumped in, and drove off to Nazareth, where, Amnon later learned, they had commandeered a public bus going to Haifa by giving the driver a huge bakshish (tip).

The rest of them got in their cars and quickly drove off to the main road that linked several kibbutzim. The fake attacks on police stations served their purpose because they didn't encounter any police or British military transport on the way to their kibbutzim, where they hid the cars. And within the hour, every member of that expedition was on an early morning bus heading somewhere else.

All rifles, guns, ammunition and other weapons were safely hidden in the usual caches in each kibbutz.

Thankfully, they suffered no casualties, but that operation did cost them six donkeys. Less than an hour later, Amnon and his men were on the bus to Tiberias, a most delightfully warm location that was a great favorite of winter tourists, especially in January. Upon arrival, they checked into a hotel where they washed up, had a light meal, and pretended to be tourists.

Amnon telephoned his father's office and told him he was taking a few days of rest in Tiberias. His father was very happy to hear from him, but knew better than to ask where he had been or what he had been doing. He did, however, ask how long Amnon was planning to stay there and was told three days. Amnon then telephoned his contact number in Tiberias and told her where he was.

The next three days were the most glorious Amnon would remember. Late in the afternoon the day after he had called his father, Amnon's mother arrived. He gave her his bed and slept on the floor that night and the next. She was concerned he wouldn't sleep comfortably on the floor, but Amnon assured her he could probably sleep standing up.

They had dinner in a fish restaurant on the wharf of Lake Kineret. Amnon ate a whole grilled fish, throwing the tiny bones into the water underneath them, and enjoyed seeing the hundreds of fish attacking every morsel. Over their meal, they talked, and for hours after that, they talked, until the waiter advised them they had to leave; the restaurant was closing for the night.

Not wishing her to worry about him, Amnon was careful to avoid mentioning anything about his activities or the extent of his involvement. Of course, being a loving mother who was very clever as well as intuitive about her eldest son, she knew he was avoiding the main issues, but asked no leading questions and said nothing. Amnon's mother had the heart of an angel.

They did talk about the British government's inflexible attitude towards

Jewish immigration, their divide and rule policies, the creation of the Arab League, and the Arab violence that was often spurred by the British authorities. They talked about her family, particularly her two brothers who were still living in Egypt.

The next day they strolled along the beach of the lake, took their shoes off and touched the waters with their toes. It was very restful, sitting on one of the dead tree trunks and just staring at the water. Amnon badly needed the rest and enjoyed every moment of it.

Suddenly his mother turned and asked, "What are your plans for the future? Invariably the day will come when this war of attrition will stop. If we're lucky, we'll have a Jewish State and Homeland."

Amnon couldn't answer, for he really hadn't thought about the future then, or any other time. There was still so much to do and so many battles lay ahead. It didn't look like the British would be giving up Palestine anytime soon. So, fudging the issue, he responded, "I'm putting off making any career decisions until we know where we stand." He preferred not to tell her that, because his life was so often at risk, he didn't think it prudent to make long-range plans. He couldn't see the point in giving her a real reason to worry.

"We must fight for a Jewish homeland," she said. "After 2000 years of Diaspora, and particularly after the Holocaust, there is no question the time has come."

Then his mother handed him the shock of his life, as if offering a surprise birthday present.

"I want you to know that your father is secretly working for the Jewish Agency."

Amnon almost fell off the tree trunk. His thoughts leap-frogged from one possibility to another as he mentally offered congratulations to his father and also to the Haganah that they had actually contacted him. Of course, being an employee of the British Government meant his father was at much greater risk than him. But on the heels of that thought he remembered the Resistance forces bombed the Ministry of Interior building, and his father had gotten a telephone call warning him to get out of the building before it was blown up.

They walked back to the hotel, had a sandwich on the little balcony, and sipped freshly squeezed orange juice. Amnon decided to take a nap, and actually slept for four hours while his mother sat on a chair next to the bed and read. Later, she gave him a cold drink and they talked a while longer.

Amnon's men joined them for supper, and during the meal a courier arrived looking for him.

"You're wanted at the Tel Aviv headquarters tomorrow night," he told Amnon. Instantly, his little holiday was over, and his mother prepared to go home the following day.

The next day, knowing his mother would leave a little later on a Jerusalem bound bus, Amnon and his men were on the early morning bus bound for Tel Aviv. His men got off at various stops on the way and each headed to his assigned kibbutz. They knew he would be in touch.

It was hot when Amnon left Tiberias, but the temperature cooled as the bus climbed the mountain toward the Jesrael Valley. The view was magnificent as the bus laboriously climbed the steep road, and several times Amnon turned his head to gaze at the glorious scenery reflected by the silver waters of the vast Lake Kineret. Finally, the bus reached the top, and from then on traveled over mostly flat countryside. He leaned his head back, and thought about their recent night attack on the unknown British building near Nazareth.

"*The operation went smoothly, thank God, just as I planned. None of my men were hurt. We were in and out in exactly six minutes, and then sped on to different destinations to avoid capture by the British. I do hope they enjoyed finding six donkeys wandering peacefully on the hillside.*"

Oh, if donkeys could only talk!

Despite everything, however, Amnon felt sorry for the young British soldiers who had to die. They must have been raw recruits, since most seasoned Allied soldiers from the war days in Europe had doubtless been discharged after their years of war service. Certainly, having been deliberately kept ignorant of the true nature of the Haganah's fight with the British, those young men had no understanding of what was going on. Amnon wondered how many had been killed, how many wounded.

Interestingly, not even a brief paragraph relating to the destruction of the unknown building near Nazareth appeared in the newspapers. That strange omission strengthened his belief that his commander was correct when he stated 'the British are preparing certain projects for future Arab use.' Similarly, though the attacks on various police stations were announced, there was no mention of casualties.

The grenades they'd dumped into the bunkers had to have killed or seriously injured at least four soldiers in each bunker. Thus, by omitting any reference to casualties, it was glaringly obvious the lives of the young soldiers in those bunkers were worth less than nothing to their government.

While Amnon understood and accepted the urgent need to get the British out of Palestine, he couldn't accept the necessity to kill ignorant youngsters who didn't know the reasons for the Jewish struggle with their government, innocent victims who had nothing to do with their situation. Their government, however, presented a completely different story, a political one at that. The British Prime Minister, Clement Atlee, and his Foreign Secretary, Ernest Bevin, were obviously committed to the Arab League and with following a pro-Arab policy because of Middle East oil, or other selfish reasons; the lives of hundreds of thousands suffering survivors of Nazi atrocities meant nothing to them. And in Palestine, British hostility continued unabated.

The Haganah needed to rescue the refugee survivors from the European D.P. (displaced persons) camps. It was intolerable and unconscionable that after six years of war, those poor souls who had lost everything including their loved ones, miraculous survivors of the Nazis Holocaust in which millions were exterminated and burned, should be relegated to yet another camp -- this time a displaced persons detention camp. Faced with that glaring evidence of the British Government's anti-Jewish attitude, the Yishuv could easily believe the British and the Nazis had more than surface similarities.

Amnon

Most of the refugees were sick, alone, widowed, orphaned, with no vision of survival. Obviously, neither their past ordeals nor the need to give them a new future, made the slightest dent in the hearts of the British Government's bureaucrats. Only made sure the refugees were deported to, and incarcerated in, detention camps somewhere in Italy, or Austria, or God only knew where else for an indefinite period, instead of letting them complete their journey to Palestine to build new lives and look toward a bright new future.

Every time Amnon thought about this, his convictions grew stronger. Not only was the battle against the British justified, but an absolute necessity. It was up to them to help create a Jewish Homeland, so that finally the Diaspora would end and a place on the earth would exist where Jews could live in dignity and peace without fear of the mindless cruelty and death that always accompanied racist persecution.

Passing the intersection their operational convoy had begun its journey from a few nights ago, climbing the road to Nazareth, Amnon enjoyed looking out at the beautiful new plantings that the gentle winter rains had nourished and kept green, and he basked in the warmth of the blazing sun inside the bus. There was still a ways to go before the bus reached the intersection where the road forks to Tel Aviv, and the road straight ahead lead to the seaport city of Haifa, his birthplace and ever the city of his heart.

Haifa was built on the bay and extended to the top of Mount Carmel, where the view looked down on ships loading and unloading their multitude of cargo at one end of the bay, and at the other end of the bay was Acre, or Akko, the city Napoleon tried but failed to capture.

As the bus neared the coast, Amnon observed a lot of British police cars on the road. And just before reaching the coast highway, a police roadblock stopped his bus. Getting no answers to the many questions the police asked the passengers, as no one seemed to understand English, the police methodically searched the bus, its passengers, suitcases, handbags, and anything else in sight. Fortunately, they found nothing, and permitted the bus to go on its way. It was typical for passengers and definitely members of the resistance, to play dumb rather than get into a conversation with the British.

Easing back into his seat, Amnon wondered about the British foreign policy. It was one thing for them to be pro-Arab, but continually prodding the Arabs' already existing hostility to the Jews, and inciting them to violent protests, demonstrations and virtual warfare against the Jews, was quite another, for it underscored the indisputable fact of a virulently anti-Jewish attitude on the part of the British.

Historically, the chain of events leading to the present struggle in Palestine began on Day One that the first appointed British High Commissioner took up his duties shortly after the British Mandate for Palestine became a declared fact. His first duty was to appoint and install the Mufti of Jerusalem. Given the choice between the heads of the two most prominent Arab families, one of whom was known to be moderate and the other radical, the knighted High Commissioner chose the radical Arab to be the Mufti of Jerusalem.

Unless the British objective, even then, was to establish an insuperable obstacle to the conditions set forth in the Balfour Declaration, the first High Commissioner's deplorable choice made no sense. In fact, that Mufti's vicious anti-Jewish speeches and hate literature widened the existing communications gap between Arab and Jew on one side, and Palestinian Jews and the British authorities on the other. In the ensuing years, the widening gap on both sides led inexorably to the more and more volatile situation in Palestine and the present battle between the Palestinian Jews and the British over creating a Jewish Homeland in the Land of Israel.

Snapping out of his wandering thoughts, Amnon became aware the bus was nearing Tel Aviv, a beautiful and lively city on the Mediterranean Sea, another city he loved. With fifteen minutes to go, Amnon sat back in his seat and contemplated soaking up sun lying on one of Tel Aviv's many white sand beaches while licking the biggest ice cream cone he could find. On that relaxing thought, his eyes closed and he fell into a light doze from which he awoke the moment the bus stopped in the Tel Aviv terminal. Stepping off the bus, he took a deep breath, moved by the strong sense of Judaism in the air coupled with the familiar feeling he was in a truly Jewish city, both of which he always experienced whenever he visited Tel Aviv.

It was raining. The skies were covered with dark clouds through which a scattering of sunbeams struggled to shine down. He stood in the bus terminal, letting the gentle January rain wash his face, taking a few moments to enjoy the magnificent gray, blue, and golden vista. A few minutes later, Amnon set out on the brisk walk that took him to a safe house where he had a late lunch and a brief nap. But as he closed his eyes, he wondered what was next. What great plan had GHQ been hatching?

When Amnon awoke, he discovered some other fighters had come in while he catnapped, and they chatted for a while. The conversation turned to issues outside Palestine. None of them were really aware of what was going on in the rest of the world, for what they knew of the latest news came from radio broadcasts, whenever they had time to listen, and sometimes during military briefings. But they were usually so heavily involved with their regular military and underground activities, or hiding from or evading the British authorities, that there was scant time for pleasure. Free time was devoted almost exclusively to sleep.

They'd heard the Anglo-American commission had begun its investigation of the problem of European Jewry and Palestine. The investigation covered Nazi atrocities in the death camps that annihilated six million Jews, and the deplorable problem of more than two hundred thousand survivors living in displaced persons camps or detention camps because the British Government refused to allow them entry into Palestine.

"*Haven't the Commission members read the Bible?*" Amnon wondered. "*Don't they know where all of us came from? Don't they know our history, and who forced us out of our land and homes two thousand years ago? Surely the entire world knows the conquerors of Palestine, the Assyrians, the Babylonians, the Persians, plus the Greek, Roman and Ottoman Empires, forced us from our homes and scattered us all over their sphere of influence.*

Amnon

Now, after more than two thousand years, it's long past time for us to finally be allowed to return home."

Maybe having initiated this Anglo-American Commission, the British Government has decided to save face with the Arabs by making another entity responsible for returning the Jews to their homeland. If that's the case, how will the Arabs view the matter? After all, the British Government installed the radical Mufti of Jerusalem who incited the Arabs against Jewish immigration. The thought that they were now seeking an easy way out was mind-boggling, especially when the latest count showed the Yishuv numbered about 600,000 and growing daily. Nothing in this world can stop the immigration of our people to Palestine, with or without British sufferance," Amnon's thoughts continued.

News from India told of mass demonstrations against the British, because the Indian people wanted their independence, which was only natural. People everywhere want to be free and independent.

"Why doesn't the British Government recognize that? Aren't the British free, and don't they have their own country? What gives them the right to claim ownership of lands where they weren't born, and therefore can't claim by reason of birthright?" Amnon's mind was working overtime.

"Hurrah for the people of India! Indirectly, they're helping our cause. Isn't it high time the world rid itself of Empires and the concept of colonialism? Let each nation determine its own destiny, live its own life, and let its citizens enjoy freedom.

Ah, yes! Freedom. That truly great, but vastly misunderstood word, which nevertheless means so much to so many people in the world. Countless men and women have died to achieve it, and countless others have died to eliminate it in this most incomprehensible world.

The mind is such a magnificent invention of God. It permits us to think as much as we want about any subject we choose, and thinking is the only real freedom a man has when he is a slave, for the mind cannot be shackled.

But here I am, thinking as I always do when I have the time, trying to philosophize about mankind. Wake up, Amnon. You have much to do before mankind will find its new course," he admonished himself.

Someone poked his shoulder, and asked if he was daydreaming.

"Very probably," he responded.

The rain having stopped, it was time to go, and soon they strolled off to their various meeting places. Hungry, Amnon stopped at a Falafel stand on his way and bought himself a double portion that he downed in seconds along with a glass of Gazoz. Hunger assuaged, he hurried on to the meeting place.

The meeting started on the dot of 8:00pm. About twenty men were in attendance. The speaker was a man whose codename was Avner.

"The British," he said, "are intensifying searches for arms in our kibbutzim. We will resist these searches. We will disrupt their approach routes and we will stop this madness. This is not an easy task, since the search parties have grown in number. They now show up in huge military convoys of armored cars with hundreds of soldiers armed to the teeth.

Thanks to many American Jews as well as various arm dealers in

Europe, we're continuously buying and smuggling arms into Palestine. It's a job of unprecedented magnitude and full of risk. Interestingly, a lot of these shipments arrive via Arab countries such as Syria and Lebanon. These deliveries will be intensified in the future and we must provide added security to the movers and smugglers. Sometimes British soldiers sell us arms. We have to guard these deliveries too. Some of you will be receiving orders tonight about your future involvement in arms smuggling. Other units may be called in to replace those, already in operation. Also, some of your units will attack and ambush the British before they reach their destination."

At the end of the meeting, Amnon was ordered to move with his unit to kibbutz Kfar Gilaadi in the northern corner of Galilee, just a short hop from the Lebanese border. They would pretend to be farmers' helpers from the city while providing security for the arms being smuggled from Lebanon, always under the cover of darkness.

Amnon asked why they were being shifted from their regular duties since they'd become so good at them. The answer was that it was necessary to move the Haganah's members around at a faster pace since the British were determined to hunt down Resistance men. Unfortunately, Amnon was told, a number of Haganah men had recently been arrested in the Galilee.

Amnon was given the code name of his contact in Kfar Gilaadi. Immediately, he sent word to his unit members with instructions to meet in Kfar Gilaadi in two days. Amnon was given bus fare for himself and his men together with a small allowance for food.

Sunday, January 20, 1946

Just over a week ago, Amnon had arrived in Kfar Gilaadi in the Galilee after a long, tiring bus trip. His men arrived either by bus, hitchhiked, or a combination of both. It was cold in the mountains of the Galilee, where the night temperatures dropped almost to freezing levels. Unused to such low temperatures, Amnon had to adjust. He wore a sweater and a British made three-quarter length gray coat to stay warm.

During the day they helped the farmers. Every night, however, they went out to learn all the mountain paths, the surrounding Arab villages, ways of communication, hiding places, and security. Within days Amnon knew the territory like the back of his hand. They even entered Lebanon by these paths, and got as far as some of the main roads. Each path received a number, which they had to memorize. Each escape route became clearly marked in their memory.

Standard operating procedures included strict instructions that in case it was necessary to retreat, all arms were to be abandoned; it was more important for the British not to capture Haganah members with their weapons. If arms were confiscated, they would be recaptured when Haganah forces later attacked British military barracks and installations.

A few days later, Nechemia, Amnon's direct commander, arrived from Tel Aviv. They spent an hour going over maps, and Amnon's markings of the mountain paths and explanation of the terrain. He took pictures, particularly of Amnon's path drawings, and told him to expect word about deliveries in two to three days.

"Smuggled arms will arrive by mule. Each mule caravan will consist of eleven mules, to be precise. Take with you eleven mules and exchange them for the eleven mules carrying arms. This exchange should take place about here." Nechemia pointed to the location on the map. "Once over the border, back in Palestine, you'll unload the arms in a central cache about two kilometers south of Kfar Gilaadi." He marked the location on an old map. " Be sure to camouflage the spot exactly the same way you found it. From there, others will attend to distribution as soon as the arms arrive. When notified of a shipment, you have to penetrate as much as four kilometers into Lebanon, to the place I pointed out. The Haganah man you'll meet in charge of the transfer will keep you informed about further shipments. Every night he'll tell you what's planned the following night, until all arms have been transferred."

That wasn't the only way arms were smuggled into Palestine. But smuggling through Arab countries was least likely to be detected by the British because it was the least likely method they would expect the Jews to use. Fortunately, just as it worked for the illegal arms merchants, the method worked for the Haganah as well.

Two days later Amnon was told the first shipment was on its way, and during dinner at the Kfar, he received the code word for that night in a coded telephone message. Most personal calls for members of the kibbutz came during the evening meal because that was when everyone was in the central dining room. That night's code was 'Shoshanat Hasharon,' which Amnon committed to memory.

After dinner Amnon gathered the unit members in the kibbutz recreation room. All of them sat on the floor in one corner and discussed the coming events. That was the first time he told them what they were there for.

"We'll need to walk slowly in two lines, about ten meters apart. A distance of about five meters must be maintained between each man so that in case of an ambush we're not all together like a herd of sheep waiting to be rounded up for shearing. When a path becomes too narrow, the first line leads and the second line follows. The last man in the second line holds the lead rope of our mule caravan. When the path widens, the first line waits until the second is in position.

There must be absolutely no talking, no matter what. A scout will be about 100 meters in front of the first line. This scout will turn on a flashlight every thirty seconds for one second only, aimed in the direction of the oncoming line. In event of any suspicious movement, the scout will flash twice. When he notices the caravan, he'll flash three times.

When the scout is about five meters from the caravan he'll ask: "Who's there, and wait for the code. When he hears the code, he flashes four times to his rear, and proceeds to meet the leader of the caravan. If all is OK, he flashes one more time. If something is wrong, he flashes twice. If there's no flash, I'll assume that something is indeed wrong.

Once we have begun our move into Lebanese territory, one man will be in charge of the eleven-mule caravan. These mules will be exchanged for eleven

Arab mules when we meet the oncoming caravan. This way we won't lose any time and the exchange can be made with ease.

In the event of an ambush, everyone falls to the ground and stays there without moving. Don't shoot, and don't reveal your position. Wait and see what develops and follow whatever instructions I give.

"If we seem to be completely surrounded, take cover wherever possible where you are, but do not return fire. This way, the enemy will not know the exact number of men in our group, and we'll have a better chance to develop our exit strategy. Arabs do not fight at night, and British soldiers have not been sighted south of Lebanon, so chances of an ambush are remote. But it's always best to be prepared for any contingency."

Amnon set the departure time for 10:00pm, but they gathered at 9:45pm next to the arms cache, which was right under everyone's nose behind the rear wall of the dining room. They checked their automatic weapons, and made certain they had enough ammunition and grenades. One man carried a flare gun and six flares. Before leaving, Amnon consulted with the kibbutz intelligence official, who reported all was quiet across the border at sundown.

It was cold, the sky partly cloudy, and a slight easterly breeze hit their backs as they set out in two lines as Amnon had ordered to meet the caravan.

The terrain was hilly, with many ups and downs, but not too hard to traverse. As the night wore on and the easterly breeze kept up, the temperatures dropped and it got colder. Amnon expected to reach his destination within two hours; the Lebanese border was just a short distance from their departure point.

When they reached the location Nechemia had had marked on the map, Amnon had his men settle into a very large circle covering both sides of the path, still keeping the same distance from one another. They'd arrived before the incoming caravan. His deputy was charged with watching for the flashlight signals. Not long afterward, they got the signal that the caravan was identified. Taking two men with him, Amnon walked toward the approaching caravan.

The lead man was a Haganah member dressed in Arab habit, who quickly introduced himself as Admony. With him were two Arabs who were not introduced, and eleven mules. Each mule was fully loaded with large boxes strapped to their sides. A few mules also had an additional box strapped on top of their backs.

Once the mules were exchanged they kept the caravan moving rapidly toward the Palestine border. The moment they had safely crossed the border into Palestine they headed to the camouflaged cache south of the kibbutz. Admony and his new mules were on the path to a destination in Lebanon unknown to Amnon.

As soon as they arrived at the cache, which turned out to be next to the road leading to Tiberias, about two kilometers past the kibbutz, they stopped and unloaded the mules. The unloaded boxes were placed into a huge underground facility that had been built sometime in the past. The cache was secured and fully camouflaged before heading back to the kibbutz. Inside the kibbutz, the mules were taken to the barn, fed and watered and left to await their next trip.

They were in bed by 6:00am, leaving the transfer of the arms shipment from the kibbutz to other destinations within Palestine to whoever was responsible.

It was not quite noon when hunger pangs awakened Amnon. Quickly, he showered, shaved and dressed before going into the kitchen where he had a huge salad for lunch. Someone had baked a cake. He cut a large wedge that tasted absolutely marvelous accompanied by a hot glass of tea, which he drank with a lump of sugar in his mouth.

Friday, February 8, 1946

Shipments of weapons arrived every night, eleven mules at a time, the same Haganah man with two different groups of mules. Amnon couldn't tell the Arab mules from the Jewish ones; they all looked exactly the same. Amnon had developed a real love for those silent animals. Their unerring sense of direction was truly remarkable. Once they knew their route, they would guide the men in the darkness without a hitch even though they carried tremendous loads. They were of invaluable assistance in their mission and to the kibbutzim, and worth all the care and affection they received from everyone.

There had been numerous news broadcasts during the past few days. The British intercepted a ship carrying 900 illegal immigrants, and the outcome was not yet known. The Haganah blew up the Givat Olga police station, and some Haganah men were caught and arrested by the police while guiding illegal immigrants.

The British military accelerated their arms searches throughout Palestine. Many battles took place as the British met with stiff resistance to their search missions. Lehi attacked a British military barracks near Holon, and took all kinds of weapons. Later, soldiers from the barracks went on a shooting spree in the town of Holon, leaving two people killed and many others injured. The Haganah's recent attempt to free its arrested members ended in failure.

However, in the remote and quiet North Country, Amnon felt like he was on vacation. There was hardly any activity by the authorities. He believed that being so far away from the Mediterranean placed them in a peaceful zone. Most of the Arabs in the villages along the Lebanese border were Christians who had no fight with the Jews. There were also numerous Druz villages. Historically, the Druz were not overly friendly with the Muslims, and many Druz Arabs living in Palestine neither accepted the Mufti as their leader, nor were they hostile to the Jews. In fact, Amnon had been told that a lot of Druz men worked with the Haganah.

Thursday, February 28, 1946

All of Palestine seemed to be in flames, and every afternoon found Amnon glued to the radio, listening first to the official broadcasts of the British Government, and then the clandestine radio station. Between the two he could figure out what must have been happening.

Resistance activity during the past two weeks reached new heights. And in another bit of interesting news from Europe, Amnon learned that a Referendum held in the Displaced Persons camps clearly indicated that 97% of the people wanted to go to Palestine. No doubt that Referendum was held in lieu of the Anglo-American Commission working on the problem of Palestine. Amnon found that particular news item of the utmost importance; the message it sent strengthened their continued fight to get the British out of Palestine, and create a Jewish Homeland.

Hurrah!

Another British radar system to intercept illegal ships was blown up by the Haganah while a simultaneous attack on all British airports throughout the country successfully deflected military and police attention. Dozens of aircraft were destroyed and damaged, as were the various installations. The British announced the discovery of an arms cache near Safed and arrested everyone in sight. Safed was not too far from Kfar Gilaadi where Amnon was with his men. But he seriously doubted the British would bother any settlements near the Lebanese or Syrian borders.

Last night, to their surprise, a group of eight survivors, five men and three women, had accompanied the mule caravan on foot. Amnon and his men were delighted to see them, and Amnon's heart quite literally jumped with joy.

He didn't go to bed that night.

After hiding the newly delivered merchandise, he sat with the newcomers in the kibbutz's dining room talking for hours, the first time in a long time he'd had direct contact with new arrivals.

This group of people, all Polish Jews, had somehow managed to get together enough money for their passports, and then made their way through Bulgaria to Turkey. In Turkey they secured passage to Beirut, where they found a synagogue. They approached the Rabbi with their problem, and he put them in touch with someone who helped them meet Admony. Admony provided them with Arab cloaks and headdresses and that night took them to his rendezvous point with Amnon's caravan, and they walked along with them to the kibbutz.

Despite his broken Yiddish, which had worsened in his excitement at meeting refugees, they talked for hours, his fluent German helping to make himself understood. Amnon was very happy with that encounter, because everything they told him further strengthened his resolve to continue his activities - not that such stimulation was necessary.

Deep within his heart Amnon knew he was committed body and soul to the ongoing fight to oust the British from Palestine and the irrevocable establishment of a Jewish Homeland. One day in the foreseeable future [please God!] their long and difficult struggle would be acknowledged, and portrayed by the rest of the world as the most idealistic battle ever fought by the Jewish people.

Visiting with those eight survivors, listening to their suffering and their sorrow over the loss of much-loved family members, Amnon was sure he could almost hear their hearts crack under the weight of their accumulated pain. Yet, even through their tears, their eyes and expressions reflected their unbounded joy and relief they'd finally come home to Palestine, as well as hope for a new life.

They asked endless questions.

"What is the country like?"

"How is the battle against the British coming along?"

"Are there any political changes for the better?"

"What do people do for a living?"

"Are there many Jewish cities and villages?"

"What is the food like?"

"How is transportation?"

"What is the weather like?"

"Is it always warm?"

"Where are we going from here?"

Amnon sat with them for hours and, owing to language differences, struggled to fill them with information about life in Palestine. As he continued to answer their innumerable questions, his Yiddish improved greatly, and with patience on both sides, Amnon managed to describe the Palestinian lifestyle, their continuing battles with the Arabs and the British [making light of the dangers], and the work Palestinian Jews did in cities and in kibbutzim. He tried to describe their transport system, but gave up because of the transport problems caused by recent Resistance activities, instead explaining the whys and wherefores of their manpower shortage and why they would all be welcomed with open arms the moment they arrived at any of the numerous kibbutzim.

Yawning, because by then it was well passed dawn, Amnon suggested they all stay in Kfar Gilaadi for a while, as the kibbutz was short of manpower, and assured them he would advise the Jewish Agency of their arrival. Until he received word back, they all needed to await further instructions; they'd be advised of the next step in due course.

Amnon had each one of them write their names, addresses before the war, names of immediate family members, dead, alive, or unknown, and explained he would have those lists sent to the immigration absorption offices. He learned two were doctors who had spent the war years with the Russian army, two had been factory owners, and one was a musician.

The three women had seen their husbands taken and killed by the Nazis. They had gotten together when they learned they had all lived in the same town in Poland [the name eluded him.] One doctor chose to stay in the kibbutz, which didn't have a permanent doctor, and the other was immediately transported to a Haganah base to serve as the base medic.

It was such a great feeling to actually see those people settle in the kibbutz. Later, Amnon was told they worked very hard, and it was obvious to everyone they loved every moment of every day. They got up early every morning and would gladly have worked the entire day, but were made to stop when everyone else in the kibbutz did.

When Amnon and his men returned to the kibbutz after their night's work, they often found the new immigrants waiting with hot tea and biscuits or whatever else was in the kitchen. Amnon assured them it wasn't necessary, but to no avail. Their response was to fiercely hug Amnon and his men, their unspoken appreciation and gratitude obvious in their eyes and their body language.

In his much-improved Yiddish combined with some German, Amnon warned them that he and his men wouldn't be staying on at the kibbutz forever;

the moment their present mission was ended, they'd be transferred. They were sad to hear this, but Amnon had to tell them so they wouldn't get too attached. Amnon also told them they'd be transported to other kibbutzim when it was safe for them to be moved.

Shortly after Amnon and his men left Kibbutz Kfar Gilaadi, he learned the immigrants had decided, en masse, to stay on in that kibbutz if the other kibbutz members would have them, which of course was a foregone conclusion, for they were desperately needed. Any time Amnon had occasion to contact or visit that kibbutz over the years, he always asked about them and found they were living in the kibbutz happily. This special piece of news always gladdened his heart.

The past week had been so hectic that an important piece of news was ignored. About a week ago mass demonstrations took place in Egypt against the British. Even Egyptian police fought against the British military. The cause of the general strike and demonstration was the Egyptian demand for an end to British rule.

First India, and then Egypt. And here they were in Palestine wanting only to retrieve their Homeland, an entirely different situation.

The Arabs of Palestine wouldn't seek independence from Britain until the Jews woke them up. Instead, they were allowing themselves to become pawns of the British who incited them against the Jews in order to remain in Palestine as the saviors of the Arabs. Amnon hoped the Egyptians and the Indians would continue their battles for independence, for these battles would aid their own cause.

The news bulletin said British soldiers fired into the Egyptian crowds, killing and wounding dozens of innocent people. Amnon wondered what was happening in other British "protectorates," as they were called. But none of those 'protectorates' faced situations in any way similar to Palestine's. They were countries that had been captured and enslaved by the armies of the British Empire; the natives surely wanted their freedom from their foreign overlords.

In the case of Palestine, however, the facts were very different. The Jews wanted, and had every right, to retrieve their homeland, the same homeland that was forcibly taken from them more than two thousand years ago by a succession of similar Empires, every one of whom wanted Palestine because it was the land route that connected Europe with Africa and Asia.

Wednesday, March 6, 1946

Their nightly runs continued. Each night eleven loaded mules dropped their merchandise, and each night the cache was empty and ready for them. The arms must be entering their second phase of smuggling with the produce and fruit delivery trucks that went southward. Amnon didn't ask and wasn't told. Each one performed their assigned functions, and knew only what they were told at staff meetings. Otherwise, they had been taught not to ask questions and not to talk with any one about what they did, including closest family members.

There was a big hullabaloo in Kibbutz Biria, which was located near Safed. The British discovered an arms cache during one of their many searches and the entire population of the kibbutz was arrested. In retaliation, and as a demonstration of loyalty, thousands of youth from all over the country set up tents on the outskirts of the kibbutz. The outcome of the arrests was not yet known.

The Anglo-American Commission arrived in Jerusalem to start their investigation. Amnon was told all Jewish resistance and sabotage against the British were to stop while the Commission was in Palestine. However, arms smuggling was to continue in full force. All of them were praying the Commission's findings would favor an independent state for the Jews.

Amnon had been thinking a lot about the need to smuggle arms into Palestine, and into Jewish hands in particular. It must have taken skilled organization to buy weapons, ship them under false papers, smuggle them through countless borders, and finally get them to their destinations.

Names, locations, intermediary storage, delivery routes and personnel had to constantly be changed to avoid the ever-watchful eyes of the British authorities. Amnon wondered how all these mouths could stay so tightly closed to avoid dangerous leaks. The obvious answer was they belonged to people who were selflessly involved in a labor of love. Motivated by strong commitment and with tireless devotion to their cause, all those people performed without complaint whatever was necessary against all kinds of adversity. The need for clandestine operations was not new for the Jews, yet Amnon doubted they were ever planned and accomplished on such a scale.

Between operations, Amnon used his down time to speculate on the future of those lost souls, the homeless Jewish survivors. Forced to pay exorbitant fees for passage to Palestine on one of the illegal vessels that plied their dangerous way on the high seas, the survivors willingly gambled their lives because the British Government refused to permit their legal entry into Palestine.

"Why won't the British Government acknowledge the desperate need of those homeless survivors for a country they can call their own?" Endlessly, awake and asleep, Amnon sought an answer to that question. But there was none.

"Thus we must do whatever it takes to finally reclaim what has always been ours since the time of the Bible. We are entitled to this country by virtue of our ancestors' and our own birthrights. The accursed homelessness and suffering of the millenniums-old Diaspora must finally and for all time be ended, and our people permitted to live in dignity and peace," Amnon reflected.

Wishful thinking kept him awake seeking answers to more and more questions. Amnon was curious what the leading men and women of various organizations did to keep their minds clear in order to make the best possible decisions about the many problems they were forced to deal with every day. Amnon found it mind-boggling to have to make so many decisions every hour, and sometimes every moment, of the day and night.

"Perhaps the Anglo-American Commission will rule in our favor, which would be a gift from God! Surely this Commission will want to meet with our leaders and also with the Arabs who've been fed all manner of anti Jewish garbage by the British. But if we're lucky, the Americans in the Commission will be astute enough to see through the deviousness of the British Government, and

something good might yet come out of the Commission's investigation. The Commission cannot ignore the basic facts of life. People seek freedom. People want independence, no matter how tough their circumstances, because people want to rule themselves rather than be ruled by others. Having waged their own Revolutionary War against the British, surely the Americans know these truths," Amnon's restless mind pondered.

Wednesday, March 27, 1946

Last Sunday, Amnon had been told their mission was suspended for a few days, and his unit was instructed to report immediately to Nahariah, a small town a few kilometers south of the Lebanese border on the Mediterranean. Always short of manpower, the Haganah couldn't afford to lose even one man to the British, so their Security measures were of paramount importance. Thus Amnon's unit split into groups of four, each group taking a public bus to a different destination from which they would eventually transfer to other buses going to Nahariah. They hardly ever traveled together on one bus, and on a bus, they sat apart as though they didn't know each other.

By Tuesday evening all of Amnon's men had arrived in Nahariah and assembled in the Boy Scouts facility in one of the parks. They were met by Nechemia, Amnon's superior officer, whom Amnon had not seen since he left Kfar Gilaadi. He immediately launched into details of their new assignment.

"We're going to shift as many immigrant ships as we can to the southern shores of Lebanon. The Haganah will have larger ships than usual, some carrying as many as two thousand immigrants. We expect these large vessels to be sighted by the British. Smaller vessels will be directed to south Lebanon. You'll have to cross the border at night; meet these incoming vessels, unload their passengers, and bring them safely into Palestine.

The plan calls for the British to capture one or two of the large ships, which will create a newsworthy international incident that will inform the world of the facts in our situation, and embarrass the British Government. The world should help bring the misery of thousands of people in Displaced Persons camps to an end. While the British concentrate on the large ships, moreover, many small craft will unload immigrants in Lebanon where it's not expected."

Perusing a map of Lebanon, they decided on the most isolated beach between Rosh Hanikra, the crossing point on the Palestinian side of the border, and the city of Sidon inside Lebanon. The vessels would be directed to sail north of Sidon, and then take a diagonal southeast route to their final destination.

Once more they would cross the Lebanese border, but this time, from a point much further west than before. The hilly terrain had many small Arab villages, several of which were Christian rather than Muslim. Night travel through those hills was not easy, and it was bound to be even more difficult because they were not able to study the territory. Most of the roads were dirt.

Fortunately, Nechemia had brought with him an intelligence officer from the Haganah's secret service, who spent an hour with Amnon. They sat with a map spread out in front of them while he described the terrain in detail, recommended where they should cross the border, and how to connect with the road leading to Sidon, although they were not to go anywhere near Sidon. Instead, they were to go to a deserted beach about two and one half kilometers south of the city. He marked the best spot to leave the dirt road and take off across the open fields to the shore.

It was to be a harrowing experience...

Soon after it got dark they left in six antiquated lorries with no covers on top that Nechemia had somehow managed to obtain. They were all dressed like Arabs and their heads covered with kefias. Rifles, guns, and ammunition as well as one case of grenades were carefully placed on the floor in each lorry and covered with empty sacks. If anyone saw them from a distance, they'd think they were returning from work, or perhaps a wedding.

In total darkness, they crossed the border. When they reached the designated dirt road, [as described,] they turned on their lights and traveled normally as though they were Lebanese citizens. Wanting to be as quiet as possible, the noise of the antiquated engines aggravated Amnon so much he had to bite on his tongue to avoid screaming in utter frustration.

Fortunately, within an hour they reached the point where they would leave the road and drive through the fields. Amnon thanked heaven it wasn't raining; just a little rain would have turned those fields to mud it would have been impossible to maneuver through. As it was, at least twice they had to get out and push two of the lorries that had bald tires.

Each lorry carried a heavy rope for emergencies. They tied the ropes between the back bumper of one lorry and the front of the other, then to each of the two towing cars, and managed to tow them along until they got to where the fields turned into sand. They turned the lorries around so they were ready for departure, then got out and walked toward the beach in small groups.

The men spread out over an area of about half a kilometer, leaving two men to guard the lorries. The rest of them dug in their positions, and in the middle of that line Amnon placed one man with a flashlight who would be receiving messages from incoming vessels and communicating with Amnon.

The risk was enormous.

Anyone standing anywhere near the beach would be able to see flashing signals from the sea, but they had no other alternative. Lacking a radio, they could not communicate with anyone. They took cover in the dugouts each man had made for himself and waited for what seemed an eternity.

Amnon's mother always used to say that a watched pot never boils. Similarly, a watched clock or watch doesn't seem to move at all. Amnon could only hope and pray the captains of those fishing vessels were expert navigators who wouldn't stray off course and sail too far to the south or north.

After waiting for a long while, they finally spotted the first signal from one of the vessels. No one, including Amnon knew the number of vessels. All anybody knew for sure was the captains of those fishing vessels were paid exorbitant fees in advance to ferry immigrants to Palestine. Since most of these fishing vessels were neither built nor equipped for long ocean voyages, their captains were instructed to stop and lower their small boats that would be filled with immigrant passengers only after the pre-arranged signal from shore indicated it was safe.

Amnon's man signaled back, and within forty-five minutes the first vessel neared the shore. Two small boats were lowered, each with two crewmembers to row, and started the short trip to the beach. The small boats made what seemed endless trips back and forth, each time unloading up to fifteen passengers.

Meanwhile, four other fishing vessels arrived, one behind the other, forming what appeared to be a wall of boats. Each lowered small boats that immediately headed for shore. When the first group of fifteen had been put ashore, one of Amnon's men walked them to the lorries, helped them get in and had them wait, instructing them not to talk because absolute silence had to be maintained. This procedure was repeated with each incoming group until all immigrants were safely on land.

The moment their passengers were on shore, the fishing vessels left, quickly disappearing over the horizon.

Regrettably, since they hadn't known in advance how many immigrants to expect, there wasn't enough space in the lorries to hold everybody for the return trip to Palestine. But they had a deadline; this phase of that operation had to be completed fast to allow enough time to cross the border and get back to Palestine before dawn. Quickly they packed the lorries as full as possible, newly arrived immigrants standing in the backs of the lorries to make room for the others. Most of Amnon's men had either to stand on the running boards or walk alongside.

In this fashion, they headed into their nerve-wracking trip back to Palestine.

All the lorries were now top-heavy, and two also had bald tires, which worked against all of them. Three times while crossing the fields the lorries stalled in the slippery dirt, forcing everyone to jump off and push from the back while the lorry in front struggled to pull the others as well. The trip seemed endless; Amnon had no idea what time it was – the night was pitch dark. He was certain his blood pressure was rising off the scale as he prayed fervently they'd cross the border and make it back to Palestine before dawn. Amnon maintained constant communications with the front scouts, directing their speedy but safe progress back to where they'd cross the border into Palestine.

When they finally reached the dirt road, he started to breathe more easily, for now they could pick up speed. Amnon could see his watch, and was relieved to note it was just passed 4:00am, meaning within the hour they'd cross the border exactly where they had earlier. Looking up and around, Amnon saw the faint red of approaching dawn in the eastern sky, and felt certain they'd be able to reach Palestine on time.

As planned, four Egged (the name of the Jewish public transportation company) buses waited on the asphalt road inside Palestine, and they rushed the immigrants into them. Then they removed and hid their Arab disguises in a special compartment under each lorry, instructing the drivers to continue wearing their own Arab garb. That done, the rest of them laid down on the floors of the lorries so as not to be seen by either civilians or the British military, and swiftly drove off to Nahariah. As they approached the intersection where they would normally turn toward Nahariah, the first driver spotted a British convoy. Immediately he drove off the road and made a U-turn, followed by the other lorries, and soon they were speeding toward Kibbutz Eilon.

By the time they arrived, the sun had fully risen. They parked their lorries with the other kibbutz vehicles and replaced the license plates with Palestinian ones. Then, having first carefully hidden the arms and Arab garb in the kibbutz cache, they dashed out into the fields and joined the kibbutz workforce. Standard operating procedures included strong instructions that if encountered by British search parties, they had to produce their identity cards and say they were city youngsters who had volunteered to help their farmers.

After about two hours they assembled in the main dining room of the kibbutz to plan their move. Amnon called his contact telephone number with a coded message telling his superior officer their location. Since it was known British intelligence monitored all telephone conversations, they used a variety of codes that Amnon doubted they ever managed to break.

Having first found a bed for his tired bones, Amnon turned on the radio to catch the latest news, and learned to his great pleasure that the British had sighted a ship closing in on Tel Aviv with a rumored two thousand immigrant passengers on board. The announcer went on to report serious clashes between the police and members of the Haganah in Tel Aviv.

Apparently, the objective had been gained, although the outcome of the seizure of the ship and its passengers was as yet unknown. They had fooled the authorities, while bringing in around one hundred fifty survivors.

Delighted with the success of their mission, and as wound up as a coiled spring from the night's experiences, Amnon barely heard the anti-climactic news that the Etzel had blown up the police station in Ramat Gan, and tumbled into bed in a state of mild euphoria, his thoughts winging in all directions.

"We're bringing in survivors, one small boatload at a time, and I'm always amazed at how badly these people want to come to Palestine, despite everything they must surely know about our problems. They must know the severity of our situation vis-à-vis the British and the hostile Arabs, yet their destination is Palestine. Of course, in truth, where else can they go?

They're fed up with being homeless and want only to live in their own Homeland, never again to have to run to another country to avoid the terrors of mindless persecution. Despite the harshness of our present situation, Palestine provides the survivors with a shining beacon of hope that they will find the peace and rest so desperately desired and needed. With their sights firmly focused on a new life in their Jewish Homeland in Palestine, this is where they want to be no matter what they must endure to get here. For our part, my men and I will do everything we must to help them get here."

On that comforting thought, Amnon finally fell asleep.

Amnon was awakened at around 6:00am the next morning and called to the telephone. It was his uncle calling from Tel Aviv; his uncle's mother had passed away and it would be nice if he could attend the funeral set for 3:00 P.M.

at the Holon cemetery. Amnon expressed his deepest sorrow and said he would attend the funeral. He quickly washed up, and leaving a message for his men to stay and help out in the kibbutz until further instructions, was on the first truck out.

He barely made it to the Holon headquarters on time. The meeting was brief, and the instructions were concise.

"All forces will be on top priority alert. If called, all members must be fully armed and ready. We will not tolerate further indiscriminate searches of farms, kibbutzim or towns. Such searches will be far more vigorously resisted.

The transport of immigrants from Europe will be intensified. Therefore, all members must be ready for stepped up military action against the British. So far, we haven't attacked British patrol boats. However, this passiveness on the high seas will stop. We've recently acquired some fast boats that are armed to fight British patrol boats whenever needed."

That last new bit of information surprised Amnon.

"When did we get speedboats, and who will man them? I had no idea, but obviously someone in our organization has been preparing for these new battles," Amnon thought.

The Haganah continued to destroy British radar equipment and radar installations as soon as they were built to stop them from tracking down ships carrying immigrants. All unit commanders were called one by one into a room and given their individual instructions.

"You," Amnon was told, "will gather your men in Nahariah, and starting the next night you'll attack the border post at Rosh Hanikra every night until the British abandon it.

"Since Lebanon is a French Protectorate, as Palestine is British, we intend to create an open door at this important border crossing. If the British send reinforcements, drive them into the sea."

Amnon received permission to take two heavy-duty machine guns, two armor-penetrating cannons, pre-made Molotov cocktails, grenades, and plenty of ammunition.

Friday, March 29, 1946

On the stroke of midnight, Amnon's unit attacked the British post at Rosh Hanikra. They swarmed on the post from three directions. It was a very short distance attack as they had crawled to a starting point of about fifteen meters from the bunkers surrounding the main post. The machine guns and the armor piercing canons were stationed to cover the main road leading to the post. As this was a border point, they didn't expect British reinforcements to come from Lebanon in the north but rather from the south. The road was thoroughly covered and no one would be able to pass through.

Since the Haganah's arms and ammunition were limited, their fighters were taught to start their assault from a point that was extremely close to the target. This was nerve-wracking, but most successful in battle.

Several men, each holding six Molotov cocktails, hid in dugouts no more than three meters from the curb along both sides of the road leading to the post.

The two machine guns were positioned on each side of the road, but closer to the post. Cannons were about fifty meters away, also on both sides and parallel to the machine guns. Instructions were very clear. The saving of ammunition was paramount. Cannons could only be used if the Molotov cocktails failed and machine guns were to be used only if rifle fire did not subdue incoming soldiers.

Jumping off their lorry, about one kilometer away from the post, they quickly unloaded all their firearms and ammunition before splitting into two groups. Amnon led his group closer to the point from which they would crawl all the way to the bunkers. The second group, according to plan, stationed itself on both sides of the road to block any incoming reinforcements.

The night was partly cloudy, only a sliver of moon sailed through the clouds from time to time. After crawling more than thirty minutes, Amnon and his men arrived at the starting point for their assault, and quickly spread out to make sure all three of the visible bunkers facing south would be covered. The British didn't need to guard the north, because they had no reason to expect a raiding party to come out of French territory.

At exactly midnight, Amnon gave his men the signal to attack the bunkers from all sides, throwing in grenades whose pins had been pulled out moments earlier. Twelve grenades were thrown at the bunkers at once. Within seconds explosions shattered the silence of the night. Immediately, they launched a frontal attack, guns blazing at the bunkers, and within seconds they descended on the bunkers. Only one bunker kept firing, the other two were silent.

Two of Amnon's fighters were killed instantly and one was wounded. Realizing what had happened, Amnon single handedly rushed the firing bunker from the side and dropped in a grenade from its rear. An explosion was followed by smoke and silence. Turning to the post itself, they saw two soldiers guarding it. They neither moved nor fired. Amnon ordered them to drop their arms and run north into Lebanon.

The guards on the French side took cover on the ground but didn't get involved. When Amnon yelled at the Lebanese guards that they better leave because he was going to blow up the post house, they ran off. The small post station was destroyed and they took positions around the frontier as ordered.

The railroad track, connecting Haifa and Beirut ran parallel to the coast, but Amnon didn't have any more explosives. However, he and his men managed to damage the tracks enough to prevent the passage of trains. He then sent two men down the track towards Nahariah with instructions to damage the tracks about half a kilometer south to block any reinforcements from coming too close to their position. If British reinforcements did arrive, they'd have to stop the train a good distance away.

So far, so good.

Phase One of their attack was completed, but in the process Amnon had lost two of his dearest friends and comrades. Their medic attended the wounded man, who reported his condition was fair. Amnon was deeply sorrowed at the loss of his men. It weighed heavily on him for days.

They then waited for the second phase, for it was sure to come.

"Surely the British aren't going to leave the frontier open, definitely not

to us. If they do attack, however, it will be during the day; the British rarely went out to fight at night," Amnon thought.

He walked down the line toward the men who were dug in on both sides of the road, and told them to try and get some sleep. Then he sent one scout about half a kilometer further south with instructions to warn him of any approaching military.

Amnon's men knew what to do. Wait until the vehicles passed and entered the ambush zone, then attack with Molotov cocktails and grenades thrown at the soldiers who jump off, followed by rifle fire. If the force numbers more than fifty men, use machine guns as well. The cannons would be used only if the Molotovs and grenades did not stop the armored vehicles.

Before lying down to catch some sleep, they buried their dead comrades away from the road, and carefully marked the site. Amnon posted men at the old post, one on each side of the road next to the destroyed bunkers, and sent an additional scout up the hill to their east. But sleep wasn't possible, though the night was silent, and the entire area seemed to have become numb with shock. On the Lebanese side, he could see lights in their guardhouse, but no one was visible.

Amnon's heart was heavy, and his thoughts busy.

"How can I face the parents of the two young men who were killed?" he asked. In his heart, he cried for them, for he knew those men better than he knew his own brother. What a terrible fluke. But that was war, and all too often men got killed in wars. He might also have been a victim.

He closed his eyes, and all he could see were his two friends smiling in front of him.

"Hey, we did it, Amnon! We accomplished our goal. Please, don't be sad. We're not."

Amnon could almost feel their hearty thumps of congratulation on his back, and smiled through his tears even as the dawn crept slowly in from the east. He fell asleep.

One of his men woke him up at a little after 7:00am. There was no sign of military movement, and the usual morning train from Beirut didn't show up. The escaping guards must have notified the Lebanese authorities what was going on. The Lebanese must have notified the British that the most important frontier crossing between Palestine and Lebanon had been seized by unknown forces. The British would almost certainly guess the identity of the perpetrators, and the ball was then in their court.

"What will the British do about this situation?" Amnon was wondering.

Hours passed with no movement whatsoever, and he ruled out an operation from the sea because Rosh Hanikra had been built on a cliff. Scaling the cliff to assault from the sea would be suicidal. Nevertheless, taking no chances, he posted one man to keep an alert eye on the Mediterranean below.

Minutes past eleven, the forward scout ran up. He had spotted a slow moving British convoy of twelve armored vehicles three kilometers down the road. They wouldn't know the exact number of perpetrators, nor if they were there at all. As far as they knew, the Jewish attackers practice was to hit and run. Doubtless, they were concerned about how to approach the post.

110

Amnon

Amnon's men had successfully camouflaged their hideouts; crouching on the other side, Amnon couldn't detect any sign of them or anything else out of place. Tension mounted as the armored vehicles neared the ambush zone. When the first seven or eight vehicles passed into the ambush zone, suddenly all hell broke loose. Molotov cocktails hit the cars along with a string of grenades. Two cars immediately exploded.

As the convoy stopped, soldiers jumped off their vehicles, but the withering fire from both sides of the road mowed most of them down before they knew what had happened. When some cars in the rear suddenly made a sharp turn and headed back the way they'd come from, Amnon ordered their small cannon to lob two shots at the departing vehicles. One shot missed, but the second hit its target, causing the car to overturn and spill all passengers to the ground. Their machine guns blasted them for the next ten seconds, and survivors were seen running south.

The retreating vehicles had all stopped dead in their tracks.

"*What a sight,*" Amnon thought, "*And how humiliating for the mighty British forces!*"

The British transmitting vehicle must have been destroyed; there was no further action. The cries and moans for help from the injured made Amnon wonder how many men had been killed or wounded. But he couldn't stop to conjecture; he was certain the next scenario would be British aircraft, infantry, or even naval forces closing in on the area, so he had to move out fast.

Around 3:30pm, not far away they saw a single car carrying a white flag driving toward them. As the car neared the old post, Amnon ordered all his men back in their dugouts and hid himself behind a rock. The car stopped, the door opened, and to his great astonishment, Eliahu, one of their politicians who worked at the Jewish Agency, stepped out with his driver.

The Jewish Agency routinely denied having knowledge of, and always denounced, any and all acts of terror and resistance. Convinced that either the Etzel or Lehi were responsible for the attack on the post, the British had approached the Jewish Agency to intervene. Eliahu knew better.

In Amnon's brief conversation with Eliahu he learned that Red Cross ambulances were on their way, would arrive shortly to remove the dead and wounded, and that they were to leave the scene immediately to avoid being the target of a full British army attack.

Eliahu was a high official in the Haganah, and they did not want this event to become an international incident.

" We made our point," he told Amnon. "At nightfall, you and your men will immediately leave this territory."

Eliahu and his driver got in the car and started back. Then, just as the car was leaving, a barrage of fire was directed at them from the distance.

It seemed logical the British had brought additional forces that were now shooting at Amnon's men with heavy machine guns. They took cover in their dugouts and waited.

It was a long wait.

Placing himself in his opponent's shoes for a moment, Amnon tried to calculate his strategy. Since a major force couldn't get there before the next morning, the constant firing was obviously meant to pin them down.

Noticing some French soldiers coming to the Lebanese side of the border, and aware of the ongoing animosity between the French and the British, Amnon decided to go and talk with them. The officer in charge was a Parisian who was surprised and delighted at Amnon's fluency in French, and they chatted for a while.

Amnon told him they were leaving under cover of darkness, and would return the way they had come, which wasn't his plan at all, but it seemed prudent to say so. Actually, Amnon's plan was to move eastward through the fields for about a kilometer, then cross the border into Lebanon and continue to march on the Lebanese side. Just before dawn, they would cross into Palestine and hide out somewhere in the mountains of the Galilee until dark when they would proceed on toward one of the kibbutzim in the area.

As darkness descended, Amnon gathered all his men. Before they started on their journey, however, they had to bury the two machine guns and the cannon, for there was no way they could carry them along with their regular battle gear. Vowing to return for them, Amnon marked the place with rocks, and they headed out. They made a stretcher using two rifles and their wounded comrade was carried.

Walking swiftly eastward for an hour or so, they soon reached the border crossing to Lebanon and continued to walk all night. At four in the morning they crossed into Palestine. The terrain was very mountainous, just what Amnon wanted. They found a good hiding place and spent the day there. Since they were all exhausted, Amnon left one man on watch, ordering a two-hour rotation watch to follow. It wasn't long before they were asleep. The meager rations and water they had left would have to suffice until they reached the closest kibbutz.

When night fell, they were on their way again, swiftly heading due south until out of nowhere a rough voice demanded in Hebrew, "Who's there?" Amnon responded with the emergency password, and was warmly greeted before they were quickly escorted to the farming community nearby.

Their guide knocked on a door and within minutes the local Haganah representative in that village greeted them. Amnon made a quick phone call to Tiberias as soon as possible after daylight and within two hours a bus appeared. First hiding their arms in the local cache, they got on the bus and were soon on the road to Tiberias.

They were delivered to the local Haganah representative in Affula who greeted them warmly and took them to his shelter, where they were safe and far away from the war scene. They had suffered two fatal casualties, and their only weaponry loss, a temporary one, was the cannon and two machine guns. That night, the news bulletin simply reported an attack on the Rosh Hanikrah frontier post by Jewish resistance forces.

Monday, April 8, 1946

Amnon's unit didn't spend much time in Affula. The next day he received instructions to attack Rosh Hanikrah again.

Amnon

"Attack it, destroy the temporary post the British set up, and get the hell out!" were his orders.

The second time around, Amnon decided to operate from within Lebanon. The Lebanese and Syrian peoples had demanded that the British and French forces leave Syria. The entire issue had gone to the United Nations for debate. Amnon had the feeling that Britain and France, Britain in particular, were paranoid about Russian plans for territorial expansion. Russian troops had entered Iran some time ago.

"*Is it possible Britain is afraid the Arabs might join the Russian camp, hence their attitude towards the Jews with their intentions of a State of their own?*" Amnon speculated. Time will tell.

The Iran issue was also brought up at the United Nations by Iran demanding Russia withdraw its military forces from their country. The news also brought an incredible item: The British had arrested over one thousand Jews in Italy who were planning to immigrate to Palestine. Now there was something new that blew Amnon's mind. "*What right does Britain have to arrest anyone in a third country?*" he questioned.

That British action in Italy brought violent demonstrations throughout Palestine and particularly in Tel Aviv. The refugees who were arrested in Italy started a hunger strike, obviously supported by the demonstrations in Palestine. Finally the British relented and allowed those refugees to board two ships for Palestine. They were given special entry permits.

"*One thousand more. It seems like squeezing water out of stone,*" Amnon thought.

The bus that brought Amnon and his men to Affula arrived and took them as far north as possible. They were armed and carried extra food. This time they carried their weapons openly. Had they encountered any British search parties, they would have engaged them then and there. But no such thing happened. They got off close to where they had crossed the border before. It was getting dark. They waited until total darkness fell, put on Arab habits and headdresses and proceeded across the border. They walked one kilometer, then turned west and continued walking single file for a few hours, about five meters apart from each other. The high hills and fields were negotiated with ease. No one was around. On occasion they heard some animal, but otherwise it was quiet. They skirted two villages to avoid being seen. Amnon found a good hiding place on the next hill and decided to spend the rest of the night and the next day there.

That evening they started their march again and arrived at their destination within three hours. The British forces didn't imagine the same post would be attacked twice in a row. This was obvious because the few soldiers who were there were sitting around a fire they'd built in a steel barrel smoking and drinking. Amnon canvassed the area carefully, found the phone lines and cut the wires, then he and his men snuck up on the soldiers and took them by surprise. The newly erected post station was demolished in seconds and the eight soldiers, were handcuffed and taken back with them. Amnon made a point of walking through a grassy area to avoid leaving footprints. They walked briskly for hours heading east.

This time they were much closer to the Palestinian Border. Amnon was looking for an isolated spot in the hilly terrain and as soon as he found what he was looking for, he had the British soldiers tied together. Their boots and fatigues were taken off, leaving them in their underwear. They left them there and crossed the border at a fast clip. Soon they were on a narrow asphalt road leading to Kibbutz Ayalon. They heard a car in the distance and took cover on both sides of the road. The car passed them; Amnon couldn't tell who was driving it. Two hours later they arrived at the kibbutz.

They deposited their weapons but kept the Arab outfits and headdresses and got into a lorry, which took them further south. Amnon decided to spend the day in a Druz village, historically friendly to the Jews. They piled into a house where they were given Turkish coffee and food. Druz hospitality was exceptional. They relaxed and slept on the thin mattresses covering the floor. In the morning their host directed them to the lorry. They were already dressed like Arabs, and as soon as they boarded, the lorry drove off for Tiberias. As they approached Tiberias they took off their disguise and jumped off the lorry in the center of the Jewish quarter. Amnon thanked the driver, gave him some money for gas and off they went towards the safe house in town. It took about two hours for all of them to assemble at the house. Always wary of British police, they spread out and appeared at their destination one by one at intervals.

Saturday, April 13, 1946

Amnon was ordered back to Kfar Gilaadi. It was four days before his entire unit arrived. British military personnel were searching cars, trucks, and buses on all roads with a vengeance. Attacks on British police stations, railroad stations, and other installations had intensified significantly during the past two weeks, and so had the searches and clashes. Demonstrations were staged in every town. Pressure on the British mounted constantly. They didn't know where attacks would be coming from, or what time of day or night. What they called illegal immigration continued unabated. Not a day passed that some vessel didn't arrive somewhere in Palestine. The trickle continued. Many young newcomers joined the Haganah forces as soon as they arrived, although most immigrants couldn't, being mostly middle aged and older.

As soon as the entire unit had arrived, Amnon sent a telephone-coded message to his commanding officer, and that night the transfer of smuggled arms resumed. They continued this every night without interruption until May 3, 1946, when Amnon received orders to proceed immediately to Ashdod with his unit. Amnon assumed the entire arms shipment had by then been delivered.

Sunday, May 5, 1946

Appalling news had just reached them. The Anglo-American Committee of Inquiry on the Jewish problems in Europe and Palestine recommended the immediate transfer of 100,000 Jews to Palestine. However, it flatly rejected the creation of a Jewish state. To make things worse, the committee stated that Christendom also had a major claim on the Holy Land, and Arabs were entitled to religious and civil rights.

Amnon

Amnon missed the enormous demonstrations staged in Tel Aviv, during which violent demonstrators killed seven British soldiers. The authorities imposed a curfew on the entire city and held the entire population of Tel Aviv responsible for the fatalities.

At the same time, rumors persisted that British and French forces were planning to leave Syria. (There were minor British forces in the French protectorates.)

"*What hypocrisy!*" Amnon scoffed.

The Jewish community was outraged; tensions were high. Amnon was advised that immigration via fishing and any other sailing craft would significantly increase. They were determined to bring the lost souls of Europe home, and they were determined to create a Jewish homeland whether the British or any commission liked it or not.

"We will continue our struggle!" was the motto of the day.

The British Prime Minister announced his government would permit the 100,000 immigrants only after the Jewish resistance forces surrendered their arms and stopped all terror and sabotage against the British.

"*Wishful thinking, Mr. Atlee. Surrender our arms while you British continuously incite the Arabs against the Jews? Not bloody likely! And certainly not to you British, who bear a startling resemblance to the Nazis,*" Amnon said to himself.

Upon hearing this news, the Etzel and Lehi organizations attacked several British police and railroad stations causing tremendous damage. At the same time the entire coastline of Palestine was covered, bringing in as many illegal vessels as possible.

"We will not be defeated. The British government and the entire world have never seen greater resolve than ours. Our hearts are the only ones that bleed for our fellow Jews, the survivors of the most gruesome holocaust in history," Amnon declared.

Despite pictures and films of the death camps having circulated everywhere, and though so many thousands were still living in camps searching for a future with broken hearts and souls, the major powers of this world did not seem to really care.

"The message is quite clear, as far as we are concerned, not only are we going to continue our struggle, but we will enhance it, increase it, fortify it, and strengthen it with increased vigor and determination," Amnon told his men.

His unit was given a territory on the coastline to cover nightly. Amnon divided his unit in two. One continued to harass late night traffic on the main road and to create disturbances. The other, which included Amnon, was dug in on the beach spread over half a kilometer. When signals arrived, they were ready. Some nights they dealt with one vessel and some nights two or three. They usually managed to bring most immigrants ashore.

Wednesday, May 15, 1946

Last night they had gotten involved in a serious battle with the British police and one of their patrol boats. Around 1:30 am a small fishing vessel was sighted after signaling to shore. A British patrol boat came out of nowhere and began shooting at the vessel. Amnon immediately ordered return fire; the boat then began firing at them. Amnon's unit was spread over a half kilometer and the entire line started firing. Amnon was certain that from the patrol boat it looked as though the entire shoreline was firing at them. They must have radioed a British station in the area, because fifteen minutes later a British platoon appeared behind them and began firing. Amnon's men were dug in the sand and had a pretty good view of the soldiers after releasing a flare. As soon as they located the British soldiers they started firing vigorously. The other half of Amnon's unit let the British soldiers through and ended up attacking them from the rear.

Meanwhile, the fishing vessel was trying to turn to get away from the firing zone, but it must have been too close to the beach and got stuck. The thirty odd immigrants jumped off the vessel into the knee high water and began swimming or wading toward the beach. The patrol boat suddenly turned on a powerful searchlight and shot at the immigrants. Amnon intensified fire at the patrol boat, and finally managed to knock out the light, then continued firing non-stop until all the immigrants reached the beach. He then sent two men to guide the arriving immigrants toward a sand dune just south of the firing line. Amnon called the other half of his unit, and both rushed in. Pinned down, the British platoon ceased firing and looked like they were ready to surrender after Amnon yelled, "You're surrounded! Lay down your arms, and we'll let you go free!"

But instead of quitting, they started firing again in all directions. Amnon ordered a wipeout attack, and within minutes that entire platoon was out of commission. One of Amnon's men was killed, and several were wounded. They found the half truck the British soldiers came with and drove their dead and wounded to the closest Haganah medic, then came back for the immigrants and took them to Ashdod; this took three trips. They stripped the soldiers of their arms, dug a huge hole in the sand next to a sand dune and buried the dead soldiers. This wouldn't have been the first time British soldiers disappeared in Palestine; the British military often announced the desertion of their soldiers.

The British knew the Haganah was very active on the beaches, and also knew its forces were far more familiar with the terrain, far better than they were. The big problem of the day was the beached vessel, which they could do absolutely nothing about. But it could serve as a warning to other ships not to land in that area.

A radio news bulletin reported that the British had intercepted a large ship carrying illegal immigrants and all 1,600 refugees were taken to Atlit camp.

"Just what these poor souls need - another camp! But at least this one is in Palestine. We'll learn the outcome of this arrest in a few days," Amnon said.

Meanwhile, Amnon received an urgent call to attend a staff meeting in Holon.

Monday, May 20, 1946

At the hour-long meeting in Holon, on a large table, as usual, lay the map of Palestine with many handwritten drawings and additions made by the intelligence staff. Nechemia, who commanded several units including Amnon's, put his pointer on the road between Ashdod and Raffah, a small Arab town on the Egyptian border, just before the entrance to the Sinai Peninsula.

On that road, and the railroad running parallel to it, he pointed to eight bridges.

"These bridges must be destroyed," he told his audience of unit commanders. "We must hamper the movement of British troops."

Assigning each of them two bridges he ordered, "Make your own plans. I have to be in Jerusalem in two hours," and he was gone.

Amnon and his colleagues divided the territory among them; he got the stretch of road between Ashkelon and Gaza. It was decided to strike at all the bridges the following night.

Since none of his men knew how to handle explosives, when he got back to Ashdod Amnon arranged for a demolitions expert to join them. He then called his men to a meeting in the safe house where he detailed the location of the bridges and told them about the explosives instructor who was to join them within the hour. When the instructor arrived, they spent the next three hours learning how to place, install, and detonate dynamite and another types of explosives developed in the Haganah labs.

As it happened, Amnon had three bridges to knock out. One was on the road to Gaza, and two were under the railroad tracks. Dividing his unit into three groups, he appointed a deputy for each before giving them his instructions.

"One man in each group will carry the explosives, and two others will help place and later detonate them. The rest of the men in each unit will guard both sides of the bridges from a distance of at least 50 meters. Each unit will have a man, fluent in Arabic, riding on a donkey and wearing Arab garb. This man will act as the scout for his unit. The rest of the units will also be dressed in typical Arab garb, their heads covered with keffiyas."

Amnon obtained two dilapidated pick-up trucks typical of those used by Arabs from the Haganah's supply depot. (He had wanted three, but two were all he could get.)

"We'll have to do the best we can. Any questions?" There were none, and they got started as soon as the sun set.

Three donkeys, the three scouts, and as many men as could jump on went in the first truck. All the rest mounted the second. They were a sight to be seen, for they clung to each other all the way. Each group would get off near each bridge. About an hour later, they reached Ashkelon, but didn't enter the city.

Nearing the city, they ran into a British roadblock. Since they were all dressed as Arabs, a British soldier asked them in his broken Arabic where they were going. One of the men told him they were returning from a wedding in a nearby village and on the way back to Gaza. He let them through with no more questions. As they reached each destination, the deputy in charge of his group had to receive an okay from the scout before beginning his operation.

All bridge areas were clear, no guards or military personnel were spotted. The explosives were laid and precisely at 12:30am all three bridges were blown sky-high. The donkeys were left to peacefully wander as all men mounted the pick-ups, and were on the road to Beer Sheva.

Beer Sheva, an Arab town, was the best place for them to hide. Unlike Jewish communities, Arab towns and villages weren't guarded by the British. They slipped into town around 4:00 am and immediately went to the market square where they bought boxes full of vegetables and fruit from the first peasants who showed up with their produce.

After piling the boxes in each pick-up, they loaded their heavy arms under the body of the truck in a special compartment, keeping enough revolvers, ammunition and a couple of grenades for each man. One man sat near the driver and six sat in the open back. The rest of them, in pairs, took public buses to five different cities, with eventual transfer to Jaffa.

Although Arab buses were hardly ever stopped and searched by British military or police, which was considerate of the British, it nevertheless seemed prudent to make sure at least one man in each pair spoke Arabic. Without conversation and without questions, they simply pretended to be sleeping during the trip so that no one would bother them. It worked like a charm, and two days later all of Amnon's men congregated in Jaffa.

Thursday, May 30, 1946

Etzel and Lehi furiously attacked British installations. Simultaneously, the Haganah attacked and destroyed many northern bridges close to the Syrian and Lebanese borders. The battle over one of the bridges exacted a heavy death toll of fourteen members, but more than ten bridges were blown up. Etzel destroyed rail communications, soon repaired by the British, at the cost of eleven members lost and twenty arrested.

Amnon's unit returned to the beaches, and every night they awaited at least one vessel with its immigrant cargo. Unable to cope with numerous fishing vessels they could neither stop nor arrest in international waters, the British resorted to stop-and-search maneuvers on every highway, dirt road, and main road. But their efforts were foiled by Resistance forces' deliberate systematic sabotage and destruction every step of their way. Thoroughly frustrated, and very likely a bit bemused by Resistance determination to hamper their every effort, the British apparently overlooked Palestine's unattended shoreline, and focused guarding their inland installations. Their oversight was the Haganah's gain, which took every advantage of it in the following weeks and months.

Tuesday, June 4, 1946

Called to an urgent meeting at Haganah Headquarters in Tel Aviv, Amnon left Yaakov, his deputy, in charge and took off. Barely making the meeting in time, Amnon slipped in to find the room packed with commanders from all over the country. The meeting was very tense and also brief, information tightly packed into less than an hour.

"Information received through our intelligence service indicates the British are planning something big. There have been numerous secret meetings with police and military superior officers in attendance together with newly arrived top brass from England.

Actually, we shouldn't be surprised. Every effort the British have made to break Jewish Resistance forces so far has failed, and in consequence they have suffered many losses during the past two years. Their constant searches for Jewish arms has yielded little to nothing, and Jewish resistance efforts have disrupted virtually every aspect of their government and military operations."

It was further reported that the cost of maintaining British forces in Palestine had skyrocketed, and so had illegal Jewish immigration into Palestine, despite every effort the British made to thwart it. Moreover, their having placed ridiculous quotas on the immigration of European Jews to Palestine gained the British unceasing anger, frustration and deepening hostility of the Jewish populace. Together with their continuing pro-Arab attitude and their policy of befriending the Arabs and inciting them against the Jews, this had stiffened the Jewish backbones and strengthened their resolve to fight.

They further learned the Anglo-American Commissioners had come up with insensitive recommendations that made no sense whatsoever.

"How dare they say Christiandom owns the Holy places and Muslims are entitled to their civil rights? What about Jewish civil rights? Or don't the Commissioners believe we should have any?" Amnon questioned.

In point of fact, the Jewish people have had no civil rights from Day One of the accursed Diaspora when they were driven from their homeland two thousand years ago. Deprived of all rights, they were forced to flee for their lives from one country to another at the anti-Semitic whim of many rulers including Hitler and his jackbooted soulless hordes.

Now their hapless descendants, the survivors of Hitler's deliberate Holocaust designed to wipe the Jewish people off the face of the earth, apparently also had no rights. And now, despite the world's knowledge of all the Jewish people had suffered to date, the British had the unmitigated gall to tell them:

"Lay down your arms and we'll allow the 100,000 Jews to enter Palestine!"

They would all have to have been certifiably insane to bow down to the British and stab themselves in the back like that. Instead, they proclaimed,

" *We'll bring our brethren to Palestine no matter how much blood has to flow. And despite all your efforts to stop us, we will finally create our own Homeland right here in Palestine. Depend on that!*"

Amnon must have seemed to be in another world for a few unguarded moments, for someone poked his shoulder and returned his wandering attention to the commander.

"We're planning a major attack on the largest British military barracks in Palestine, and we're working with Irish soldiers inside the camp, to ensure we take as many arms as possible, particularly heavy machine guns and ammunition. We're in great need of Bren guns as well."

"Besides," he went on, "We need to show the bastards we're not afraid of them, and that we'll fight hard to achieve our goals. So, here's the plan…" he activated a slide projector and a picture of the northeastern corner of the British military barracks appeared on the screen.

Pointing first to the ammunition stronghold and storage warehouses, then the parking area adjacent to the main warehouse where a number of trucks could be seen, the commander continued: "We're going to employ four units to spearhead the attack. Three other units will be responsible for entering the main warehouse and loading the arms into the trucks. Those units will be introduced to an Irish officer whose men will drive the trucks to a loading position, and his men will also help load. The attack will start at 11:00pm. Four of our units will attack the other end of the barracks."

The next slide came on.

"Four different roads lead to the two main entrances. Each entrance is gated and posted with sentries and each serves a different purpose. An exit gate used by vehicles leaving the barracks is situated about 100 meters to the left of each entrance and is also manned by sentries.

All four will be attacked. The impression we'll create is that we are trying to enter the barracks from the front. Remember, the barracks is over two kilometers long from one end to the other. Meanwhile, the other units will cut through the fences from the back and penetrate the compound.

The Irish officer will meet you at the point of entry and direct you to the warehouse entrance. His men will bring the trucks to a loading position and help load. If anyone questions the loading, the Irish officer will produce paperwork authorizing the loading and transfer of arms.

The frontal attack on the entrances will automatically trigger a call for help. The British officers in charge will obviously concentrate on the area of attack. The attacking forces are to create the impression of a major attack without actually going anywhere. Some aggressive advance movements will be necessary here and there, but nothing more.

They're to think they're holding us back. As more help arrives in that direction, their fire will intensify. It's also possible they'll call for outside help. Be prepared to block any movement from the outside.

This battle should last at least an hour, during which our units will enter from the rear, which is at least two kilometers away. They'll load the trucks and leave through the crushed fences, drive through the open fields, which we determined are passable, to this dirt road." The commander's baton pointed to a small narrow road leading to the main road to Rishon le Zion. "Any questions?"

Amnon's arm was up before he finished: "The British use wireless communication systems and could call police stations in the entire area. Roads may be blocked, and who knows what might happen?"

Reassurance came just as fast.

"Not to worry. On the seat next to him, the first driver will find documents authorizing the transport. All drivers will wear British uniforms, and the first one will present papers to any roadblock officer. The rest of you hide in the back of the covered trucks. If you're discovered, you'll have to shoot your way out.

All trucks will drive in one convoy, which is typical for the British military. Once you're on the road, you'll proceed to Rishon Le Zion. One of our men will wait for you at a side road on a motorcycle leading to our warehouse.

After you've unloaded, the trucks will be driven by other men to a garage where they'll get a face-lift. All fighters involved in the confiscation of arms will proceed to designated safe houses in Rishon and Rehovot. Frontal attack will stop and a full retreat will take place once the trucks have left the barracks.

Now, for the most important part of the plan: While you're loading, our explosives expert will lay explosives to go off about five minutes after your departure. We want the entire warehouse to blow up so as to destroy the British army's largest arms storage facility. All commanders will report here, at 8:00pm, one day after this operation. Clear?"

"Yes, Sir!" They immediately responded, and hurried back to their men.

Sunday, June 9, 1946

British military were known to drink a bit on their days off, which would be extremely helpful to their operation. So this was the day they selected for their major break into that most famous British military storage barracks.

As planned, their units attacked the front entrances and created the impression that they meant to enter the barracks. While this charade was going on, Amnon's unit and two others that had been placed under his command sneaked towards the northeastern corner of the barracks. Crawling the last 200 meters, they cut through the lines of barbed wire and fences to the location where the Irish officer, wearing a major's insignia, waited with his men.

To Amnon's surprise, trucks were already in position, and in the still of the night they could hear the noise of the battle being waged at the other end of the barracks.

Within minutes, the main gate to the warehouse was opened, and they promptly started loading the trucks. Leaving room for those men who would sit on top of the cases, all trucks were loaded to capacity. They waited the few minutes required by the demolition experts to place explosives with their timed detonators in strategic locations. The moment they jumped aboard, the trucks departed.

Before the hour was out they drove through the cut fence, and minutes later they were racing along the dirt road headed east. They were almost to the road to Rishon when the skies lit up with the force of the explosions demolishing the greatest known British arms warehouse in all of Palestine. Grinning gleefully at each other, they settled into the rest of the trip.

On the road to Rishon, they were easily cleared through two British roadblocks when the driver of the first truck presented his papers documenting shipment of food supplies to a military barracks near Be'er Sheva, and they continued on their way. When British military men at each of the roadblocks asked what the explosions and fires were all about, the driver just shrugged and assured them he had no idea.

Their booty comprised three dozen heavy machine guns, three dozen light machine guns, a variety of light cannons that were mostly two pounders, some six pounders, 50 cases of Bren guns, hundreds of rifles and hundreds of boxes of ammunition. They also took mortars, grenades, and an assortment of revolvers.

Not a bad haul!

The next day Amnon reported to the designated meeting place. As everyone filed in, he noticed the Irish major in the little crowd. Since he'd been the first to greet him at the entry to the barracks they had raided, Amnon greeted him in English, and was nearly shocked speechless when he responded in Hebrew.

"Fooled you, didn't I?" he crowed before explaining he and his men's participation in the operation.

As it happened, they were all Haganah intelligence officers who had entered the British military barracks with faked papers, driving a typical military command car. They made their way to the arms storage area and took the guards out of commission. That explained the lack of security at the warehouses when Amnon and his men reached them, which was one thing that had puzzled and surprised him. But with his mind focused on the operation, Amnon hadn't let himself dwell on that detail. Now the mystery was solved.

The guards, having saluted the major on arrival, were told his men were replacing them. As they departed, they were knocked out and taken to a nearby shed, gagged and tied up. All twelve guards were thus neutralized within minutes, and the way was cleared for Amnon and his men.

About a half hour later, the commander in chief walked in. First, he complimented them on a job well done, and then announced the casualty toll for the attack on the front of the barracks was two men lost, several wounded. Later that day, a news bulletin reported that a Jewish resistance attack on the Sarafend barracks had been beaten back, which gave Amnon and his men a hearty laugh.

New assignments were given.

After being told it was imperative for all units to command every possible conflicted territory throughout Palestine, Amnon's unit was transferred to Jerusalem. Amnon was overjoyed by his new assignment, knowing it meant he'd be able to see his mother again. But he was concerned about his father's reaction to his skipping school, wondering what he'd said to the Headmaster who'd almost certainly called him, and how he had handled the matter.

Thursday, June 13, 1946

In high spirits, Amnon jumped on a Jewish bus departing the Tel Aviv terminal, then relaxed into the trip to Jerusalem. The bus was stopped no less than four times enroute, and each time British military police asked first for identification papers, then they asked where the passengers were traveling to and who were they visiting. Each time Amnon responded he was returning home after visiting a sick relative.

Arriving in Jerusalem, he hurried to his parents' apartment. His mother first kissed and hugged him, exclaiming over how much weight he'd lost, and immediately started stuffing him with what he was certain she felt would be enough food to replace the lost pounds. Later, when his father had returned from work, he also embraced him, refraining from asking any sticky questions.

It was a wonderful reunion after so much time, and they talked for hours. One of the topics they talked about was Amnon's truancy at school, and his father surprised him with the story of the events since Amnon's disappearance.

Soon after Amnon had disappeared, his father received a telephone call from the school's Headmaster asking why his son had not shown up at school. Amnon's father told him that he had sent Amnon to England to complete his schooling. Amnon's mother having finally filled him in on his son's involvement with the Haganah, including his alias, he had produced departure documents, and even faked Amnon's departure. He apologized for not having contacted the Headmaster sooner. Unfortunately, the political situation in Palestine had kept him very busy with urgent government work...

That evening, Amnon's father, who had always been a model of stiff-upper-lip British deportment under any and all conditions, actually entrusted him with a full disclosure of the intelligence service he was providing to the Haganah, and even told him of his great pride in his son's involvement. Feeling honored at his trust, and more than somewhat surprised, Amnon felt very proud of his father. Unable to verbally express his feelings over the lump in his throat, he settled for giving him a fierce hug, which was returned. Somehow, in his deepest heart, Amnon must always have known of his father's strong, but necessarily unspoken commitment to the irrevocable establishment of a Jewish Homeland.

A product of very strict Victorian parents combined with an equally Victorian upbringing, Amnon's father had always reflected the typical English gentleman's distinctive style and character. While he never hid the fact that he was a Jew -- for he was very proud of his heritage -- neither did he draw attention to his strong streak of human [menschlechkeit.] Jewishness. He kept his feelings private, for it went against his grain to display his strong feelings about anything, least of all his personal politics.

At this juncture Amnon began to look deeply into British Middle Eastern politics, which seemed contrary to normal British behavior and belief in fair play. Very likely it was their colonialism, along with imperialism, that was responsible for the peculiarly unbalanced British foreign and political policies, both of which had incited past and present demands for immediate independence from the people in the British colonies. First, there was the American Revolutionary War, more recently Egypt, India, and the Sudan had demanded their independence, and now Palestine also wanted out from under British rule. Exactly how much more would it take for the message to get through, and how long would it take before the British Government finally got the point of that message? People want freedom from foreign occupation, and they also want to run their own lives, and enjoy their own independence.

Realizing his thoughts had not always been fair to his father, Amnon finally understood that he was caught between two worlds. As a British Jew, he was brought to Palestine by his British Government employer, and once in Palestine he had finally acknowledged his secret heart-felt Zionist feelings coupled with his unspoken commitment and long hidden dream of a Jewish Homeland. Even now Amnon's father couldn't easily discuss that subject with him. But with his mother's loving encouragement and gentle support, his father finally let go. The next few hours were a revelation that finally spawned the long-standing bridge of silence between them, and made it a night Amnon would always remember.

Naturally, the next topic on the agenda was Amnon himself, and his father and mother took turns with their questions.

"You look so thin. Don't you eat well?" she asked.

"God forbid, have you been ill?" he asked.

"Your eyes are so red, and they have such dark rings under them. Don't you get enough sleep?" his mother added.

"What are you doing out in the sun so much that you're so tanned?" queried his father.

"Believe me," Amnon assured them, "I'm as healthy as a horse. I'm lean, which is healthier than being fat. I have a huge appetite and eat like a ravening vulture. I get as much sleep as I need, and working in a kibbutz out in the sun several hours a day, of course I'm tanned. So you can both stop worrying about me, and we can get on to more important stuff."

With that out of the way, Amnon spoke briefly of his activities in rescuing immigrants off the boats. Ever mindful of the looming possibility of capture by the authorities and preferring to spare his parents real cause for worry, he said nothing of his military and terrorist activities - what they didn't know couldn't hurt them. Many Haganah members had been caught and deported to prison camps in distant countries like Cyprus, Eritrea, or Mauritius. Others had been jailed in Palestine, and still others had been hung. Fortunately, thanks to Haganah intelligence services, Amnon, like most of his comrades had legitimate identity papers in several different names.

When his eyes would no longer stay open and he couldn't stop yawning, Amnon kissed his parents goodnight and finally tumbled into his warm, cozy comfortable old bed. Out cold the moment his head hit the pillow, he sank into a dreamless sleep.

Thursday, June 20, 1946

In a new and ominous move, the Etzel abducted five British officers and shot two others before demanding the release of their men jailed in the Akko prison. This launched a wide-ranging British military offensive throughout Palestine. Total curfew was imposed on all cities and communities, and searches were conducted everywhere. More armored cars than ever prowled the streets and highways accompanied by patrol cars, and the authorities announced that anyone seen on the streets at night would be shot.

Ernst Bevin, the British Foreign Secretary, made his most hateful speech against the Jews and Zionism to date, his language offensive enough to merit comparison with that of Hitler's worst anti-Semitic diatribes. Predictably, this triggered additional retaliatory action by the Etzel and Lehi forces, attacking police stations, railroads, and any British installations along their way. In retaliation British courts swiftly handed down death sentences on two captured Etzel members. The fate of the abducted British officers was not yet known.

At Haganah headquarters, frenzied activity had all of them near the boiling point. Amnon's new instructions were to study first hand the entire line dividing the Jewish and Arab neighborhoods, from the northernmost point of the Old City to Sanhedria, the northernmost suburb of Jerusalem. Tensions were high on both sides. The Jewish population was under strict curfew while the Arabs were permitted to roam free.

With the British military stopping and searching and questioning everyone on the streets, Amnon spent the next week walking the entire dividing line with an English novel, Magnificent Obsession, under his arm. Stopping to view every alley, passage, fence, possible attack and escape routes, and possible bunker and roadblock locations, he committed everything to memory, written notes would have been suicidal. He had a designated Haganah girl friend, to be used as a reference if necessary. Every time he had to study a location, he sat down on a bench, fence, rock or curb, opened his novel, and pretended to be reading.

Owing to the newest curfew, operating at night was the trickiest and most dangerous part of this scrutiny, for British military and civilian police were so jittery they were ready to shoot anything that moved. Anyone out walking in the streets after dark was at high risk of becoming a moving target for their itchy trigger fingers, making covering his assigned line at night more than somewhat difficult. But despite all the dangers, Amnon managed to do his job.

Fortunately though, the armored cars with their lights on roared at high speed through the streets, and were so noisy he could hear them from a distance. That gave him time to climb a tree, jump a fence or simply hide in any niche available. No soldiers were visible at night, and only a few intersections harbored watchful policemen. Unfortunately for the stray animals of Palestine, they were again at high risk; well aware of the Resistance movements' well-honed nocturnal expertise in sabotage and terror, the nervous British military and civilian police shot at any noise or suspicious movement, too often ending the lives of innocent stray cats and dogs out scavenging for food or water.

Sunday, June 30, 1946

Yesterday was "Black Saturday." British military and civilian police arrested all the leaders of the Jewish community as well as thousands of Jews suspected of anti-British activities. The authorities set up two camps for all the people placed under arrest. The British Government resolved to break the Jewish will, which only proved they had learned nothing at all from the Jews' long history. Etzel released two of the abducted officers and the third one supposedly escaped. However, they held two more officers. Amnon doubted that would change anything, and the mood throughout the country was bleak.

"*What next?*" Amnon wondered.

Representatives of the Yishuv decided to sever all contacts with the British authorities until their leadership was released and the 100,000 refugees allowed to enter Palestine. The British suddenly announced they would reverse the death sentences on the two Etzel members, and Etzel released the last two officers, resulting in a total of four lives saved.

Amnon's men had spent the last ten days in Kibbutz Ma'ale Hachamisha outside Jerusalem, helping farm work, and Amnon decided to pay them a visit.

Daniel Rosenfeld

The Haganah hadn't been active for the past couple of weeks, and most members were working in kibbutzim and community farms. Some were engaged in espionage, spying on British military movements throughout Palestine, for the Haganah's intelligence service had to know every move the British made.

Saturday, July 6, 1946

Amnon joined his men at the kibbutz. He loved that mountainous area. The air was crisp and clear and it cooled down in the evenings. With their help, the kibbutz built additional terraces for growing vegetables. That was hard work, for they hauled large stones and rocks to build the terraced steps into the mountainside.

With the completion of each wall, dirt was poured in to create a large terrace. These terraces ran downward, and the entire mountainside became usable. It also required little or no irrigation as the heavy morning dew provided moisture. Although backbreaking work, they thoroughly enjoyed every moment.

The level of idealism they all worked and fought with was indescribable. Not a day passed that Amnon didn't think of the plight of the Jewish refugees still lost somewhere in Europe without a destination, without hope of reaching Palestine, without knowledge of what their tomorrows would bring. For a refugee family to be together and desperate was one thing, for at least they had each other. But it was something entirely different when the refugee was alone in the world, having lost his or her dear ones. Their suffering was undoubtedly greater, their hope extremely difficult to maintain, and every passing day worsened their already desperate situation as the British Government continually issued new edicts against immigration to Palestine. News of ships being intercepted and their passengers transferred to foreign detention camps further discouraged the refugees. Lacking an alternative and because they had no place to go, they were forced to stay in the camps.

Amnon's burdensome thoughts nagged at him, particularly when he went to bed at night and had time to reflect on the lives and endless suffering of his survivor brethren. Though a year had passed, Amnon couldn't forget the poor woman who had sat on his bed caressing his hair and called him her son. Similarly, Amnon continually saw his fallen comrades as well as the dead British soldiers -- young men who had no idea why they were killed, nor, probably, what they were fighting for. Poor souls! He felt sorry for parents losing their young men in far away countries. As for his lost comrades, Amnon shed tears, just thinking about them.

How could the British be so stupid they didn't realize they could achieve their political objectives cooperating, instead of fighting, with the Jews. What had the Arabs ever done for Britain? Every Arab in sight had been living under the rule of the Ottoman Empire for hundreds of years. Some Arabs, and Iraqis in particular, had offered to help the Nazis at the beginning of the Second World War, whereas the Haganah fought alongside the British to rid Lebanon of these Nazis sympathizers. The history of the British pointed to usual modus operandi, including the judicious use of bribery and deceit.

Doubtless in the case of Palestine, the British were motivated by oil, or the land route to India, or their Suez Canal. It was so hard to find logic in political decisions when so many people were suffering. There was no justification for people to suffer that much. The decision of the Jewish leadership, to fight for independence and kick the British out of Palestine, was the only solution. In this at least, the Jewish leadership and the general Jewish population, the Yishuv, were in agreement. The entire Yishuv was united in its aspirations. Amnon's own idealism was strong, just as he sensed it was in every one of his men. Amnon could see it in every Jewish settlement and in every Jewish worker. Productivity was high, every man, woman and child contributed to that enormous effort.

They had to succeed.

The British were putting tremendous effort into their battle against the Resistance, and the Jewish Agency had decided to cool things for a while and concentrate more on the immigration issue. The big push was to try to bring to Palestine the 100,000 stranded refugees. So far Amnon couldn't see any improvement. Statements issued from official government offices, and made by high officials in public or over the radio were hateful, pro-Arab, and blatantly anti-Jewish.

Time and again they were told the British were seeking to stop the violence in Palestine, the British asked the Jewish resistance to denounce terror and lay down their arms. But so long as the British incited the Arabs, and as long as they rejected the idea of a Jewish Homeland, that was not going to happen. Amnon couldn't foresee any change in the Jewish leadership's approach to the subject. However, in the interests of some semblance of deescalating, the Haganah stopped most sabotage operations for a while to calm the British Government and its local authorities. It was hoped the change in pace might affect a more positive attitude and affirmative action.

Monday, July 22, 1946

Apparently, the Irgun (Etzel) neither accepted nor trusted that sudden calm. This very day at noon, they launched one of their worst terrorist activities against the British, blowing up the southern wing of the King David Hotel, which housed the offices of British military headquarters in Palestine. Ninety people were killed and hundreds more were wounded. The Yishuv were shocked, and the British launched their own retaliatory reign of terror in a series of extremely thorough searches throughout the country. Thousands of troops were deployed. Both Tel Aviv and Jerusalem were put under nightly curfew, and the military conducted methodical, thorough house-to-house searches for the terrorists.

Tuesday, July 30, 1946

A great news item was broadcast. The Anglo-American Commission announced that it recommended regional autonomy for Jews and Arabs under a British protectorate, definitely a step in the right direction. Whether the British could or would implement such a plan was questionable.

Ironically, in the earliest days of the development of Palestine, the Zionist Organization would gladly have accepted a Jewish Homeland under

British rule. Now, owing to the British pro-Arab and other unacceptable policies, Palestinian Jews would sooner trust a cobra than the British. Moreover, it was doubtful the Arabs would accept this proposition after having been so long the beneficiaries of British political incitement and favoritism. Yet there was something positive about the Commission's recommendation, for it indicated a change of heart from its earlier statements.

Tel Aviv was still under strict curfew, and British forces were searching frantically for Jewish terrorists, but it was doubtful they would find any. The British Commander-in-Chief made a public statement to all his soldiers not to befriend Jews, adding the anti-Jewish sentiment that the Jew's pocket was his weakest point, a reference to the myth of Jewish avariciousness. But to young British soldiers with only a vague idea of what a Jew was, the hate-filled reference meant nothing. Moreover, even a cursory review of British history attested to the Empire's continuous exploitation of its far-flung colonies for the sole purpose of increasing the Empire's wealth. An unbiased British history provided a much more accurate example of pure avarice than that attributed to the Jews by the anti-Jewish Commander-in-Chief.

Thursday, August 1, 1946

To day was Amnon's father's birthday, and he went home for a short visit, bringing with him a bag full of vegetables and fresh grapes. Owing to the curfew, which began at 8:00pm, he'd have to either spend the night or leave early enough to return to base before the curfew. For some reason, just the thought of spending the night gave him a headache, and he was anxious to get together with some of his buddies to learn more about the underlying reasons for the high tension in the Jewish community.

Fortunately, Amnon's father arrived home early. He wished him a happy birthday, kissed both his parents goodbye, and was on his way within minutes. Regretfully, he had not had sufficient time with his mother, and he knew she felt bad about that. However, he was certain she would understand, and he rushed to reach his safe house before curfew, barely making it in time.

Inside was noisy. The sun had just begun going down, and the main living room was semi-dark. No one bothered to turn on the light. Looking around, Amnon saw everyone there was roughly his age, with perhaps a handful of men who were older.

They were all discussing the Jewish Agency's decision to temporarily stop sabotage activity. Some felt if the Resistance continued at the violent pace it had been going, the British would become even more vengeful concerning the immigration issue. Amnon took the position that the immigration issue was not related to the terrorist activity, but rather to the underlying British insistence on their retaining control of Palestine because it was the key point in the route linking Europe with Africa and Asia. He further insisted that sooner or later Great Britain would have to abandon Egypt, leaving Palestine the only strategic point from which the British could guard the Suez Canal. In addition, there was the land route to India and the fear of Communist expansion.

Most of his comrades did not appreciate his comments. They were not as globally oriented or astute as he was. Their opinions were based on simple occurrences within Palestine. Fortunately, all of them agreed on a dual goal of getting rid of the British in Palestine, and the establishment of a Jewish state.

The phone rang. Amnon was called to speak to his cousin. A feminine voice at the other end of the line, said,

"Amnon, I have to see you in the morning. Grandma in Tiberias keeps asking for you. She misses you very much and wants to see you. Could you possibly visit her tomorrow? And, if you can, could you bring her a basket of cucumbers? You know she loves to pickle her own cucumbers."

Amnon asked his "cousin" how she was and they shared nonsenses for a while. The coded message indicated he was being called to an urgent meeting in Tiberias, and must get his unit there ASAP.

Telephoning Ma'ale Hachamisha, Amnon instructed his deputy to round up all the men and move out to Tiberias immediately.

Monday, August 5, 1946

With all the curfews, endless roadblocks, searches, and interrogations, it took most of his men two days to reach Tiberias. Few buses went to Tiberias every day for one reason or another, but lots of people were on the move to other destinations. That was good, because they were less visible and mixed well with the crowd. Arab buses also plied that route, and some of Amnon's men used them. In fact, Amnon traveled on the Arab bus quite often.

At the safe house in Tiberias, the entire unit was told they must prepare for a major operation in Haifa. Haganah intelligence had reported the British were bringing two large passenger ships into Haifa harbor to deport thousands of immigrants they'd been holding, primarily in the Atlit detention camp, and other camps in Palestine.

Plans called for their sabotaging those ships, even if they had to block the port of Haifa. Maps were spread out on the large table and Amnon, together with his deputy and the visiting commanders, went over them in detail. His instructions were clear.

"You'll be responsible for guarding the sabotage units, which will act at the wharves and in the waters. You'll have to knock out any guards guarding the entrance to the port, and inside the port grounds. You'll receive two additional units, both of which will be under your command. This will be a major operation, and we want you to take charge of it."

Amnon asked to meet with the commander of the sabotaging units to fully understand his attack plan. To ensure the success of the mission, there had to be faultless coordination between the units charged with damaging the ships, the unit charged with rendering the harbor impassable, and the covering ground forces.

Amnon was introduced to Meir the next morning. Meir wasn't as tall as Amnon, but very muscular, and heavier. His dark brown eyes penetrated anything he looked at. He was quick on his feet despite his weight.

The map covering Haifa Bay and downtown Haifa lay in front of them on the table. It was an English map prepared by the British military and doctored by Haganah's intelligence personnel. Meir pointed to the entrance to the harbor from the bay, and explained that his forces would come by small craft with his men rowing four explosive-laden boats. He suggested Amnon's men secure the tower, communications room, and the grounds as quietly as possible before his men began their operation. Entering the harbor compound was Amnon's problem. They discussed timing, and determined the earlier they started, the better.

It became clear that the only way to enter the compound would be in disguise, and Amnon assured Meir it wouldn't be hard to accomplish. They set the time for the attack at 10:00pm, giving Amnon an hour to secure the grounds. All they needed was the date and ETA of the British ships, so that they could sabotage the ships the night of the same day they arrived. If the British started loading the immigrants too early, their mission would have to be aborted. Meir and Amnon decided how they would communicate while waiting for the start of the mission. The next morning Amnon left for Haifa with a pair of binoculars in his backpack.

When he got to Haifa, Amnon took the bus to Mount Carmel and got off at a point where he could view the harbor from the top. He located a suitable position next to a small group of pine trees and hidden from the road, sat down on the ground and scrutinized the port from the main entrance to the wharves.

Slowly scanning the many buildings and warehouses in the compound, Amnon searched for the communications room knowing it had to be in one of the buildings. The first sweep was not successful. In his second sweep, seeking anything that even looked like antennas, he came across a set of wiring that made sense. He finally zeroed in on what had to be the communications room and committed the location to memory.

Next, he carefully made mental notes of the route leading from the main entrance to the building that housed the communications room, also noting the number and locations of the guards, making specific note of those locations with two guards or more. After mentally reviewing the entire plan and attack procedure, Amnon committed both, the plan and procedures to memory, pondering that this had to be the most complex operation he'd undertaken to date.

Preparation for entry, elimination of guards, and silencing of all communications had to be precise, as did their retreat, Haifa's harbor being in the dead center of the city's downtown area. Besides being ringed with police stations, it had a central police station within the compound. Not wanting to lose any men, Amnon had to ensure the retreat would be as foolproof as the entry. In several other operations the British had caught some Haganah men.

Though Amnon considered himself a bold, hard fighter, he was definitely not any sort of gambler or unnecessary risk-taker. He carefully planned this operation with meticulous attention to the slightest detail to make sure absolutely nothing was overlooked.

Carefully observing the guards at the main gate and other locations over the course of the day, he noted that each shift was four hours, meaning there would be a change of guards at 8:00pm, which further meant they would have to spring into action precisely at eight.

Just before it got dark, Amnon left his observation post for a brisk walk down the mountain's winding road with its beautiful trees along both sides. The long walk led him to Hadar Hacarmel, the main Haifa suburb built on the slopes above the city, and he swiftly walked straight to his uncle's house, a block away from City Hall on the edge of the Arab quarter.

As always, he was welcomed with love and warmth. Uncle Mordechai was more of a role model to him than his father, and Amnon loved his cousins Dror and Rachel more than any other relative. Immediately, he was fed and also given a glass of wine, something he had not had in ages. As it was obvious he was exhausted, his aunt prepared the guest bed for him.

However, with the upcoming operation staring him in the face, Amnon couldn't fall asleep. Concentrating on his mental picture, he saw the gate, the streets inside the compound and the wharves as clearly as if he were right there. Lying on his back, Amnon formulated his plan:

"We'll arrive in three big military trucks, each carrying one unit completely dressed in British military uniforms. Our Irish major, sitting next to the driver of the first truck, will present the entry papers to the guards. Having been cleared for entrance, we drive to Point 'A', a dark side street where everything is closed for the night. We will park all vehicles there.

Two men will then proceed to the front gate, silently sneaking up on the two guards, taking them out and replacing them. The British guards will be tied, mouths taped, and will be hidden. At the same time, six other pairs will move on foot to the six locations I've identified, and do the same thing. Everything must be accomplished in absolute silence.

When we've taken out the guards at the entrance to the communications building, I, our Irish major, and four other men will enter the building and take out the men on duty. This part of the operation must begin at 8:50pm, ten minutes before the explosive-laden craft arrives with the other unit assigned to sabotage the ships. The rest of the men will find their way to the wharves, under another unit commander, to make sure the wharves are clear and secure. To avoid any unnecessary noise at all cost, no arms will be fired. This must be a totally silent operation.

Knowing it would take about thirty minutes to place all the timed explosives, one of our trucks will drive slowly towards the wharf and pick up all men. The timers will be set for 9:45pm, by which time we should have just left the harbor compound. " As Amnon smugly envisioned the satisfactory completion of the operation, he fell asleep.

Awakened by his uncle, at 7am, as requested, Amnon took a quick shower, got back into his clothes and enjoyed a breakfast of salad and eggs with a strong cup of coffee before taking off.

Walking briskly, Amnon got to the Haifa safe house and immediately contacted his superior to request that the Irish major join the operation, to serve as their front man regarding any contact with British personnel. Nechemia agreed, and the Irish major was dispatched to Tiberias where all their preparations were being made.

British military uniforms, arms, and equipment, including rubber-soled boots, were immediately delivered to the small forest next to Lake Kineret, where they were carefully hidden. As each man arrived, he was given a bag containing his new uniform. The arms were hidden in especially built compartments under the bodies of their trucks. Everything was ready; the only thing still needed was the date and time of the ship's arrival.

Sunday, August 18, 1946

Early in the morning, Amnon received word that the two ships were due to arrive in Haifa sometime that afternoon, that the docks had been cleared, and all wharves were unoccupied. He instructed his men to stay where they were, but to be completely ready to meet at 4:30pm so that he could brief them about the operation taking place that night, and have them leave for target at precisely 5:30pm.

At that time of year, Tiberias was always hot and sweaty, with so many men in the large living room at the safe house it felt as if they were all in a steam bath.

Very carefully Amnon went over the plans before designating pairs for guard replacement, and gave them detailed maps he had prepared showing all the routes in the interior of the harbor compound, and which maps would be destroyed at completion of the operation. Each received a bag containing a full British uniform, to be worn over their khaki clothing, and put on as soon as they got to the trucks' hiding place.

Four of Amnon's men, in full Military Police uniforms, walked out to the highway, and as soon as the road was clear, their trucks rolled out. Amnon's plan called for arrival soon after sunset. To avoid arriving too early, their convoy drove slowly through the streets of Tiberias heading toward Haifa. No one stopped a British military convoy, not even the police, and they passed quite a few on their way without incident.

Arriving in downtown Haifa, they stopped next to the central bus terminal. The Irish major, Amnon, and the four phony military policemen stood on the sidewalk next to the first truck and pretended to be chatting. The place where they were waiting was no more than a three-minute ride to the port's main gate.

As planned, they arrived at the gate one minute before 8:00pm. While the guard was checking the documents the Irish major provided, the replacement guards arrived. They automatically saluted the major, who responded according to habit, and were waved in.

"*Boy*," Amnon thought, "*Do our Haganah labs know how to produce false documents!*" Driving slowly, they turned into the designated side street and parked. Soldiers were ordered out and were placed in formation. Each pair knew exactly where to go and what to do. Amnon's men walked up to each pair of guards. In their British military uniforms, everyone looked the same. The semi-darkness also helped. In each case the two guards were ordered to raise their hands and their arms taken away. Then, having been tied, gagged, and knocked out, each pair was dragged into a dark corner and hidden. Amnon's men made sure none of them would awaken too soon. Within less than thirty minutes all the British guards were taken out.

Amnon

The Irish major walked briskly toward the communications office. Amnon followed him with the four military policemen behind him. As soon as they reached the building, the guards standing at the entrance saluted the major, who told them to surrender their arms to the police as they were under arrest for smuggling cigarettes. The military policemen handcuffed them, and as soon as they entered the building, they too were knocked out, gagged, bound, and crammed into a nearby closet. Two of Amnon's men remained standing at the doorway.

Next, they proceeded to the communications room, a very small room on the second floor. The door was open, and inside men were talking and laughing. Amnon and the major waited in the corridor a few minutes until exactly 8:50pm, when the major walked into the room. The men jumped to their feet and saluted. The Irish major, revolver in hand, ordered them to turn around and face their equipment with their hands up. Their revolvers were liberated and he told them they were under arrest. One of them asked why, protesting they'd done nothing wrong. With a perfectly straight face, the major told them British intelligence had evidence they were aiding the Jewish Resistance.

"*What an actor!*" Amnon had to bite his tongue so as not to laugh. "*He really is good.*"

The men were handcuffed and gagged, one smack of a rifle butt on the head rendered them motionless. While they waited, Amnon checked on the two "military policemen" he had posted at the entrance. The major sat down in front of the wireless communications equipment, and was soon easily chatting with someone. Amnon told the major to disconnect all equipment at 9:25pm, disable it, and move rapidly toward the wharf where their trucks would later pick up all the men.

While all of this was happening, the other unit quietly spread out through the docks, but stopped short of the wharves, where about two-dozen British soldiers were guarding the ships awaiting the delivery and loading of the immigrants to be deported in the morning. Approaching the wharves, Amnon was stopped by one of his men who drew his attention to the soldiers. Realizing he lacked the capability to warn the underwater demolition team about the soldiers on the wharves, and knowing that once the explosives had been planted on the ships, the team would soon be surfacing, Amnon realized they were about to face a very serious problem. But there was no time to deal with it, for a moment later all hell broke loose.

One of the British soldiers noticed a man in the water and began shooting. Amnon ordered his men to fire, causing an exchange of heavy fire. Trained to always change their firing positions for safety and tactical reasons, they fired from different locations, confusing the British soldiers and buying them a few minutes, since the British didn't know the exact number or what direction Amnon's men were firing from. They fired constantly, but with no place to hide, they were visible to Amnon's men, who easily pinned them down.

Running to the far side of the second ship where the man had been spotted, Amnon motioned the men in the water to pull out onto the wharf. Under heavy fire cover they all ran and in minutes were behind the first warehouse where the trucks were waiting. At Amnon's signal, they piled into the trucks, and a few more minutes saw them in convoy form heading for the main gate. They slowed down periodically to pick up the men left behind as guards, including the Irish major. As they reached the gate, they found the road ahead blocked by three British armored cars supported by at least a dozen police officers on foot. Confused by the sight of a British convoy, policemen took no action.

Amnon instructed the first truck to ram the middle armored car and drive through, then ordered his men to shoot at the policemen, taking them by surprise. Seconds later, having successfully rammed the armored car out of the way, Amnon's convoy picked up speed. Some British policemen fired back at them from behind the overturned car. Under cover of the ensuing pandemonium, and despite a fierce exchange of heavy fire between Amnon's men and the police, they managed to make their getaway, continuing to shoot at the police until they were out of sight.

His immediate problem was which way to drive to avoid detection by the British. But before he could make a decision, deafening explosions short-circuited his thought process. With no idea of the outcome of their mission, they all cheered at their obvious success. Amnon ordered everyone to strip off the British uniforms post haste and pile them up in the trucks.

Heading east away from Haifa, Amnon reviewed the recent events, and tried to figure out what had gone wrong, or still might with his original plan.

"How had the police who'd tried to block them come to be there in the first place? Had they been alerted by the communications silence, or had they heard the soldiers' shots from the wharves? Was it possible a guard had untied himself and called the police?" Amnon's mind was racing. *"Any additional police may come from the direction we're headed in. When we rammed our way through the blockade, the Britishers must have called for additional help. I need to decide our next best move while on the run."*

A few kilometers from Haifa, as he was mentally mapping the route to the nearest safe destination, Amnon noticed two armored cars following them at a distance, their searchlights sweeping both sides of the fields. That had to mean they hadn't yet been spotted, and driving without lights helped them avoid detection for the moment. Amnon calculated they needed to lose the armored cars fast, they had to split up and go their separate ways.

As they approached the Megido intersection, Amnon had to make a fast decision. From the intersection they could drive north to the Galilee or southeast toward Jerusalem, and driving straight ahead would take them either to Affula or Tiberias. He ordered two trucks to head north with instructions that each should go to a different kibbutz and carefully hide their trucks and arms. Maintaining distance between them, with Amnon in the lead, the remaining trucks headed straight along the road leading to Affula where he knew there were more than a dozen kibbutzim along the way. Within minutes, they saw the first kibbutz, and one of the trucks peeled off. At the next kibbutz, another of the trucks turned into its entrance, and it wasn't long before all of the trucks had split up, with each to a different kibbutz.

Amnon's instructions were clear. As soon as a truck arrived at a kibbutz, if it couldn't be safely hidden, so as not to endanger the kibbutz in any way it would either be taken apart if necessary or destroyed. Kibbutzim members were used to helping Haganah fighters at any hour of the day or night. Amnon's main objective after each operation was to prevent British military or civilian police from catching any of his men, including the residents of any kibbutz they took refuge in. Capture meant a guarantee of seven years to life in prison. What's more, prisoners were deported to a prison in a distant country where chances of escape were nil.

Amnon's truck drove into Kibbutz Nahalal, where all arms and British uniforms were stashed quickly away. When they inspected the truck, they discovered bullet holes in its rear and sides. The truck was driven into a large barn and dismantled. Within a half hour, with all sides, tires, and certain engine parts removed to make the truck look like it was being repaired, it also looked like one of the flat beds kibbutz farmers used for carrying produce from the fields.

With all the usual safety precautions taken care of, Amnon finally learned that one of his men had been killed and several wounded in the operation. No one had said a word to him about this earlier because during their escape from the harbor he couldn't think of anything but getting them out and finding them all a safe place.

A doctor was summoned to attend to the wounded. Fortunately, most of the wounds were not too serious, except for one man who was carried to the kibbutz infirmary. If he was discovered during a search, the standard answer would be that Arabs had shot him while working in the field, a commonplace fact of life in any Jewish settlement in Palestine.

It was past midnight. Amnon felt completely drained, but couldn't help wondering how many wounded or dead they had in the other trucks. Standard operating procedure after all operations included strict instructions to maintain total silence, and definitely not to call during the night to avoid alerting the censors. Knowing daytime calls were far more difficult to trace, Amnon anxiously waited for morning to call his commander.

Soon the Haganah commander of the kibbutz arrived, and they sat in the little kitchen in his house. He offered Amnon a drink, and only then did he realize his mouth was dry and he was very thirsty. Anxiously, Amnon asked if the commander had heard any news, and was not surprised when he said no. That was also standard. Questions were never asked, and information never given. Knowing nothing was the best insurance in case of a search and interrogation.

Sleeping arrangements were made and all of them collapsed into their beds, to be awakened at the usual hour of 5:30am, when all of them joined different crews and went out to work in the kibbutz vegetable or fruit fields. In case of a search, the story was the usual - they were city boys helping out in the kibbutz. Two hours later, work stopped for a half hour break, and most workers found their way to the central dining room for a light breakfast.

The radio was on, and the news reported that Jewish resistance forces had sabotaged two British ships in Haifa harbor and the authorities were searching for the perpetrators. By late afternoon the following day, Amnon had learned where all his men were, and that the operation had cost three fatalities and eleven wounded. Everyone was to stay and work in their respective kibbutzim for at least a week, then head for Tiberias by whatever means available.

Monday, August 26, 1946

The evening's news surprisingly reported that Kibbutz Sdot Yam had been encircled by thousands of British troops and searched for arms and the men who had sabotaged the ships a week ago. Knowing that the authorities were always anxious to capture Haganah men, it seemed odd the search hadn't begun immediately, for the authorities were always hot to capture resistance men.

The news went on to report that arms had been found, and over eighty members of the kibbutz arrested as suspects. In reality, none of Amnon's men were anywhere near that kibbutz, which was located about fifty kilometers south of Haifa, and it was a real mystery why the British had gone there. Amnon wondered if Haganah intelligence had steered the British in a bogus direction using one of their fake Arab informers. The news also reported that exhaustive searches for arms were being conducted in dozens of kibbutzim south of Tel Aviv.

In August, as all other months, good things and bad things alike took place. Interestingly, executives of the Jewish Agency convening in Paris decided to stop all Resistance activities against the British. The leaders of the Yishuv seemed to have taken a leaf from the British in the art of deceit, for the executives' carefully worded and advertised letter, that from now on, the Jews of Palestine would concentrate on bringing their brethren to Palestine by peaceful means.

Not mentioned was that the Jewish Agency had no control over the Etzel or Lehi, two organizations not likely to stop their operations. In fact, eighteen members of Lehi who had been caught in a railroad operation had been sentenced to death. But the British soon changed this to life imprisonment, afraid that hanging the eighteen Lehi members would trigger a bloody war. Deportation of immigrants to Cyprus continued.

Not much was said about the heavy British casualties. The British censors worked hard to hide such information from its own men. Other interesting recent news was that the British Government retracted the public statement made by its chief commanding officer to his troops telling them not to associate with Jews.

Amnon found that interesting because in the British Isles, especially England, where anti-Semitism was then virtually unknown, Jews lived in a free society and enjoyed as much freedom as their non-Jewish friends and neighbors. Since there were Jews in Parliament as well as in British Government offices, why had there been no comment from any of them?

By the end of August, Amnon was back in Tel Aviv, his men still scattered through numerous kibbutzim. While awaiting further instructions, Amnon visited the Tel Aviv safe house twice daily, and for the first time in a very long while, he spent time on the beach. He loved the warm waters of the Mediterranean, and for the first time in months, began to relax.

But it was almost too quiet; he kept waiting for the other shoe to drop.

Amnon

Relaxing a bit at last, and trying very hard to forget all the troubles in his world, Amnon still found his ever-active thoughts reviewing the Haifa harbor operation.

"Exactly how did the police learn about our activities that night? Had the shots from the wharves alerted them? Was it the unresponsive communications room? Fortunately, the British military forces were scattered in numerous barracks, the closest to Haifa being the one at Atlit, at least half an hour from the harbor. Moreover, the cars blocking the road were local police armored patrol cars."

From that point, his thoughts jumped to the enormous British force that had descended on kibbutz SdotYam seeking the harbor perpetrators. Not only had the search party found no significant amount of arms, the arrest of eighty innocent people was doubtless a retaliatory measure against the Yishuv.

"The British will have to release all of them very soon." Amnon thought.

After a few days of unmitigated pleasure, Amnon decided he should really be with his men; informing his office where he'd be, he departed for the Emek. (Jezrael Valley)

Tuesday, September 3, 1946

Finally, new instructions had arrived. His entire unit was to report to the Negev office. When Amnon arrived in Rehovot, he was told plans were underway to establish eleven new kibbutzim in the Negev area, mostly between Beer Sheva and Gaza. Since the Jewish Agency had decided to stop sabotage activities for a while, they were to help build those new communities. As soon as all members of his unit arrived, as did many other units, they began a huge transportation project of lumber, sheet metal, cement blocks, mortar mix, and water tanks. All 11 locations were clearly marked and looked to him something like a defense line. The question was -- defense for what?

Saturday, October 5, 1946

During the past month numerous Haganah units, including Amnon's, willingly slaved as construction crews. During the day, the Negev temperature soared into the high 90's and the sun was brutal. At night though, temperatures dropped to almost freezing, so they needed only light blankets. Working hard from sunup to sunset, they were all agreed that unloading and carrying cement blocks from one location to another had to be the worst of all jobs; it left them so exhausted they literally collapsed into their cots every night. Lacking cranes, the blocks had to be taken off the trucks one by one at every future building site.

Many times, Amnon stood looking at the land, to the north, to the east, to the south and to the west; all he could see was desert. Sand, sand, and more sand. Amnon knew Jews were expected to perform miracles, but this seemed a bit much.

"How can anyone live in or somehow wrest a living from this arid desert land? There must be a political reason for this enterprise," he kept telling himself. *"The men at the top must know what they're doing."*

Daniel Rosenfeld

Whenever he looked at the map of Palestine marked with the new and prospective settlements, he could see the progress being made in settling new Jewish immigrants into Palestine. This would be a strong basis for their future Jewish Homeland.

The British announced that illegal immigrants would be deported to the island of Cyprus where they had established detention camps. Again, camps! Amnon's heart bled at such news. Shutting his eyes, he visualized the emaciated men and women who had miraculously survived the horrors of Nazi death camps. Having nowhere else to go, they had struggled their way to displaced persons camps, then onto illegal boats that were supposed to take them to freedom in Palestine but were intercepted by the British. Now they'd be shipped to detention camps on Cyprus. What an unmitigated horror for the survivors. And what a hateful description that word "survivor" must have been for them.

"How long does a person have to survive all sorts of horrors to earn that hateful description? Haven't they suffered enough? Can't the world see and feel the agony of these poor human beings? How can the British Government be so heartless?" Amnon could find no answers to those nagging questions. In his mind's eye, he envisioned those suffering souls on their journey from a European DP camp to an illegal fishing boat that would take them on a dangerous voyage through unfriendly seas to the shores of Palestine. Caught by the British, their hope and vision of finally coming home shattered, they had to have felt totally crushed.

"But despite all obstacles, we men of the Haganah will achieve our goal -- to bring them all to Palestine, where they will have a new life," Amnon swore.

At night they sat around a fire to eat their evening meal, into which some sand always found its way. After dinner they sang lusty patriotic songs, and there were always discussions about British proclamations and their inflexible policy against Jewish immigration. Their single radio was the sole connection to the rest of the world. Strong in their belief that the Negev desert would one day bloom, they worked hard, with an enthusiasm that beggared all description.

When all the raw materials arrived and were unloaded, their construction work began under the eagle-eyed supervision of one civilian; a semi-engineer who directed the work. Overnight all of them became construction workers. After unloading cement blocks, the second hardest job was digging the trenches into which concrete mix would be poured to form house foundations. As the trenches were made ready, they mixed the concrete mix with water on top of a sheet of metal, then shoveled it into the trenches. Sweat rolled down Amnon's body as he dug, mixed, and poured, and often he was so thirsty he felt he could have drunk the entire Mediterranean Sea and it wouldn't have been enough to quench his thirst.

All houses were one-story. Some were built of cement blocks, others of lumber. Most roofs were made from cut sheet metal, nailed on the wood. There was virtually no rain, but lots of sun and unbearable heat. Thankfully, the cool nights helped reduce tension as they cooled down their bodies.

They continued to work under the guidance of the semi engineer or architect, or whatever he was. He seemed to know what he was doing. By the end of the month, Amnon's unit had built the first housing facilities for one kibbutz. Other units working in other locations did the same. Food and water had to be brought in daily. There was no refrigeration, no running water, no toilets. In fact, there was nothing except for what they built in the dry, sweltering Negev desert.

A fascinating news item reported that the British Government decided to hold a conference in London on the future of Palestine, and neither the Jews nor the Arabs showed up. Amnon could understand the Jews not showing up, but the Arabs?

"What new twist is this?" he asked.

The British had supported the Arabs and incited them against the Jews and they had blocked all possible Jewish immigration to Palestine to please the Arabs. "So why hadn't the Arabs attended the British-sponsored conference in London where the future of Palestine was to be discussed?" Amnon kept asking.

"Maybe the Almighty is with us, for if the Arabs had showed up and the Jews hadn't, the Arabs and British would have had additional ammunition to use against us," he reflected.

However, the most wonderful news of the day was that President Harry Truman of the United States of America announced in Washington he would support the establishment of a Jewish State in Palestine. Interestingly, President Truman's announcement was made on the eve of Yom Kippur.

"At last, we're making some real progress," Amnon shouted for joy!

"If the United States supports the creation of a Jewish State, they will be diametrically opposing Great Britain [or the United Kingdom, as it was now called.] Clearly, no world power should base its governmental policies on its need for Arab oil, nor on its fear of Russian expansionism. Doubtless the U.K. will fight for its ideologies, and the U.K.'s spoiled rotten baby, the Suez Canal, still needs its Palestinian nanny."

"Now all we need is for the baby to grow up and stop being spoiled so that its nanny can finally break free," Amnon declared.

When all the houses and other structures had been completed, they built a fence around the entire complex, involving endless digging, this time holes for fence posts. With the posts in place, they stretched the fence wire that came in large rolls, and connected the wire mesh fence to the posts. Now they were done. According to one report, it was the first time in the settlement history of Palestine that eleven kibbutzim were established at once.

Soon the settlers arrived. Most were young couples, some with children. They brought with them their boundless courage and unbridled hope for the future, and they also brought a few cows, goats, some chickens and what appeared to be a veritable nation of dogs. Apparently unfazed by either the unfriendly landscape, miles of arid yellow sand without tree, flower or the smallest bush or plant, or the formidable task before them, they were all happily ready to settle into their new homes and new lives.

Though it was difficult to fathom how they'd manage to live or make a living in such sparse conditions, Amnon and his men were elated at their arrival, and threw a party for the settlers on their first night in the wilderness. They sang, drank wine, ate stale sandwiches, and at the party's end wished the settlers good health and good luck in the future. The next day Amnon and his men left the kibbutz for another project.

Sunday, October 6, 1946
A special bus came to pick them up and they were on the way to civilization. They arrived in Rehovot around noon. Amnon left his unit at the bus terminal and went to the Rehovot safe house for instructions. There were none, but he was told orders would arrive the next day.

Amnon returned to the bus terminal and instructed the men to find their way one or two at a time to the safe house where they would have to stay until the next morning.

Monday, October 7, 1946
A long meeting with various Haganah commanders was held at the safe house. The main focus of which was how to sabotage and take out of action the vessels used by the British to intercept ships and boats arriving with immigrants. First, they needed to know the exact location of their land base, how frequently they went out, and how long they stayed at sea, as well as crew changes, and method of obtaining supplies. After some discussion, they decided the port of Haifa had to be their main base, so Haganah operations would have to be launched from there. Smaller craft could possibly use Atlit and Jaffa.

They decided to mount a major study of all aspects of that issue in order to come up with a logical plan for the destruction of these British vessels, whilst ensuring the safe arrival of the many illegal vessels engaged in bringing ever greater numbers of immigrants to Palestine. If tens of thousands of immigrants were caught and deported to Cyprus, the population explosion in the camps would create more problems for the British. Destroying or damaging high-speed British patrol boats and high-speed interception vessels would significantly reduce their capability to block incoming traffic, thus smaller crafts arriving with their smaller passenger loads could continue to arrive safely.

Before the meeting closed, it was decided Amnon's unit would be spread out from Natania to Akko for two weeks to evaluate and scrutinize the vessels' activity from their base out to the sea and back, plus supply shipments and crew changes. It was decided to reconvene in Haifa at 8:00am Friday, October 25th.

For the next fifteen minutes Amnon sat over the map showing the coast of Palestine, deciding on the best locations for the study. Splitting his men into pairs, he assigned each pair a specific location. For himself, he chose Mount Carmel, from which he could comfortably observe the entire port of Haifa. They left for their destinations that afternoon.

Thursday, October 24, 1946
It had just occurred to Amnon that his birthday had come and gone and neither he nor anyone else had celebrated it.

"*My mother and father surely remembered and I was in their prayers,*" Amnon thought.

The following day he was supposed to meet with his superiors to report his unit's findings over the past two weeks.

"*Maybe I'll have time to visit my uncle and his family.*" But snapping at the heels of this selfish thought was the demurer that he didn't want them endangered in case he got caught, which was why he settled for the occasional visit whenever he passed through Haifa on his way somewhere else.

During those two weeks he often visited the bars in downtown Haifa, most of which were frequented by British soldiers, sailors, and other British employees. Nonchalantly, he sipped his beer and casually struck up a conversation with whoever sat next to him.

It never ceased to amaze him that you could learn so much in a bar, especially from someone who had downed several glasses of beer or whiskey. Regrettably, Amnon could never be described as a seasoned drinker; he couldn't hold more than a bottle of beer. To keep his casual acquaintances company as they drank and talked while he listened intently and squirreled away everything he heard, Amnon pretended to match them drink for drink. Just like them, he made numerous trips to the restrooms, but unlike them, he poured out his beer, and re-ordered when he returned.

While visiting bars was expensive and dangerous, it was also very informative. British soldiers, unlike tight-lipped members of the Haganah, talked too much. He gained several bits of useful information corroborated by his spying from the top of Mount Carmel. In record time, Amnon learned where the target vessels docked, when the crews changed and how and when those vessels were supplied.

Interestingly enough, he discovered while observing the port through his binoculars that food items were delivered in boxes bearing Hebrew lettering, which meant the British bought their meats and produce from Jewish wholesale trade. Amnon sent a man to cover the produce terminal with orders to make mental note of the main supplier's name, how and when orders were delivered, and how the delivery was checked at the entry to the port.

Two weeks passed quickly with daytimes spent on the mountain and nighttimes in the bars. Though he slept little, Amnon wasn't tired, for the fresh cool air on Mount Carmel kept him invigorated. Slowly, each day that passed, his plan of attack formed in his mind and became increasingly more feasible. Certain that his plan would work, he could barely wait to discuss it with his men that night, before the meeting with the brass the next day.

By 9:00 all of Amnon's men arrived at their safe house as planned. Amnon was extremely happy to see them for the bond they had developed was strong. They felt like brothers. Each would have willingly sacrificed his life for any of the others. Amnon was also elated that some of his wounded men had rejoined his unit.

The cumulative result of their spying showed there were neither bases nor landfalls anywhere except in the port of Haifa, and Amnon and his assistant had thoroughly covered the Haifa docks. Moreover, as the Haganah already knew, the rooftops of all police stations in Natania, Hadera and Atlit carried special radar systems to detect ocean-going ships; these would need to be destroyed. They were facing a real challenge.

Daniel Rosenfeld

There was no real need for Amnon to disclose all his findings in that meeting with his men, so he simply said it seemed the British ships assigned to intercepting immigrant ships operated solely out of Haifa. Assuring them that he had all the information he needed, Amnon closed the meeting with the request they all be available tomorrow noon.

Wednesday, October 25, 1946

The previous week Amnon had reached his 17th Birthday. This was a milestone because he felt he had become a man in every sense of the word. But at the opening of the meeting, like the teenager he really was, Amnon asked if anyone wanted to wish him well on his birthday that had just passed without notice. They all did. He was hugged, and even kissed, by his commanding officer.

"Amnon, " Nechemia spoke, "I feel like I've known you all my life. You are the symbol of idealism and spirit in this outfit. I can't think of anyone more devoted to our cause than you. So, I congratulate you, not only for your birthday, but for your personal achievements and contributions to your fellow men and homeland."

It was a most touching statement, and Amnon blinked back the tears that had welled up in his eyes.

Asked to deliver the findings of his unit, Amnon launched into his report. "The British Navy's intercepting vessels operate solely out of Haifa harbor. They dock at the outer side of the bay. Each vessel is at sea for four days, departing at 6:00pm, returning four days later at around 7:00pm. The sailors are given shore passes, and all except two or three leave their vessels on a four day pass, free to move around the City during their leave. The sailors use a barracks provided for them in a converted warehouse on the north side of the harbor complex."

"Around 3:00pm, the day of departure, a truckload of wooden boxes containing food supplies is dropped on the dock next to the ship's gangway. Returning sailors then carry the boxes aboard, probably to the vessel's galley or storage. By 4:15pm, the loading is complete. I noticed that all boxes are nailed shut, probably to make it harder to steal food."

"Since most vessels lack storage space inside their galleys, chances are boxes are opened in the storage pantry next to the galley. This is important, because my plan calls for placing dynamite inside some of the boxes, which will explode when a hand grenade's pin is pulled out the moment the lid is opened."

"This is a delicate mechanism, but it can be done by one of our experts. We'll also pour gunpowder on the bottom of each box containing dynamite so that the flying metal fragments from the first explosion will detonate the gunpowder, which in turn will detonate the dynamite. With this chain of events, there's no telling whether the vessel will sink, or simply be so damaged it will be unable to sail for a while."

"These intercepting vessels are not battleships. They are large high-speed patrol boats that can hold fifty sailors, and carry various cannons and automatic machine guns. If we choose this as our plan of action, we won't risk the

142

lives of our men."

Asked how he was planning to place the grenades and dynamite into the boxes, Amnon replied, "This is the simplest operation of all. We know where the boxes come from; so we get some and place the gunpowder, dynamite and grenades on the bottom covered with vegetables or fruit. We intercept the delivery truck, take its driver away, supposedly for questioning about some labor union business since he's a union member, and while he's away, we replace some boxes. The driver is returned, and he continues on his way."

"This is great for the first one," the commander said. "But what comes next? According to your report, every day at least one or two vessels sail away. How do we deal with the other vessels?"

"We can sabotage the first two vessels. If both explode, all the better. But if only one explodes, so be it. Other vessels will have to be destroyed in a different way. I believe our second main objective in this, as in all other sabotage operations, is to demonstrate to the British in no uncertain terms that there is nothing we won't do to achieve our goals."

Amnon's next statements concerned the speedboats the Haganah had obtained to harass British ships seeking to intercept immigrant vessels.

"Can these speedboats fire two or six pounder cannons?"

"Yes, they can," one of the commanders answered.

" Then we should attack their vessels at night from close range."

"I don't have orders to mount such an operation as yet," the commander responded. "Keep thinking about this project. I'll let you know when the next meeting will be to discuss this matter in greater detail. At that time I'll have a starting date for this operation as well as its magnitude."

"In the meanwhile, I would like your unit to replace a unit that's been on the beaches too long. Resume operation 'Nightly Immigrants' until further notice."

"Will do," Amnon said.

Tuesday, November 5, 1946

British authorities in Palestine announced the leaders of the Yishuv would be released from detention in Latrun. Obviously, the British had not achieved anything by imprisoning the leaders of the Jewish Agency. Though they had no proof, they had also accused the leaders of the Jewish Agency of being the heads of the Haganah. If they but knew it, their charge was truly laughable, for virtually every Jewish child knew that the Haganah was directed by the supreme Jewish Authority in Palestine, the Jewish Agency.

Once again, Amnon and his men have set up shop on the beaches. This time, however, they were replacing a unit near Natania.

Ships of all sizes continued to arrive at a regular pace. The British intercepted two big ships, each carrying over 2,000 immigrants, and all were immediately deported to Cyprus. Amnon had no idea how many survivors were in detention camps in Cyprus, but none of that made any sense to him.

"Immigrants have traveled from camps in Italy and Germany to camps in Cyprus, which may soon run out of space to hold them all. Don't the British

realize that sooner or later they'll have to release those immigrants altogether? Why can't the British face up to realities?" Wondered Amnon.

The Haganah had been quiet since they received orders to cease sabotage activity. However, Etzel and Lehi, who were controlled neither by the Jewish Agency nor the Haganah, continued to defy the request for calm to resolve the immigration issue politically. Both Etzel and Lehi continued their terror and sabotage activities against the British, and not a day passed without some incident provoked by them.

Haunted by his thoughts and memories of the immigrants he'd met, especially in the dead of the night as they waited to welcome another immigrant vessel, Amnon wondered when the immigrants would finally have a happy ending.

Their operations might be 'illegal' to the British, but to them it was a moral obligation to bring those lost and suffering souls into Palestine, which would one day be an irrevocable Jewish Homeland.

The British could have achieved so much more had they simply welcomed immigration into Palestine. Instead, they permitted their misbegotten and miscalculated political objectives to form the basis for their deceitful decisions.

"Don't they know that a Jewish State would be a far greater deterrent to communism in the Middle East than all the Arab League countries put together? And don't they know that the Jewish State would be by far a more dependable ally for the west?" Amnon's mind wouldn't let go.

Amnon could only wonder what kind of minds directed the British Government's foreign policies. *"Are they still motivated by the dreams and past glories of the former British Empire, in their present-day policy making? Can't they see that colonialism no longer works? All they have to do is look at present day Egypt, India, Iran, the Sudan and such places as distant as Indonesia and Siam [now Thailand.]"*

"Why don't they wake up and stop living in the past?"

Awake or asleep, Amnon's mind was always active. Sometimes it seemed he was floating inside a huge barrel, spinning in ever-widening circles with no end in sight.

Somewhat impatiently, Amnon waited. Finally, word reached him that three fishing vessels were approaching the shore. In the far distance, Amnon and his men could hear shots and two or three kilometers away a flare suddenly shot up into the night sky. Obviously, one of Amnon's neighboring units was engaged in some activity.

"Why would our leadership begin to talk about destroying British intercepting vessels only to suddenly declare a moratorium? Was it that they were making some progress on the immigrant issue?" The men on the battlefield were at a loss to understand what was going on, as was the Jewish population in general. The entire Yishuv was thirsty for news about developments, but there was nothing. There must have been some significant conferences between the British Authorities and the leadership while the latter was jailed in Latrun.

Shots were getting closer, pulling Amnon from his wide-ranging thoughts. It seemed one or more British civilian police patrol were chasing a retreating Haganah unit to the north of Amnon's location. Instructing his men to take positions in the form of an open triangle, they quickly dug in the sand and within minutes they were almost entirely buried with only their heads and rifles above the ground. Praying the fishing vessels wouldn't arrive in the next five minutes, they let the men of the other unit retreat to their lines, and lacking time to dig, Amnon had them lay on the sand.

A large British unit was in pursuit, and no sooner did they enter the center of the open triangle than firing began. The heavy barrage hit many British targets that fell to the ground; others, realizing they'd been ambushed, quickly began to run back in the direction they'd come from. With several small immigrant craft due to arrive momentarily, Amnon ordered the newly arrived men to give chase for at least one kilometer, hoping the boat captains wouldn't lead toward the beach if they saw any signs of battle.

"*Flares work both ways,*" Amnon thought.

After a long hiatus from their work on the beaches of the Mediterranean, Amnon and his men were once again aiding new arrivals. Even as Amnon wondered what had caused the earlier fracas with the police, he decided he must speak with his counterpart later that morning. One of the men suddenly came running up to warn the fishing vessels had arrived.

Amnon had two small rowboats and with two men in each; they immediately started rowing toward the two incoming vessels, which had begun lowering their own boats. Everyone tried to be first into the rowboats, but they managed to get them under control by telling them the unloading had to be done quickly to avoid the prowling British patrol boats. They calmed down and cooperated. Soon they had all the rowboats filled to capacity and were on the way to the beaches. After ten trips everyone was on shore and well hidden until the final group arrived.

Half the men were sent ahead to the safe house with their immigrant charges; Amnon and the rest of his men started back to the ambush area to see to the dead and wounded policemen. But just as they drew near the scene, sirens cut the night air and Amnon decided they'd better leave fast.

It was almost dawn when they reached their safe house. All the immigrants were there, most already wearing the Palestinian style clothing they always provided to their immigrant charges. Having taken a glass of tea, Amnon was getting ready to sit down on the floor in the dark room when one of his scouts came running in panting that numerous armored cars were spotted coming in the direction of the safe house. First he cautioned the immigrants not to say a word, and if the British police came, to resist but do whatever they were told. He then gathered his men, and arms in hand they ran out the back door.

The safe house was built at the northern edge of town directly above a canal; nearby were a few housing projects. Heading right into the canal, they spread out and tried to keep down as they silently sloshed through the water. But they definitely couldn't stay there because the cover of night was swiftly giving way to illuminating daylight when they would all risk being captured by the police. Cautiously, Amnon led the men into a wide valley covered with tall weeds, and cautioned, "Listen, men, if we can't get out of here before daylight, we're going to have to spend the daylight hours hiding in this weedy place. If God forbid! the police have dogs, we'll have to shoot our way out. But let's hope it doesn't come to anything like that."

The very last thing Amnon needed was a shootout with the police in broad daylight! Fortunately, in the quiet of dawn they heard no dogs, the armored cars had passed by and were gone along with the threat of imminent capture. With all clear, they filed back into the house and relaxed in relief. Amnon's glass of tea stood waiting on the floor exactly where he'd left it, and, even though it was cold, he gulped it down. Later, the immigrants told him none of them had moved or uttered a single word until they saw their rescuers return.

With nothing much to do but wait for further instructions, Amnon dozed off sitting on the floor, his back up against the wall. The few beds in the house had been given to the women while the rest of the immigrants sat or stretched out on the floor. For them, the past four days and tonight had to have been harrowing. A risky 4-day ocean voyage topped by a near-miss encounter with British police, but the worst was over. For Amnon and his men, the night had also been long, extremely risky, and exhausting. With the perilous night over, they gratefully collapsed into sleep wherever they found space.

Around noon, people began to come awake. Amnon was hungry, as were the immigrants. He explained to them in his broken Yiddish that regrettably there was no food, not even coffee, in the house, and they'd have to wait until the supply car arrived. Only then, for the first time, could Amnon clearly see their sad and scarred faces, some with wrinkles, many tracked with tears, and all with tired eyes sunk deep into their dark-ringed sockets as a result of their long, difficult, and probably sleepless journey.

Thankfully, just then his scout, who had been on the last shift, told Amnon the supply car had arrived, short-circuiting his usual heavy thoughts on the subject.

A man and a woman in their sixties got out of the car, opened the trunk, and quickly hauled several large packages into the house. Apologizing that it had been a hard night everywhere, they opened the packages, placed on the small kitchen table coffee, bread, cheese, and a bag full of tomatoes, at that time of year usually impossible to find. The woman put everything neatly away and then left on foot to buy milk at the nearest grocery store, returning in half an hour.

Meanwhile, they boiled water on the gas stove and added ground coffee and sparing amounts of sugar found in the cupboard. Small dollops of milk from the supply the woman had brought were added to the coffee, which they laughingly said tasted like ice cream, but actually was pretty bad. Oblivious of the bad taste, they toasted each other with a hearty "L'chaim!" to celebrate being alive, that the British hadn't caught them, and that they'd successfully brought in seventy-eight new immigrants.

A woman asked who was in charge, and being directed to Amnon, asked him to join her in one of the locked small rooms at the back of the house. The moment she unlocked the door and closed it behind them, she voiced her apprehensions.

Amnon

"The situation here is getting more difficult by the day," she said. "British police are investigating every house, checking who lives there, where they work and asking for identity cards. Sooner or later they'll get to this one."

"My husband and I are listed as the owners of this house, and he has certificates that state he's disabled." She showed one to Amnon; it showed he was disabled by some illness Amnon had never heard of.

"I'm afraid," she continued in agitation, "If the police come here and find so many people, we'll be arrested for helping illegal immigrants."

"First of all," Amnon assured her, "We take every precaution to avoid being seen or caught by the police. Secondly, we all take many risks, some more than others. Normally, we stay only a few hours or a day, leaving with all of our charges when the time is right. The men and women of the Haganah in charge of removing new immigrants from safe houses work in teams and will only move people when the coast is clear. Sometimes they move people during the day and sometimes at night. They are particularly careful when British activity has intensified. This time, owing to circumstances beyond our control, we've had to remain longer than usual."

"However, please be assured," Amnon calmed, "by tomorrow morning everyone will be gone, and you'll have no further need to worry."

She stopped wringing her hands, and Amnon heaved a big sigh of relief as they walked back into the kitchen.

A newcomer to this neighborhood, Amnon wanted to get a better feel for it. He asked his scout to sneak outside and take a good look around. He reported back in 15 minutes.

"This is a fairly new housing community, expanding Natania to the north. Most are two family houses. This particular section was built along a wadi, [shallow gully] which only has water in it after heavy rains. If you follow the wadi west, you'll reach the Mediterranean."

They didn't have enough cups or glasses for all, so they let the newly arrived guests enjoy their first cup of coffee in Palestine. It must have tasted okay; the coffee seemed to perk them up. Soon, with a slice or two of bread and a thick piece of good old Tnuva cheese, everyone began feeling better. With plenty of time to kill until they were taken elsewhere, they began to chat.

Most of Amnon's men were Sabras, born in Palestine, who spoke mainly Hebrew with a smattering of English and Arabic. Of Yiddish, they knew nothing at all. Thus it fell to Amnon, with his own broken Yiddish, to serve as a translator. Although it wasn't easy trying to converse with so many people speaking so many different languages, somehow they managed.

They talked a great deal amongst themselves, then turning to Amnon they asked what seemed like hundreds of questions, all of which he patiently tried to answer.

First Amnon detailed the situation in Palestine as regards to the British authorities and Jewish immigration.

"It's extremely important that you know the British try to intercept all ships carrying immigrant   passengers. If they succeed in catching a ship, they take all those they call 'illegal immigrants' to a holding camp called Atlit here in

Palestine, and the next day they deport them to a detention camp on the island of Cyprus, which is near Lebanon and Turkey."

"We do everything we can think of to make it very difficult for the British to catch anybody. Like last night, for example, when we got all of you and brought you here. And today or tomorrow we hope to move all of you out of here and on to your temporary or permanent homes."

"Refugees like yourselves whom we succeed in bringing in, are smuggled into one of our kibbutzim, communities, farming collectives or cities, depending on each case. Do you understand so far?"

They nodded, and Amnon went on. "Hopefully, tonight, or maybe tomorrow, you'll be talking with our Absorption personnel who'll decide which is the best temporary home for you. Then, one by one, so as not to call attention to our movements or arouse suspicion, you'll be taken to your new home, in Palestine. Do you understand?"

Receiving another collective nod, Amnon continued. "Obviously, if you have relatives in Palestine, that will be taken in full consideration. Your relatives will be notified of your arrival. Then, if at all possible, you will settle with them until you have your own place. Also, in due course you'll receive your own identity cards so that you can move freely about."

They knew quite a bit already. The Jewish Agency's representatives in the Displaced Persons camps had provided them with a lot of information on the situation in Palestine, especially the British attitude and policies, but they remained unfazed. In fact, despite the known hardships, most of the survivors chose to come to Palestine, which they all thought of as their homeland. This made Amnon feel very proud of both them and Palestine, his birthplace and his own homeland.

"Here we are in Palestine, fighting for a homeland so that we can call a piece of land our own. And here these suffering people have willingly taken numerous risks to come home to Palestine, without a clue to what risks or sacrifices might lie ahead, and they stand willing and ready to join our fight to make this land their own," Amnon reflected.

He was more proud of them than they were of themselves.

Thursday, November 28, 1946

Three young men who had arrived three weeks ago insisted on joining the Haganah. They'd demanded this to the Aliya Absorption man who came to pick them up. He had placed them in a kibbutz near Tel Aviv, and promised to refer their request to the proper authorities. Their story was a fascinating one.

Seized at the age of 16 by the Russians, they were sent to Siberia with many others. Their parents were sent elsewhere, and they had no communication with them until the war was over. Actually only two of them found relatives. One found his father, and the other found his mother. The third one found no one.

They became acquainted in the camp in Italy. The boy's mother married the other boy's father at the camp, and all of them decided to take one of the big ships to Palestine. But the wife was very frail. She and her husband decided going on a fishing boat was too risky. The young men had no problem taking a small boat. They decided to meet in Palestine. The two large ships, which were intercepted by the British, probably carried their parents, and they had to assume they'd been deported to Cyprus.

The three youngsters insisted on joining Amnon's unit. They were taken to training grounds, and trained for a week, then sent to join Amnon's unit. When they were brought in, they hugged and kissed Amnon, overjoyed at having been accepted. Although Amnon couldn't for the life of him figure out how they knew about him and his unit, their insistence on fighting only under him and no one else made Amnon feel very proud.

Fortunately, this could be arranged. One of them had a pretty good knowledge of Hebrew, which he told Amnon came from having attended a Cheder as a child. The other two knew only a few words. Amnon couldn't get over it. It was usually rare to see such young immigrants; most of the new arrivals were much older.

This was the first time Amnon learned first hand what it was like to sit and wait in the displaced persons camps. He was furious at the British in behalf of those suffering human beings. Thought Amnon, *"What an ungodly and unconscionable waste, keeping tens of thousands of people in tents, with no vision of tomorrow, dependent on welfare organizations for their very food. These poor souls had miraculously eluded gas chambers, seen loved ones taken away and shot or incinerated in huge pits before their very eyes, or often had no idea whether their loved ones were dead or alive. And now, due to the crass insensitivity of the British Government, they had again been relegated to camps -- British detention camps on Cyprus or God alone knew where else -- awaiting the redemption of British permission to resume their journey to Palestine, their own homeland."*

The entire situation defied reason; the psychological impact upon those suffering souls must have been lethal in many cases.

Despite everything the enlightened world press reported about the suffering of the survivors, not only in the concentration/death camps of Europe but also in those deplorable detention camps, representatives of world powers in the United Nations couldn't make the simple decision that would force the United Kingdom to "let those people go!" When 97% of them told the world they wanted to go to Palestine, why couldn't the powerful United Nations decisively move on their behalf?

The European Holocaust survivors weren't only Jews. Other Europeans-- the French, Dutch, Norwegians, Poles, and Russians -- also suffered the Nazis' beastiality. They also lost loved ones under circumstances similar to Jews. However, when the war ended and the Nazi killing machine destroyed, unlike the Jews, those people could go home to their own countries where they were welcomed back into the fold. The Jews of Europe, however, had no such luxury or warmth awaiting them. They couldn't possibly return to countries that had betrayed them, rounded them up like cattle, and turned them over to the Nazis for transport to those infamous concentration/death camps.

"Why can't the United Nations understand that these people desperately need their own homeland here in Palestine?" Was Amnon's inner pleading.

The last two weeks hadn't been too difficult. No real action, although a few more fishing vessels had arrived and a few more immigrants successfully reached their assigned destinations. Amnon kept wondering why the plan to sabotage the British intercepting ships had been shelved, and just when it might be re-activated.

With no new instructions for him and his men, he decided to take the bus to Tel Aviv. No sooner said than done; Amnon caught the next bus, and when he got to Tel Aviv swiftly made his way to the safe house where he briefly met with several commanders. His superior, he learned, would arrive around 8:00pm, so he decided to walk around the city for a while.

Months had passed since he'd last browsed around a store, and telling himself it was high time for the next few hours, he pretended he was a tourist and pleasurably browsed, looking at all sorts of merchandise, taking mental note of prices; he felt like a visitor from another world. Without the slightest idea of what everything cost, he found most prices unbelievably high. Still, he greatly enjoyed his window-hopping, and since he was hungry, and did know the cost of a falafel pita and an ice cream cone, he treated himself before walking back to the safe house.

Arriving before 8:00, Amnon ran into Nechemia, his commanding officer. Delighted to see Amnon, Nechemia told him he had approved the three young immigrants who so demanded to join his unit.

"Thanks very much for thinking of me," Amnon told him. "But what's happening with the plan to sabotage the British intercepting ships?"

"We must be patient, Amnon. It takes all kinds of careful deliberations now going on at high levels. On the one hand, the Jewish Agency is trying to show the British that we are capable of restraint, while on the other the Agency continues to funnel its support and assist legal or illegal Jewish immigration into Palestine. Believe me, all of this takes an unimaginable amount of calm and patience."

"But of one thing you may be absolutely certain," he assured Amnon, "if the British don't ease their blockade, and continue refusing to let more survivors come into Palestine, and also continue their campaign to break us, we will attack them every way we can to bring them down. We will know for sure one way or another, in a few weeks."

"Meanwhile, whenever you have the time, go to Haifa and have your plan ready to put into action. Knowing you, I'm sure you'll come up with a plan nobody can beat." With that, he slapped Amnon heartily on his back, and departed.

"*I'll have to be satisfied with that,*" Amnon told himself, knowing it would be difficult.

Amnon headed briskly for his friend Levi's home. Levi and Amnon had been classmates in the first grade and good friends ever since. He, too, was in the Haganah, but they hadn't seen each other for more than two years. He was not home, but his parents warmly welcomed him, and following a light meal, Amnon spent the night.

Amnon

Friday, December 6, 1946

Amnon stopped in Natania, assigned command to his deputy, and left for Haifa with two men. One he assigned to scan the docks from the mountaintop and make mental notes of the comings and goings of the British vessels. Amnon and the other man set out to investigate the food supply companies. He quickly located the same label he'd seen on the boxes the British were supplied with, noted the company's name, and went right away to the Haifa safe house where he requested a report on the company's owners.

Inside a day he had all the information he needed, including the owner's name, address, and how long in business. Next he consulted with Uncle Mordechai, a Haifa resident for over 40 years and owner the only Hebrew printing press in town, who Amnon was certain would know that person. He was right. Uncle Mordechai told him the man had an impeccable reputation and was well liked. It was important to Amnon not to ruin him.

That night they broke into his warehouse. They took a dozen address labels and one of his shipping boxes, the same type of box widely used in the citrus packaging industry, thin strips of lumber connected by wire; the box was collapsible, and when filled, its lid would be nailed in place. Delighted with his find, and knowing those boxes were easily obtainable near Natania, Amnon asked his Haifa contact to get twelve of them right away.

Their next project was to spy on the truck that delivered the supplies to the British Navy, learning its route, its stops, and timing. This was an easy job, for downtown Haifa was a big commercial center where many trucks came and went all the time. Being a port city, ships were constantly arriving and departing with imports and huge exports of citrus fruits and other merchandise marked for numerous global destinations.

Traffic to and from the port was always heavy. Taking careful note of that particular company's truck, Amnon became familiar with its driver's habits and the truck's daily route to pinpoint the best spot to intercept it. The whole time Amnon was engaged in his research, his overall plan for the operation developed and finally became set in his mind.

All that he needed was the target date around which to work. He sent an immediate message to his superior requesting he be given a few days prior notice so he could investigate and act on any changes in the truck's route, type of box, and delivery time.

Then, fully satisfied with all the information he had collected, Amnon returned to Natania to await further developments and instructions.

.

Sunday, December 8, 1946

An immigrant ship with 800 on board sank somewhere in the Aegean Sea, all but eight of the passengers were rescued by a British ship that was cruising in the area, which transported them directly to Cyprus without stopping in Palestine. It was lucky the radio Amnon heard this report on was not his, for he was angry enough to throw it on the floor and stomp it to pieces for having announced that worst of all news.

"What rotten luck that a British ship happened to be cruising in the area,

and took the refugees directly to Cyprus without even a stop in Palestine so the refugees could at least have had a breath of air in our land. There was no explanation given for the sinking. Could it be this innocent British ship was responsible? And what the devil was it doing there anyway?" Amnon's suspicion of the British was obvious.

"None of us would trust any of these British people, and with very good reason!" he announced.

Monday, December 23, 1946

Amnon was called to a meeting in Haifa. The Haganah was planning a major break-in into the Atlit barracks with the objective of removing weapons that had been confiscated by the British authorities. Date and time, they were told, were set at 9:00pm Christmas Day, December 25th. This major operation would employ ten units, the biggest operation ever. The Haganah wanted not only to recover the arms the British had taken during their searches, but also to supply themselves with additional weapons for future use.

The Haganah planned to block all roads so no one would be able to enter or leave the barracks after they'd gone. Amnon's instructions called for his unit to be in Zichron Yaacov by noon Wednesday. Trucks were constantly in and out of the Zichron vineyards, so no one would get suspicious.

Thursday, December 26, 1946

The year 1946 concluded with news of the most astonishing arms robbery of all time.

Eighteen truckloads of variegated weapons plus limitless ammunition were taken from the Atlit warehouses. An elite commando unit of the Haganah broke through one of the entrances to the barracks, surprised the guards, and took them prisoners. From there, the small commando unit convoy went straight to the officers club and arrested everyone in sight. Not a shot was fired.

While all this was taking place, their own truck convoy entered the barracks and headed for the marked warehouses. Heavy gunfire was heard somewhere behind the barracks, doubtless the result of word having gotten out that the barracks was under attack, possibly through an officer who managed to escape undetected.

Amnon and several units under his command were in charge of securing the blockade so that no military reinforcements could enter or leave the barracks after the trucks left. They took up positions around the main entrance gates and all exits from the compound. Several units were inside the trucks to take care of the loading.

When the commando officer ordered the British officer to open the main gate to the warehouse, he refused. Forthwith, the commando officer ordered one of his men to shoot off his legs, and shots were fired into the ground about ten centimeters from him.

"Next time, we shoot off your legs," he was told.

The British officer immediately produced a set of keys and opened the locks. Two men took him away and handcuffed him to an outer gate. There was no way he could move. While fighting continued at another end of the barracks, Haganah men held the military guards at bay. With the help of cranes, each truck was filled to capacity.

As soon as all the trucks were loaded they drove out of the barracks compound heading north toward Haifa, however, at the first intersection, about four kilometers from the barracks, the convoy turned east into Arab territory and circled south through a number of dirt roads toward Zichron. The idea was to make the British believe that the trucks were on the way north. From that point on, that entire stretch of road and all others leading to the barracks were under Amnon's control.

Within fifteen minutes, dozens of assorted military vehicles loaded with personnel came roaring out. Amnon's men stopped them cold, and kept them at bay for over an hour. No one left the barracks.

After an hour they slowly began to abandon their locations. Mines had previously been laid on the road to delay pursuit. By the time they'd gone on their way, they heard explosions behind them. Not a single vehicle followed them.

This operation cost the Haganah two men dead, six men wounded. Though Amnon never got a complete count of all the booty, he knew it must have been tremendous. And the commando officer left a note for the British, the gist of which was "You stop seeking and taking our arms, and we won't take yours!"

They got a real kick out of that man's sense of humor.

1946 was drawing to a close, and as usual Amnon mentally reviewed the past year. Actually, he thought it had been quite an interesting year. The British had intercepted twenty-two immigrant ships and sent their passengers to detention camps in Cyprus. However, although specific statistics were lacking, numerous fishing vessels managed to get through the British blockade with over 20,000 immigrants, all of whom safely arrived and were assimilated into the Jewish population of Palestine. Despite the Jewish Agency's moratorium on major sabotage and terrorist activities against the British, during the final months of the year the Resistance forces staged many minor operations just to let the British know they weren't likely to give up the fight.

Though the Haganah complied with the Jewish Agency's request for restraint, continued stealthy harassment by Etzel and the Lehi rubbed British noses in the Yishuv's anti-British feelings. In retaliation, the British handed down heavy sentences on captured saboteurs, including three death sentences that caused violent protest demonstrations throughout the country, and British military and civilian police continued their purposely irregular searches for hidden defense weapons, clearly indicating they would have liked for the Jews to be defenseless against the British-armed Arabs.

British pro-Arab policies continued along with their inflexible anti-Jewish immigration policies. The Zionist Congress convention that year accepted the resignation of Chaim Weitzman and gave David Ben Gurion the responsibility for all Defense activities, which meant that the hawks had won. To compensate for all the disturbing events of the year, the most heart-warming news was that Haganah members had helped to establish twenty-five new settlements in

Palestine, the highest number of new settlements in any year to date.

Saturday, January 4, 1947

As the New Year began, it became clear that the Yishuv and the Resistance forces were in a very combative mood. Fishing vessels, with as few as twenty immigrants slipped through the British blockade. Maybe the British didn't bother with such small ships. If so, British oversight worked in the Yishuv's favor, and the Yishuv rejoiced over every new arrival, for traditionally, saving one life meant saving a nation.

At yesterday's meeting, in keeping with the Jewish Agency's policy of restraint, the Haganah was requested not to conduct any overtly militant anti-British harassment until further notice. However, ignoring the Agency's request, the Etzel and Lehi's forces intensified their daily sabotage and terrorist activities. The Yishuv, which included all the Resistance forces, was evidently engaged in a political balancing act, its leaders claiming they had no control over the radical Resistance organizations, meanwhile praying their harassment would so frustrate the British they'd finally give up and leave Palestine.

"From all our mouths and hearts to God's ears!" was the quote of the day.

Amnon's commander judiciously suggested the Haganah might turn to general annoyances to drive the British up the wall. Huge rocks were to be placed in strategic locations to block traffic on main arteries and side roads, slashing telephone wires and short-circuiting electricity and other utilities to British installations and military barracks was also to be carried out.

Taking Amnon aside, Nechemia led him to a sofa where both sat down and briefly chatted.

"It looks like that operation against the British intercepting ships may take place sometime in February. Have you come up with a feasible plan?"

"Yes, I have," Amnon said. "I plan to use boxes full of explosives to replace the regular supply boxes, and they'll be delivered by the same trucker who delivers supplies to the port every day. They're ready to go. If all goes well, when the explosive mechanisms in the boxes have been activated, at least two ships will be destroyed, or at least damaged to the point of being unusable. This leaves four similar ships out on the high seas, and all of these must dock at regular intervals to resupply. But since the British aren't likely to fall for the same trick twice, we'll need to use another method to destroy the remaining four ships.

" Since these ships will return from duty and dock after the first two are out of commission, I suggest we prepare an explosive device our frogmen can attach to the ships' undersides at night. They have experience performing similar maneuvers against docked British ships, so they should have no problem with this one."

"There will also be two other British vessels at sea, which should be attacked by our own boats. All of these attacks should be launched during the same night."

Nechemia always enjoyed listening to Amnon's verbal explicate of his attack strategies.

"I like it, Amnon," he said, "and I'll keep you posted on developments. Meanwhile," he slapped Amnon's shoulder and grinned, "I suggest you keep your men ready to move at short notice," before they went their separate ways.

"*So what else is new?*" Amnon asked himself -- there was never anything but short notices. But this was the first time an operation was being planned for an as yet unknown future date.

Jewish Agency leaders continued their talks with the British authorities in Palestine. Amnon understood there was also lobbying being done in England without much success. Atlee's government, represented by Ernst Bevin, was uncompromising on the issue of Jewish immigration into Palestine. The British continued to believe the Arabs were their best allies in the Middle East, a misguided stance that militated against a favorable decision for the Jews.

British history showed that only bribes and other material benefits to the Arabs had helped the cause in the Middle East. Regarding the issue of Jewish immigration into Palestine, the Arabs were so divided amongst themselves that no consensus was possible. Thus the British belief that the Arabs were their best allies in this matter was patent demonstration of their sheer blindness, if not utter stupidity.

"*As long as Atlee's government continues on its stubborn course,*" thought Amnon, "*there's no chance the Haganah will quit its sabotage operations aimed towards creating a Jewish Homeland in Palestine. To achieve this objective, we must first somehow evict the British from Palestine. Regrettably, it's becoming more and more clear the stubborn British only pay attention to hard action.*"

So, off they went, on a new plan designed to frustrate the hell out of the British!

Amnon called his men to a meeting and laid out a huge map of Palestine on the floor, pinpointing the locations of British installations from Natania to Haifa. From their equipment and supply depot Amnon requested an old half-truck as well as a telephone company repair van to use in disrupting telephone service in British installations, police stations, and any place else they could think of.

Four of Amnon's men posed as telephone repairmen in uniforms identical to those worn by telephone company personnel. One man climbed the telephone pole, one waited on the ground, and two were inside the van with weapons ready in case of need. Telephone wires were prepared for collapse in 10 hours so service would be disrupted at night, or long after the saboteurs had gone. The half-truck was filled with nails, and as soon as darkness fell they spread nails on roads connecting to police stations and military barracks. Other units did the same in other parts of the country. Huge rocks and boulders were hauled in from outlying areas and used to block important intersections.

The British government in Palestine was so thoroughly frustrated by all those disturbances that their personnel were driven up the walls. Meanwhile, the Etzel and Lehi continued attacking and bombing anything in their way that looked even vaguely British. They too spread nails, cut telephone wires, blocked roads with boulders, knocked out electric power for hours, and cut off water to

British military barracks.

The Haganah's continued harassment, along with ferocious attacks by Etzel and Lehi, caused the British to establish security zones. Hoping to improve security for themselves, the British declared certain areas of the country Protective Zones, which the Yishuv immediately dubbed "Bevingrads." By establishing those zones, moreover, the British actually increased the Haganah's freedom crucial in its operations, to transport men and supplies and communicate in areas outside these zones.

Friday, January 31, 1947

Today the British announced all women and children of British military men and administrative government personnel would be evacuated from Palestine. Amnon immediately began to speculate, *"Does this mean we're getting somewhere? It shows the British no longer considered Palestine a place where they and theirs can stay peacefully. On the other hand, it could also mean the British and their Arab buddies might be planning an all out war against us."*

A second British announcement stated the Yishuv leadership had acceded to the British demand for a cessation of sabotage and terror activity.

Amnon's response was, "Yeah, right. We'll stop all action against you the moment you open the gates to our survivors." To date, however, there was absolutely no change in the inflexible British anti-immigration policy, and as long as the British blockade continued to intercept and block refugees from Palestine, the sabotage and terrorist activities would not only continue, they would increase.

When Amnon's scouts reported the British had been clearing nails and other debris off the roads, they simply returned to the scene that same night and laid down more. While this sabotage work was going on they continued meeting illegal fishing vessels to ensure their immigrant passengers' safe arrival. Every week brought another illegal vessel with more new arrivals. It must surely have been with God's help that those boats and their passengers slipped through the British blockade in dozens of trips from Italy to Palestine and back.

They were busy on both fronts. With the main arteries impassable due to their sabotage, the Haganah reverted to using the dirt roads and fields where they maneuvered just as well. In the long run, it took a little longer to get from place to place, though it was also much safer for them and their immigrant charges.

Tuesday, February 4, 1947

Amnon received an urgent summons to go to their safe house in Tel Aviv. At the commanders' meeting they were told that despite all efforts -- the Jewish Agency's talks with the British produced no change whatsoever concerning "immigration" to Palestine. Therefore, sabotage would resume within days.

Amnon was instructed to immediately activate his postponed plan to destroy all British naval vessels engaged in intercepting immigrant ships. The date set was Thursday, February 13, 1947. Unless Amnon received orders to the contrary, he was to go ahead with it.

Immediately, he called a meeting of the unit commanders working with him to go over every aspect of his plan. Returning to base, he called on the Haganah's explosives expert, and instructed him to construct twelve food boxes using hand grenade pins to set off both the gunpowder and dynamite that would be in each box. As Amnon stood watching, on the bottom of each of the twelve boxes the expert first laid a layer of gunpowder about three centimeters high. Then, into each bed of gunpowder he laid as many dynamite sticks as could fit in the box. In the center he lodged a hand grenade with a pin that would slide out at the slightest pull of the lid. The hand grenade was secured in place, surrounded and covered with potatoes to the top and the wire connected to the pin was attached to the lid, which was then nailed down.

Address labels that exactly matched all the other boxes were affixed to the sides. Amnon was now ready for act one of the big show.

Friday, February 14, 1947

Last night they blew up four British naval vessels used to intercept immigrant ships. The sequence of events began Thursday afternoon, February 13th, when Amnon's men intercepted the target supply truck on the selected street where they had stored the explosives-laden food boxes. One of his men asked the driver to get out of his truck, and one of the older operatives borrowed from the Haganah's back office took him aside and began questioning him about his membership in the Histadrut. (Labor Union)

The older operative infuriated the driver by telling him that because he hadn't paid his dues, his membership would be terminated and he would lose his health insurance. During the ensuing heated discussion between the driver and the operative, Amnon's men quickly removed six boxes from the front of the truck and another six from the rear, and replaced them with the doctored boxes in such a way that half of the dozen doctored boxes would be deposited next to each of the ships. After they'd finished up in about ten minutes, they signaled the operative who then apologized, saying he had somehow gotten the wrong man, and hurried away, leaving the driver cursing profusely as he got back into his truck and drove off.

One of Amnon's scouts followed the truck on a bicycle. At the same time, two of his men disguised as mechanics and each with a fake entry pass, drove into the harbor compound, continued from the main gate headed directly to the wharf dividing the docks. They parked their car and hid until dark. Each of their toolboxes contained two powerful bombs attached to timers.

Soon after nightfall, they slipped from their hiding places and lowered themselves into the water. They attached one bomb to the outside of each vessel, just twelve centimeters under the water level, each bomb set to explode an hour later. The moment they were done, they swam around the divider and out into the bay, heading north towards the shore at Kiriat Chaim, where they went ashore.

Act Two began when, as on any other day, the truck and its unsuspecting driver entered the port compound with the driver showing his entry permit through his window. Since he and his truck were familiar to the guards, they waved him right through. One load of boxes was dropped off next to the first

157

vessel, the second load by the second vessel.

As usual, sailors carried the boxes on board and disappeared from view. Within an hour, all boxes were out of sight. The first vessel left at exactly 5:00pm, the second vessel about fifteen minutes later. Ironically, the second vessel, which had barely left the bay, was the first to blow up. The first explosion triggered the others. The key was that all the boxes exploded exactly as Amnon had planned.

The first grenade that exploded sent shrapnel into its neighboring boxes, which detonated them one by one. A series of explosions were heard, followed by fire, and the ship began taking in water. Ten minutes later, there was a repeat performance when the first vessel, by then quite a distance from the dividing wharf, burst into a similar series of explosions and sank within half an hour. An hour later, there were two more huge explosions, and since the water wasn't deep enough to cover them, the two docked vessels were only partly under water. The successful operation left four British intercepting vessels out of commission.

Additionally, two more British vessels in the Mediterranean which had been followed from afar by Haganah speedboats got a nasty middle-of-the-night surprise. The speedboats' four 2-pounder cannons each fired a withering salvo at close range, penetrating the vessels' steel hulls. That exploit marked the first Haganah attack at sea.

Taken totally by surprise by the sneak attack, it took the British naval men some time to collect themselves and snap into retaliatory action mode, by which time the speedboats had safely gotten away, and the shots fired in their wake did no damage. Though two pounders make only small holes, those holes take in water, and a boat taking in water through numerous small holes in its hull has very little chance of staying afloat unless it's very close to shore. As this was not the case, both vessels soon sank, which brought the tally of destruction in this operation to six British intercepting vessels.

Both the owner of the supplies company and the truck driver were arrested, but later released because no incriminating evidence was found against them. Later, Amnon was called to the main safe house in Tel Aviv, and warmly congratulated on a job well done.

Tuesday, February 18, 1947

There couldn't have been greater news! The British government announced it was referring the Palestine issue to the United Nations.

"Hoorah!" The Haganah's clandestine radio station repeated that statement over and over again.

"Finally, there will be some light at the end of the tunnel. Surely in the United Nations we will find people with more heart, who are not guided by either outdated ideas of colonialism or imperialistic policies," Amnon declared.

While at this stage they knew little or nothing of exactly what the United Nations could or couldn't do, they did know it had to be better than the British.

"The United States, which has been pushing the United Kingdom to allow 100,000 immigrants into Palestine, will surely be on our side. And Russia, who released most Jewish detainees from Siberia and allowed them to go west, will almost certainly be on our side also. Guilt ridden Germany was engaged in a full-scale reparations program to benefit the Holocaust survivors, as were many European nations that had surrendered their Jewish populations to the Nazis, and it seems safe to assume these countries will also range themselves on our side in this matter. In the United Nations, we and our cause will finally receive a fair hearing, and the new support that might come from every corner may actually work a miracle for us," Amnon continued.

"If I had ever had any doubts about the success of our Resistance war against the British Government and local British authorities, they have nearly all disappeared. It's working," he said gleefully. "We have succeeded in creating a hostile environment to make the British want to get out of Palestine as soon as possible. My gut feeling is that in order to speed their early departure, our Resistance activities should step up considerably."

Sunday, February 23, 1947

Yesterday, a rare day of rest was unusually hot and humid for this time of year. Amnon grabbed a large towel and went to the beach where he rolled the towel up into a makeshift pillow, stretched out on the sand, closed his eyes, and simply relaxed. Few Palestinians went to the beach in winter, so it was virtually deserted. It was almost spring-like, though a little cooler than inland, and a gentle breeze caressed his body as Amnon relished those rare few hours of almost total solitude.

Laying there in the sun, and getting even more tan than he needed, his mind went to the impending discussions of the Palestine issue at the United Nations General Assembly in New York.

"Since the British have referred the matter to the United Nations, they might possibly have some argument similar to that broached to the League of Nations after World War I, which had earned the British Palestine as a Protectorate. Assuming they did have such a plan, mightn't it detail the necessity for the United Kingdom to retain control over Palestine, in order to also retain control of the Suez Canal?"

"At no time had the British Government ever taken a chance that the cards would not fall their way. Moreover, everyone in Europe and especially in England knew of Britain's long obsession with the Suez Canal, which explained its tremendous military presence in Egypt, Trans-Jordan, Iran, Iraq and Palestine. But with the advent of the refugee problem, now being relegated to the United Nations, one could be forgiven for wondering what skullduggery the UK had planned at this precise moment in time."

On the heels of this thought came the equally disquieting question:
"Since the British Government had fought so hard to win control of Palestine after World War I, why would it now voluntarily relinquish it because of the Jewish refugee problem?"

"Britain has the greatest fleet in the world, so where does Palestine fall into this equation?"

"And what about India?"

Having heard and read so much about the British obsession with the land route to India through Palestine, coupled with India's successful struggle for independence, Amnon wondered what the British would do about that situation in relation to Palestine.

"Having taken over Palestine from the Turkish Ottoman Empire, could the UK now prefer that Palestine remain an essentially uninhabited protectorate as it was when they first took over, and might that be the reason for their inflexible stance against admitting the Jewish refugees?"

Trying to second-guess the British gave Amnon a king-sized headache, and he decided to clear his mind with a short snooze.

But sleep was simply not possible, and his ever-active thoughts flew on to other aspects of the same problem.

"Where are we now? At what stage is our struggle? What will come next? What if the United Nations votes to permit the establishment of our own state, how will the Arabs react?

"The British installed anti-Jewish Mufti of Jerusalem, who over the years had taken his cue from Palestine's British overlords and continuously incited the Arabs against the Jews, was not likely to tamely accept the creation of a Jewish State. Moreover, his continuous hate-filled sermons together with vicious Arab attacks on Jewish settlements were not conducive to any sort of conciliatory climate in the Middle East".

"Thus if the United Nations threw its weight behind the establishment of a Jewish State, the result would almost certainly be an all-out war, the Arabs against the Jews. Continuously ignoring the truth, which was that Jewish settlers had purchased from the Arabs only arid desert and deadly mosquito-infested marsh or malarial swamp land which they'd slaved and died to change from arid desert or swamps to flourishing farmland, the Mufti claimed the Jews had taken or stolen Arab land. This radical and unscrupulous personality would incite the Arabs to mindless violence in the form of a no-holds-barred war that would start as soon as the United Nations approved the establishment of a Jewish State."

The more Amnon reflected, the more certain he became that the United Nations, after reading truthful reports of the successful development the Jews had achieved in Palestine, would vote in favor of a Jewish State. With the whole world aware of the many Holocaust survivors stranded in the limbo of European displaced persons camps and British detention camps on Cyprus and other British-owned territories, the entire Yishuv in Palestine and the rest of the world anticipated the United Nations finally resolving the immigration issue in Palestine by voting in favor of the establishment of a Jewish State.

The whole world was aware of the Jewish resistance to their British overlords in Palestine. Daily news broadcasts and newspaper articles reported the Resistance forces' continuing attacks against British installations and intercepting ships that kept Jewish immigrants from Palestine. It wasn't possible for the British government and the British press to ignore mounting British fatalities and wounded; their hospitals were filled to overflowing with severely wounded officers as well as soldiers and sailors that had been transported from Palestine. British authorities would be hard put to provide adequate explanations for this situation.

Furthermore, a close look at the British statement in which they referred the matter to the United Nations clearly showed the British-sponsored conference between the Arabs and the Jews on the problems of Palestine had been a total failure.

The British continued in the misguided belief they could control the Arabs as they'd managed to do for the previous thirty years. All the men in the Arab legion were British-trained as well as British-armed and directed in all their campaigns by British officers. It was, therefore, all too probable the British would incite their Arab buddies to launch a full-scale war against the Jews the moment the establishment of a Jewish State became fact.

No clear-thinking Jew in Palestine would trust the British as far as he could throw them, which explained why the Yishuv spent every shekel they could get their hands on to buy every manner of defensive and aggressive weapons for the growing armory, also explaining the many operations designed to denude or deplete every British military and police armory depot. Moreover, the reason for all those impromptu arms searches by British military and civilian police, which had occurred long before the Resistance operations designed to steal their weapons, suddenly became clear. They were motivated by the sole purpose of weakening Jewish defenses against the Arab enemies.

Amnon's heavy day and night work schedule left little time in which to simply sit and ponder all of the possibilities of the upcoming United Nations debate at its General Assembly meeting in New York. This is where member nations would hear all aspects of the total Jewish immigration and Palestine's long struggle for independent statehood. Having analyzed all facts, and with the picture clear in his mind, Amnon felt much better for having sorted out all these vexing puzzles.

He'd spent more time than he realized on the beach. Picking up his towel, he shook out the sand, slung it over his shoulder, and headed back to base, where a lot of work was waiting for him. As he strode along Amnon continued his mental reviews:

"My belief and commitment to our cause had always been well defined and very strong. It's a cause for which, if necessary I'd willingly die. But although being a soldier didn't leave much time to think, it didn't stop my thoughts from roaming free. And, even though I was obliged to follow orders, this didn't make me, or my Haganah comrades, regular soldiers involved in a World War."

"Our war, if it could accurately be so described, was actually a pitched battle for our independence in the same way as the Americans fought the British for their independence in the 18th century. Ours is a fight for the right to establish our own Jewish Homeland after 2000 years of the Diaspora and after the Nazi Holocaust, their master plan to annihilate the Jewish people. The time has come for all Jews, especially the Holocaust survivors, to finally have a country of their own. And what could be a more fitting location for a Jewish Homeland than the Land of Israel, the biblical land, long ago wrested from the Jews by force?"

161

"In the course of the Diaspora, the Jews were never fully assimilated into the countries in which they had settled. At the whim of anti-Semitic despots or emperors, they were often made scapegoats and accused of heinous crimes for which they were hounded down like animals and forced to flee for their lives. Surely the United Nations will take all this into account, and despite the deviousness of the British, we will finally win our own Jewish State."

Amnon wished that his way of thinking would go from his mind and heart to God's ears. He decided to bring up all his analysis of recent British behavior at the next commanders' meeting, plus he had a few ideas to discuss with his own commander.

Sunday, March 2, 1947

In one of its fiercest attacks to date, the Etzel killed twelve British officers inside a British Officers Club, wounding numerous others. In direct retaliation, the British authorities imposed a martial law on Tel Aviv and part of Jerusalem. It was believed that this violent Etzel attack was in reprisal for the hanging of three Etzel members sentenced to death some time back.

Whatever the case, the fight continued and was soon joined by the Haganah, which would resume its own sabotage and terrorist activities.

March seemed to start like every other month, a continuing flow of immigrants trying to get to Palestine by every means possible. A ship with 1,300 immigrants managed to get through the blockade but was caught as it reached land, and all of its immigrant passengers were immediately transferred to another ship, which took them to Cyprus. The game continued unabated, the Haganah managing to bring in some immigrants, and losing others to the British who transported them to detention camps.

"Tomorrow, I'll head for a meeting in Haifa, and put my cards on the table. We must have more information," Amnon decided.

Monday, March 3, 1947

Apparently Amnon wasn't the only one who felt they needed more updated information and knowledge of the latest affairs. The lull in activity against the British had allowed others to think as well. Answering to their main question, they were told the British had called for a conference in London to discuss the Palestine problem, and the Yishuv had felt perhaps there might be some change in the British attitude regarding immigration, but that proved not to be the case. The Yishuv had also thought the Jewish Agency honoring the British request for restraint in hostile acts might also work to soften them up, but that didn't work out either.

The Jewish leadership had given both possibilities a try. But since the Etzel and Lehi had never stopped their anti-British operations, the Yishuv's leaders disavowed either affiliation or control over those two organizations, accompanied by official statements that they opposed violence against the British. At this juncture, it appeared obvious the Yishuv hadn't had any real chance of changing either the British inflexibility against immigration or their pro-Arab policies; both gambits had proven to be exercises in utter futility.

Amnon

Amnon and the other commanders had their answers, and their course was set. They would use every means at their disposal, take any action necessary, hopefully without too many Jewish fatalities. In short, the Haganah would do whatever it took to force the British the hell out of Palestine!

The key statement made by the Haganah's northern regional commander concerned the Yishuv's efforts at the United Nations.

"The great majority of our work is being done behind the scenes by a variety of United Nations diplomats, some from friendly countries, including Russia. This is why our leaders felt that we should show some restraint," the commander told them. "However," he continued, "we must continue aggressively to arm ourselves."

"As you know, we have a number of members who specialize in buying arms, and who are working in certain countries. With the help of contributions by Jews inside and outside of Palestine, primarily in England and America, we have enough money to make such acquisitions."

"However, the more difficult and complex problem is smuggling these arms into Palestine. So far, we've been successful, and the British haven't caught a single shipment," he knocked on the wood table. "And speaking of arms shipments, huge quantities are about to arrive, and all units who've been involved in arms smuggling will soon be called on to help."

As the meeting wound down, the Regional commander advised Amnon that a replacement for his unit would arrive Wednesday, and his unit was to proceed immediately to Kfar Gilaadi, and be there by the end of the week. Though they received only hints rather than candid answers to all their questions, most commanders understood not every issue could be made public. They also clearly understood that the Yishuv must be prepared to move in the event of a war. It seemed that like the majority of the Haganah, the Yishuv also felt the British were not to be trusted.

Monday, March 10, 1947

As instructed Amnon's entire unit arrived in Kfar Gilaadi by Friday. All the unit's members kept busy working with the kibbutz staff until the call to action came through. That had occurred yesterday, and last night they resumed their work of arms smuggling. When Amnon went to the barn where the mules were kept, it felt as if he was renewing old friendships. Amnon had learned to love those funny, but very smart animals, and felt very close to them. Whenever they worked together, his life, as his men's, depended on their phenomenal night vision, and he valued their ability to carry heavy loads while also directing their every step along treacherous mountain paths. To Amnon, every one of the mules was worth the care they needed; they were worth their weight in gold for their invaluable assistance in the smuggling operations.

Friday, April 4, 1947

Aware this would be the last trip into Lebanon for a while -- the last shipment to arrive in Lebanon was now safely in the hands of the Haganah-- Amnon wondered which other locations were involved in the arms smuggling.

Such information was divulged on a need-to-know basis only, and he squelched his curiosity by telling himself, *"You should know only that which is necessary for you and your men to accomplish your job."*

The entire Haganah organization by now comprised of close to eighty thousand members, had become a worldwide underground network of operatives working under cover of night and in secret, their operations known only to themselves and their Haganah superiors. Taught from day one to keep their mouths shut, and not even talk to closest blood relatives about the most negligible aspect of even the most minor action, Haganah members were continuously engaged in sabotage and other hostile action against the British as well as fiercely defending kibbutzim and other Jewish settlements against Arab attacks.

Haganah members worked in displaced persons camps and British detention camps to help Jewish survivors make their way to Palestine by any means possible. They continuously bought and smuggled arms, engaged in multitudinous diplomatic efforts and lobbying, raised funds for Haganah operations, and, of course, stubbornly fought to bring immigrants arriving on illegal fishing vessels from every seaport into Palestine, and help them settle comfortably into their new lives in the Yishuv.

Every free moment he had, Amnon was glued to the radio. A British Court sentenced another Lehi member to death. The British caught an immigrant ship with over 1500 people on board. Lehi forces attacked the oil refineries in Haifa Bay and caused severe damage. Amnon felt sorry for those Lehi men, considered radicals for their relentless violent war against the British by most of the Yishuv, who preferred more moderate action.

The problem, as Amnon saw it, was that the Etzel and Lehi organizations wholeheartedly believed the biblical Land of Israel was the only future Jewish Homeland. They wanted the biblical boundaries of Israel to be the modern boundaries. Amnon didn't believe that was going to happen, and it was in fact ridiculous for them to hold on to such a wish, for such fantasy boundaries would mean the future Jewish Homeland would include millions of Arabs, none of whom would meekly submit to Jewish domination.

Unfortunately, radical thinking did not lend itself to rational solutions of problems. But if not for the radicals in their midst, the Haganah would have no basis for comparison in its own more moderate solutions to the problems. Amnon felt they must therefore be gracious enough to salute the Etzel and Lehi for their courage in their persistent tilting at what seemed like windmills.

"We must acknowledge that just like the rest of us, they want a Jewish State, and many have died fighting for that cause," Amnon declared.

After Lehi forces severely damaged the British oil refineries in Haifa Bay, it was to be hoped the United Kingdom would soon, if it wasn't already, become desperate. There wasn't a single British installation in Palestine that hadn't been hit, and many of them more than once.

Saturday, April 12, 1947

After it successfully completed the latest arms smuggling project from Lebanon, Amnon's unit was ordered to report to Naharia, where they would again disrupt British military and civilian police transportation in an area spread between Rosh Hanikra and Haifa.

Split into small groups of three or four, each with some sort of vehicle, they nightly dumped debris in locations that greatly frustrated the British. During the day, in kibbutzim, farms, or moshavim, they loaded their vehicles with anything that could help achieve their objective. Locations they felt were of critical importance to the British were spread with nails and sharp slivers of glass; they were always armed and ready for a British attack while they worked.

Last Wednesday night, on the road to Rosh Hanrika, Amnon narrowly avoided being ambushed by a small police force. Thankfully, unlike the Haganah, the British lacked the expertise and nerve for night fighting. Without waiting for Amnon's car to enter their ambush zone, they started firing too soon. Had they waited, Amnon and his two companions would have been killed.

Instead, at the first wild shot, Amnon's driver stopped the car, and Amnon, one man sitting in back and the driver jumped out, and quickly rolled over to the left and right of the road. The British civilian police kept firing blindly at the car. Amnon and his men didn't return fire right away. Instead, they silently crawled in the trenches along both sides of the road towards the police, their rifles slung over their shoulders onto their backs.

The policemen kept firing at the car sporadically. Lacking any response from the vehicle, they probably thought all passengers had been hit, and eventually stopped firing. By that time Amnon and his men could clearly see them from close up. Knowing the next ten seconds were crucial, Amnon threw a pebble across the road, which alerted his men to be rifle-ready, and instantly fired the first shot, followed in rapid succession by his comrades.

Firing as they went, they cautiously crawled forward, stopped, crawled forward again. When Amnon was ten meters away from the police, he pulled the pin out of a hand grenade and hurled it in their direction, and three seconds later another.

Decimated by the two explosions, no further firing came from the police, only silence punctuated by cries and groans of wounded men.

Cautiously, rifles at the ready, they approached and saw the policemen were in no condition to move. Looking around, Amnon spotted their armored car parked in a nearby ravine. He drove over to the six wounded men, piled them in the back of the armored car and drove it about a quarter of a kilometer from the frontier. There, they placed them carefully on the ground before taking their police badges, identity papers, rifles, revolvers and all their ammunition, plus two cases of hand grenades.

With all their loot piled into their newly acquired armored car, they sped off to their hideout, dropped off the confiscated arms, picked up enough sufficient food for the next day, then drove back to the scene of the failed police ambush. They pushed the bullet-riddled car to the side of the road where it would be visible, especially to the British authorities. "The British police will be totally confused when they discover this shot-up car without any of us in it. Eventually they'll discover the wounded policemen near the border and that their armored car has disappeared. That's when they'll really be confused," Amnon said, adding, "This is not the end of the confusion, because when they check out our shot-up car they'll find out it's a police car which was stolen from a government parking lot." They had a good laugh.

In those days, all acts of violence were automatically blamed on the Etzel or Lehi; Amnon was delighted that they'd inadvertently become honorary members of the two radical organizations.

Shortly past the shot up car left on the side of the road, Amnon and his men drove off the road into a ravine. They continued to drive north through the hills and stopped just before the Lebanese border. The armored car was parked deep inside a small, almost totally isolated forest of trees, which Amnon decided would be a perfect place to hide during the day. They settled in to rest.

One of Amnon's men took first watch while Amnon and the other man stretched out on the ground; in no time, both of them were down for the count. It was their routine to stand watch in two-hour shifts, and it wasn't long before it was Amnon's turn. They saw no one, and there wasn't anything to disturb them in that lush green glade covered with wild flowers in bloom. They spent the beautiful spring day sleeping, talking, and just generally relaxing while waiting for the night.

At nightfall, they drove the armored car toward the single road that connected Rosh Hanikra to Haifa and stopped a short distance from the road. Taking out the large bag of nails they'd brought with them, they systematically spread the nails on the asphalt while walking north toward the border checkpoint at Rosh Hanikra. The darkness grew thicker around them as they approached the well-lit checkpoint. When the checkpoint became visible, they left the road and walked east, parallel to the Lebanese border, for about twenty minutes. Then they crossed the border, and continued north another twenty minutes until they reached a dirt road heading toward the Lebanese checkpoint and followed it almost up to the checkpoint, which they circled around. They saw only three Lebanese guards at the post.

Amnon had one of his men lay down on the ground while he and the other man hid behind a parked car. Amnon's man on the ground began to call for help in Arabic, the Lebanese guards came running, Amnon and his man jumped them, knocked them out, and laid their bodies on the ground behind their car. They took the guard's guns, put on their hats, and walked back to their position. A few minutes later Amnon called the British guards at their checkpoint, and offered them fresh coffee.

A minute or so later, the two British guards walked over and Amnon gestured them to go to the side of the post, where his men waited to knock them out. Quickly, they were stripped of uniforms, guns, and ammunition, and checked to make sure they were out cold. A few minutes later, there was a call from the Palestinian side looking for their comrades. With no answer, it wasn't long before two more unsuspecting men walked over, only to be knocked out as well. They too were stripped their uniforms and arms. All four British guards were piled onto the back seat of the Lebanese car, which Amnon drove a kilometer north toward the city of Sidon. As soon as he saw a turnoff leading into a ravine, he drove the car into it and parked.

Amnon

He sprinted back to the Lebanese post where he'd left his men. Not a soul came by. He couldn't see anyone on the Palestinian side either. Though Amnon was sure there were more than four guards at the post, possibly only four guards were on duty, and the rest sleeping not too far away. Quickly and cautiously, Amnon and his men confiscated all the local documents, rubber stamps, and log books, as well as the British uniforms and weapons, and retraced their steps to the Lebanese side.

The night was quiet and peaceful around them as they found their way to the armored car they'd left behind, and drove it south to their safe house near Naharia. They encountered no traffic on the dirt road they used; the entire area, in fact, seemed totally deserted. They hid the car in a barn together with their loot before sleeping away the remainder of the night.

When Amnon woke up the next day, hungry and thirsty, it was almost noon. There wasn't much of anything in the house, so he walked to the nearest grocery store, where some people stood talking and laughing. He asked what was so funny, and one of the men told him Radio Beirut had reported the kidnapping of four Palestinian border guards who'd been found in their underwear in an abandoned car.

Amnon bought a loaf of bread, cheese, tomatoes and a bottle of milk and walked back to the safe house, thinking, a lunchtime breakfast tastes more delicious than breakfast earlier in the day. While they ate, Amnon told the men what he'd heard in the grocery store and all of them shared a good laugh. Then, still tired, Amnon went back to sleep for another two hours.

When he awoke, he showered, changed clothes, and walked to the nearest public telephone where he had a friendly conversation with one of his contacts. Certain the Haganah's intelligence service had listened to the Beirut radio station, Amnon knew it wouldn't take long for his commander, knowing who was operating in that area put two and two together.

Walking back after his call, he found himself thinking that lately it certainly made good business sense to be in the tire trade in Palestine.

Saturday, April 26, 1947

It was a time of unrelieved tension in Palestine. The previous week four Etzel members on death row had been executed. Their executions, followed by apparent suicides in their cells of another Etzel member and one Lehi member, unleashed the fiercest series of incessant retaliations by Etzel and Lehi forces to date. Daily attacks on British installations, police stations, railroads and barracks ensued, which left the entire Yishuv and the British on edge. In fact, the crackling tension in Palestine reached new heights that Amnon had never before felt or seen. The British creation of security zones were only marginally effective as the attacks continued mercilessly.

Jewish Agency and Haganah leaders feared the level of the Etzel's and Lehi's terrorist activities would unleash a far-ranging British attack on the Yishuv. A serious rift developed between the three Resistance organizations that Amnon feared would lead to a fierce internal struggle, for the two more radical organizations refused to either talk or listen to anyone.

Certain strong emerging political signs suggested the British might be considering a possible departure from Palestine. On the one hand, Amnon felt the increased sabotage and terror activity would push the British into a mood of defeat. But the United Kingdom had always been a major power, and nobody could predict what its next move might be. Just recently, for some unknown and probably unsanctioned reason, British soldiers were seen indiscriminately firing at civilians on the streets of several cities.

Simultaneously, what the British called 'illegal aliens' continued to arrive nightly at an intensified rate. Amnon's unit was diverted from nightly harassment work to that of aiding arriving immigrant vessels; the past few nights had been exceptionally hectic due to the arrival of more than a dozen ships. The security zones created by the British helped them a lot, for the British contained themselves in those areas. Their armored vehicles were seen patrolling all over during the day, but less often at night.

Demonstrations held everywhere in Palestine displayed every variety of slogan ranging from "Free the Jews!" to "Get Out of Palestine!" with infinite variations. Surprisingly, the Arabs were unusually quiet during this period of mounting tension, possibly afraid the creation of a Jewish state might not be too far off.

Wednesday, April 30, 1947

Radio, radio, and more radio. Every free minute lead Amnon to the radio to catch news of the latest developments. The best news that week was that the United Nations General Assembly was reviewing the Palestine problem. It seemed likely that a special committee would be created to study the issues and recommend a solution. There was a great deal of unrest in the Displaced Persons camps in Europe, aimed at drawing the world's attention once more to its misery.

During the past three weeks a number of large ships with over 1500 immigrants were intercepted by the British and all passengers were immediately deported to Cyprus; however, small fishing vessels continued to arrive at an alarming rate. Apparently nothing fazed the arriving refugees, not even news of the ever-increasing struggle by the underground forces to get the British out. All of that fell on hungry ears; the survivor refugees knew that a Jewish homeland was their best hope, since no other nation was doing anything constructive to end their suffering. Those survivors, in fact, wanted no other solution than to be part of the creation of a Jewish Homeland.

Monday, May 5, 1947

Yesterday, in a remarkable display of rare courage, the Etzel attacked the famous Akko (Acre) prison where a large number of their comrades were held. Fighting their way into the prison, leaving numerous British casualties in their wake, they freed dozens of their men, doubtlessly causing untold damage to British egos.

Amnon and his unit were busy at the beaches, day and night smuggling immigrants into Palestine. Amnon was very proud of those refugees' persistent courage and fighting spirit. It took real inner strength to board small fishing vessels and travel across the great Mediterranean from Italy, without any assurance they'd actually make it into Palestine, or wouldn't be forced by the British to land in Cyprus.

These fishing vessels were normally used for day trips only, and lacked appropriate facilities for passengers. But oblivious of the lack of comfort aboard, or of any bad weather the vessels might encounter at sea, and desperate to reach Palestine no matter what, the refugees came with nothing more than the clothes on their backs. Hungry, thirsty, often freezing cold and wet to the skin, the moment they realized they were safely on Palestinian land, they bent to kiss the sandy beach at their feet.

Even as Amnon's men tried to rush them away from the beaches and the unfriendly eyes of prowling British military patrol cars, the refugees jumped to hug and kiss their saviors for their help in getting them safely ashore. As often as they had experienced it, not one of Amnon's men could control the lumps in their throats, and very often had tears in their eyes at seeing the survivor's great joy and relief at having made it safely home to Palestine.

Some of Amnon's men were hidden all over the beach on the alert for British patrols, and only occasionally were there any confrontations with British military or civilian police. Diversionary action continued, but it was apparent the British felt sufficiently confident in their recently created security zones to decrease their nightly patrolling, making transporting the refugees to the safe houses less dangerous for all of them.

Thursday, May 15, 1947

Yesterday, the United Nations had appointed a special committee to investigate the Palestine problem. Committee members represented countries totally uninvolved with the Palestinian conflict, among others Holland, Guatemala, Peru, Sweden and Poland. Andrei Gromyko, the Russian foreign minister, surprisingly announced his country's support of the establishment of a Jewish State.

Amnon was absolutely amazed at the workings of international power politics.

"How was it that Russia, a country historically known for its anti-Semitism as amply evidenced by its many anti-Jewish pogroms and persecutions in the 19th and 20th centuries, could in this year of 1947 announce to the entire world it supported a Jewish State, and expect to be believed? In point of strict fact, Russia's violent anti-Semitism, bloody pogroms, and persecution of its Jews were the motivating force behind the original 19th century pioneers' settlement and development of Palestine. And that was long before the British even dreamed of being given the Protectorate of Palestine. How very interesting," Amnon said.

"*Possibly,*" he thought, "*Russia felt a Jewish State in Palestine would be of some political advantage to them, although given the country's history of violent anti-Semitism, one could be forgiven for looking askance at such a contradictory belief and also for asking why they would have made such a statement. Whatever the case, it is one giant step toward the resolution of our*

169

plight".

"Hopefully, this committee won't take long to devise an acceptable recommendation in our favor."

Amnon's nightly work continued unabated. Due to the large numbers of arriving migrants his men spent part of the day getting them through to their final destinations. That morning, after a harrowing night, Amnon took a man and his pregnant wife (they had married in a Displaced Persons camp a year ago) to B'nai Brak where their relatives lived. They had the names, but had lost the address, which Amnon promised to help them find when they reached their destination.

When he asked why they hadn't waited until they got to Palestine to start their family instead of endangering the mother by taking such a long and dangerous trip, they fervently replied that this child, and every child they hoped to have during the woman's childbearing years, would add to the strength of the Jewish people in Palestine. Their convictions were unshakeable, their love and aspirations for a Jewish homeland were intense. And the man assured Amnon that whether they settled with their relatives or on their own, he would definitely become active with the cause.

As soon as they arrived in B'nai Brak, Amnon took them to City Hall where he inquired about their relatives. Once found, he was given the address and quickly took them there. When the woman who opened the apartment door saw the pregnant woman standing next to him, she froze. Actually, both women appeared to have gone into a catatonic trance for a moment before they literally jumped at each other, and couldn't be separated for several more minutes. The new arrival introduced her husband and Amnon to her relative, who graciously offered tea and cake, which Amnon declined; he had no time for such pleasantries. Quickly, he kissed his charges goodbye, and left with their thanks filling his eyes with tears as they all waved until he was out of their sight.

It was a real pleasure for him that he had been instrumental in those two women meeting again after their long separation during which neither had known whether the other was dead or alive, and if alive, whether sick or in need. Having found each other again, they could both look forward to enjoying their newly regained relationship in this new country. Amnon not only felt redeemed, he felt his work was well worth all the risks he and his men faced nightly to bring the refugees safely into Palestine.

"And if all goes well, the United Nations will vote in our favor at their next General Assembly meeting in New York," he told himself.

Elated at his conviction that this would be the case, Amnon returned to his safe house and grabbed a few hours rest before joining his men who had come in for a snack, and off they all headed to the beach.

Tuesday, May 20, 1947

When Amnon had gotten back the night before, he found urgent instructions. More shipments of arms had arrived in Lebanon, and the first mule convoy would be arriving the following night. Without time to rest, he quickly washed off the sand and sweat, changed his clothes, and he and his men headed off in different directions with kibbutz Kfar Gilaadi as their ultimate rendezvous.

He felt that his unit had become the Lebanese experts, and that bringing arms safely across the mountains into Palestine was as important as bringing immigrants safely into the country. The only difference between the two jobs was that guns didn't display emotion.

Leaning back in his seat on the bus to Haifa, Amnon let his headrest on the seat back, closed his eyes, and tried to doze. But as usual, his turbulent thoughts wouldn't permit it. Bus trips always allowed too much time to think, speculate, and analyze all aspects of all situations he was now or might become involved in. Amnon also enjoyed looking back and remembering the joy and relief people expressed having safely arrived on the shores of Palestine.

Each time the bus passed a city or a large settlement, it was stopped by the police who got on the bus, looked the passengers over, and asked questions which met mostly with blank stares; most people didn't understand a single word asked, or didn't care to respond. Some people tried to answer in their broken English. When they asked Amnon a question, he gave the hand motion that indicated he didn't understand English. That happened three times during the short trip, and each time his line of thought was interrupted. Neither afraid nor discomfited by the police or their questions, Amnon simply sat in his seat as if he owned the bus, and after they left he quickly picked up the thread of his interrupted thoughts.

As the bus wound its way to Haifa, Amnon focused on the tension that could be felt everywhere in the Yishuv. The continuing British interception of immigrant ships and deportation of immigrants to Cyprus or other British detention locations caused many, sometimes violent demonstrations throughout the country. People everywhere in the Yishuv felt they had to express their outrage and anti-British hostility, and demonstrations were the outlet of choice. Not too surprisingly, no members of the active Resistance, at least that Amnon knew, were ever involved in such demonstrations.

All this made him realize he wasn't the only one whose heart went out to the immigrants. An invisible chain bound all of the people into the unceasing effort to help the immigrants safely negotiate the British blockade that sought to keep them out. To that end, Haganah representatives worked openly and tirelessly in the Displaced Persons camps in Europe. They also worked secretly with ever-expanding network of illegal vessels bringing immigrants safely into Palestine.

While the objective was to get more Jews into Palestine to strengthen the Yishuv, it was the immigrant Holocaust survivors who took all kinds of risks to get there because they believed they belonged in Palestine, their only true home.

"Why is that simple truth so difficult for the British to grasp? What more can we do to make them open their eyes to it?" Amnon thought.

So many times had Amnon pondered these questions only to be brought up short by remembering the malicious anti-Semitic speeches of the British Prime Minister, Clement Atlee, and his Foreign Secretary, Ernest Bevin.

"With such cold-hearted politicians representing the United Kingdom, it's truly a wonder the Palestine issue made it to the United Nations at all. But the Yishuv lacks the luxury of time to wait for any significant change in the British Government. With their luck to date, the British Labor Party will win the

elections, leaving the same men in place. So we'll just have to pray our luck will change enough to permit the United Nations to work a miracle."

Amnon's thoughts shifted to the last immigrant arrival he'd handled, and he could still feel the hugs and kisses of a woman who kept asking who was in charge. When she finally caught up with him, she grabbed him in such a tight embrace he barely managed to extricate himself. She thanked him over and over in a language he barely understood. No other words were needed. Amnon knew exactly what she meant and how she felt at having made it safely onto the beach. But what she didn't know, and he found so difficult to explain, was that not only was there a long distance between a Mediterranean beach and her ultimate destination in Palestine, but also that dangerous British patrol cars lurked every step of the way.

Later, after they'd reached the safe house, the woman confided to him experiences in Auschwitz. Thinking it cathartic to let her talk of the horrors, it occurred to him she might have thought if he knew more he would do even more to help the survivors. However, he hoped she knew she had finally come home.

Saturday, May 31, 1947

Nightly work continued, more mules were added and the loads increased. Amnon was curious about how and who attended to all those shipments and methods of delivery, but knew better than to ask questions not likely to be answered. Nevertheless, he was certain larger equipment than usual was arriving, for the boxes packed on the mules were larger and longer, and the mules, bless their hearts, were silently indefatigable carriers.

The news bulletin his group was listening to reported that when the Etzel, attacked the Akko prison, they managed to free close to two hundred imprisoned members. "What a coup! And what a humiliation for the British!" Amnon crowed. The news announced that the first immigrant ship had arrived from North Africa, which must be a new port of immigrant embarkation.

"Were they European Jews?" Amnon didn't know, for it wasn't clear whether or not this ship was intercepted. What was important was that immigration continue, which it clearly was, and he felt that he was playing an important role in the entire plan. But then, he and his men were bound together in the determined mechanism that would one day create the Jewish Homeland.

Night after night the mules labored across the mountainous and hilly terrain, and night after night they delivered fresh, rested mules without knowing whose mules were Arab and whose theirs. They all looked alike to Amnon. Amazingly, the British felt so secure with the Arabs they hardly ever went into Arab territories. Their only concerns were in the Jewish areas, for the official broadcasting system news bulletins always reported British police and military action in Jewish towns and settlements. Fortunately for Amnon and his men, the obviously skewed British interest worked in their favor and helped them accomplish their vital role without interference.

Admoni, the man in charge of the nights' deliveries, told Amnon there would be no deliveries for the next three nights, but would resume on the fourth night. In the meanwhile, Amnon and his men had three nights rest. But though the next three nights were free, the manpower shortage left a lot of daytime work needing their attention at the kibbutz, for which they gladly volunteered.

Tuesday, June 10, 1947

Earlier this month, the eleven members of the United Nations Committee on Palestine had arrived in Palestine and began interviewing Jews, Arabs and British leaders. Amnon wondered how long their visit would last and what the outcome would be.

"Surely, they'll recognize the plight of the survivors, and accept that this land is ours. But, above all, they will have to consider the main issue -- that it's time the Jewish people had a homeland of their own. Hopefully we'll soon learn the outcome of this visit," Amnon told his men.

In the meanwhile, at the start of their visit, the Jewish resistance forces had significantly quieted down.

The radio reported the Arabs had resumed their attacks on Jewish settlements and there were daily skirmishes. In Kfar Gilaadi, official Jewish guards worked around the clock, for they were the only men holding British permits to bear arms, which meant they were permitted one rifle and a dozen bullets. However, the kibbutz had many more unofficial guards who patrolled the territory day and night. Men who worked in distant fields always carried arms, as they were often targets for attack.

The mule trains resumed as they continued their arms smuggling. Fortunately for Amnon and his men, the British never discovered that nightly activity, and all arms reached their destination.

Ordered to appear at a special meeting in the nearby town of Safed, Amnon hitched a ride on top of a produce truck headed in that direction and arrived just as the meeting was beginning.

Thursday, June 19, 1947

That was the first time a meeting was devoted entirely to discussions of the future. Those attending the meeting received some information about the United Nations Committee's travels and research in Palestine. So far, their interviews with the Yishuv's leaders had gone well. But their meetings with the Arabs were reportedly made unpleasant by Arabs demands for the expulsion of all Jews from Palestine. It was believed the Arabs' hostile demands would weigh heavily in the Yishuv's favor because most Bible-reading Christians knew the history of the Jews and the Holy Land. It was further suspected the British had made little sense with their anti-Jewish/anti-immigration arguments. The Jewish leadership concurred that the committee's recommendations would be in favor of the Jews.

Unfortunately, the underlying problem with this expectation was that the leadership was convinced that when the Committee's report was made public, the Arabs would go ballistic. It was well known the British had no real intention of leaving Palestine, and inciting the Arabs against the Jews served their purpose. Believing they had British support, the Arabs might wage war against the Jews; therefore, the Jews had to be thoroughly prepared for any contingency.

The fact that Arab attacks on Jewish settlements had escalated lately, even while the Commission was still in Palestine, strengthened that feeling. In fact, a few attacks, albeit small ones, began to take place on the Jaffa-Tel Aviv border.

On the other hand, it should also be noted the Haganah had numerous Arab supporters and informers. There was an Arab minority that welcomed Jewish settlement in Palestine, and who were well known for their opposition to the Mufti and his radical anti-Jewish behavior. Moreover, the Haganah's intelligence operatives were well entrenched in most neighboring Arab countries.

Commanders at the meeting also discussed the Arab Legion, which the British had set up in Trans-Jordan, and which was still commanded by British Military Officers. Logically, there was no reason for a small country like Trans-Jordan to have such formidable military power. It was not under threat of attack from either the Jewish population of Palestine or any other Arab country. The British therefore must have had ulterior motives for creating the Arab Legion with its base in Trans-Jordan. There was also unconfirmed rumor that one Yishuv leader had met with the King of Trans-Jordan, purpose unknown.

The commanders were also told about a serious incident that had happened yesterday that caused the death of a Haganah member. No details were available other than he'd discovered several Etzel men digging an underground tunnel towards a British main office building in one of their security zones in Tel Aviv, intending to blow it up. They were told a very serious rift was developing, with the Etzel whose actions were out of control.

As the meeting ended, they were advised there would be future meetings to discuss security for the projected Jewish State.

Wednesday, June 25, 1947

An urgent summons to the Tiberias office informed Amnon that the British had rebuilt a new radar station on top of Mount Carmel. His orders were to proceed immediately to Haifa with whatever help he needed, spy on this installation, and develop a plan of attack to destroy it. The rest of his unit could stay and work in the kibbutz while he was away. Just as he was leaving, he was also informed a major immigration push was being planned for July. Filing this information away, he left for Haifa with two of his men.

Saturday, July 12, 1947

Knowing that in order to detect ocean movement a radar installation had to be built in a high location facing the water, when he got to Haifa, Amnon took a bus from the downtown bus terminal to Ahuza, the highest community on Mount Carmel; the radar installation proved easy to find. Built high on Mount Carmel, it overshadowed all other evidence of the tremendous British military presence seen in bunkers built around an intersection from which a road led west towards the sea.

From where he stood, Mount Carmel formed what seemed, at first glance, a cliff. Having seen it from the coast, though, Amnon knew it to be more of a sharp incline than an actual cliff. The road up to it curved down and around as it wound its way southward to the coast. He also remembered the unforgettably spectacular view of the entire Mediterranean coast from Haifa to Zichron and beyond.

Amnon decided to explore the radar installation from all sides, and arranged to stay in the apartment of a Haifa member who lived on the Mount.

Since Mount Carmel was tree covered in undeveloped areas, they strolled in the forest, each day advancing a little further towards the radar installation. By the fourth day, Amnon knew its northern parameter, the number of bunkers guarding it from that direction, and that there were at least six soldiers in each bunker with one Bren gun facing the forest. Altogether there were eight bunkers facing north and northeast.

The following four days he studied the southern side of the installation with findings similar to those of the northern side. Constant movement by British military between the intersection and the installation made it difficult to spend much time spying on the eastern section. However, Amnon did notice that a regular bus service, from Mount Carmel to the beaches below, traveled on the road that passed by the installation. He took that early bus service to the beach with bathing trunks and towel in hand, and observed two bunkers on each side of the road, approximately twenty five meters from the main entrance, and one bunker on each side of the entrance itself.

"This place is fortified like Fort Knox," Amnon thought.

His next project was to take a good look at the side of the installation facing the sea. The next day, he took the bus to Haifa's terminal station, walked to a safe house, borrowed a pair of binoculars, and took another bus to Zichron. In Zichron, he found a good spot behind a storage building belonging to the wine company where he could observe the top of Mount Carmel where the radar installation was. Amazingly, there appeared to be only one bunker facing west, at the very top of the mountain.

With all his questions answered to his satisfaction, he could formulate his plan of attack.

Friday, July 18, 1947

With complete plans carefully memorized, he took an early afternoon bus to Haifa, and headed to the main safe house to contact his superior officer and discuss the plan, what day to attack, and logistics. However, as the bus descended the mountain, he saw tremendous crowds of people in the streets of downtown Haifa. He wasn't aware of any demonstration, and couldn't figure out what was up.

Not until the bus arrived at the terminal, and he had literally ploughed through the crowds, did he learn from the outraged citizenry that the British had intercepted a huge immigrant ship. It was rumored that all the passengers were being transferred to three other ships were standing by as they spoke for the immigrants' immediate deportation.

In fact, had he looked out the window of the bus, he would have seen the so-called Exodus ship, but he'd been so preoccupied with the radar project he wasn't looking out. Few people were on the bus with him, and he guessed no one else had noticed anything either.

Amnon stood there for a while, talking with people who knew little or nothing. Some people were running back and forth with all kinds of stories about resistance on board the ship, and claiming that British military personnel were abusing the immigrants. Nothing could be seen from the street, so he decided to proceed to the safe house. Not surprisingly, upon arrival he found nobody there.

He turned on the radio tuned to the official broadcasting station, and listened avidly to the reported interception of a ship carrying over 4,500 illegal immigrants, who were being transferred to three other vessels, to be returned to their original ports of embarkation instead of Cyprus.

"Now there's a brand new maneuver by the British," Amnon muttered to himself.

Precisely how, he wondered, would the Yishuv handle this new development?

"*So this is the big deal that was alluded to briefly during the last meeting,*" Amnon thought. He wondered if the Exodus incident had been deliberately created for the benefit of the United Nations Committee while they were in Palestine. There was a real need to create an emotional experience for them to include in their report to the General Assembly, and Amnon thought this is what was going on.

Back at the safe house, members returning from the streets or their assignments talked of nothing but the Exodus. Haganah members who had traveled with the immigrants had carefully orchestrated the immigrants' resistance on board ship, which had resulted in British action against the unarmed Holocaust survivors. The objective had been won.

World attention would be drawn to the suffering of the Holocaust survivors, their plight at the hands of Palestine's British overlords who would not grant them admittance, and most importantly the glaring need for the immediate creation of a Jewish Homeland for them and the rest of the world's Jews.

One of his commanding officers arrived and Amnon took him aside, asking for an immediate conference. Amnon was told he'd have to wait till tomorrow to discuss his plans since the commander directly in charge wouldn't be arriving until the next day. Amnon hadn't eaten anything since lunch, and he was ravenous. He walked into the kitchen, found some vegetables he cut into a salad, and devoured it. Replete but exhausted, he went to bed in an adjoining room, and slept like a log through the night.

Saturday, July 19, 1947

At six o'clock Amnon was awakened by the area commander, joined by three other commanders. "There's no time to waste," he told Amnon. Amnon sat up on the bed, and they pulled chairs around him.

"What is your plan of attack on the radar installation?" the regional commander asked. Amnon recited his plans to the last detail. They liked it a lot and it was approved on the spot.

"When should this mission take place?" Amnon asked.

Amnon

"On the night of July 21st. Your men are already en route. They were instructed to depart for Haifa last night and should be arriving today and tomorrow. All the arms and explosives you'll need are in Zichron, in the usual place. Good luck!" The chief's right fist lightly cuffed Amnon's right shoulder, and he left with the other commanders.

Tuesday, July 22, 1947

Last night Amnon and his men demolished one of the biggest British radar installations ever built in Palestine.

It all began at 9:30pm when the eight fighters Amnon had selected joined him on board a small truck he had commissioned. Starting their trip on a back road, they drove along until they reached a dirt road which they followed to the end of the vineyards at the foot of Mount Carmel. They continued to drive slowly without lights until they reached their destination where Amnon had the truck turn around so they could make a quick getaway. From there, at least two kilometers from their target, they began climbing to the top of the mountain. They lumbered up the mountain until they were about half a kilometer away from the western bunker. Here Amnon split his unit into two groups. He assigned four of his men to take the route to the left side of the bunker, and he and four other men took the route to the right. They crawled very slowly upward for about an hour and a half until they reached his predetermined positions about 50 meters further east of the bunker.

Amnon had calculated that the bunker was at least 200 meters from the radar installation. It was then 11:30pm, and the shift would change at midnight. His plan called for capturing the bunker and the soldiers inside a few minutes before midnight, which they achieved by 11:47pm.

Doubtless thinking their replacements were a little early, the British soldiers weren't suspicious when they heard Amnon and his men marching in. Walking in with drawn Tommy guns, they ordered them to freeze, and in less than two minutes their mouths were taped, their hands cuffed behind their backs, their feet tied with a sharp steel wire, and they were all lying on the floor in the far corner of the bunker. All their weapons were piled in the other corner. Amnon waited for the replacement group to arrive.

At exactly midnight, six cheerful soldiers walked into the bunker to the greatest surprise of their lives. Minutes later, their weapons confiscated, Amnon ordered them to strip before they too were taped, handcuffed, and wired. Within three minutes, six of Amnon's men, including the two explosives experts, dressed in British uniforms, walked straight to the radar installation. The explosives were placed and detonation timed for 12:15am.

At exactly 12:05 am, the rest of Amnon's unit already positioned in front of the radar installation's entrance began firing at the bunkers. The idea was to create the impression the resistance forces were attacking from the front. That firing lasted exactly 10 minutes, whereupon the building blew up. The shooters retreated into the woods, picked up the van that had brought them, and drove north to the end of Ahuza. From Ahuza they followed a dirt road, leading down the mountain. This tactic not only fooled the British into thinking the installation was being attacked from the front, but saved lives and casualties.

By the time the radar installation blew up, Amnon and his men were almost half way down the mountain. The load of weapons they'd liberated was heavy, but Amnon wasn't about to leave them in the bunker. The massive explosion and confusion with the shooting in front of the installation caused the British to lose precious time, and once they realized what had happened, Amnon and his men were gone.

Amnon had no idea how long it took the British to find the tied up soldiers in the bunker. He wished he knew. As it happened, they had plenty of time to reach Zichron, hide the weapons, and vanish into thin air. This was high season for grape picking, and there were more than 80 men and women working in the field. Pretending to be workers in the vineyards, Amnon and his men simply mingled with the other workers and no one knew the difference.

Amnon instructed his men to leave after three days and make their way to Tiberias, then called the regional commander from the vineyard's office, assured him the harvest was wonderful that year, and that he'd be leaving for Tiberias on Friday for a short vacation.

Amnon was very proud of himself. Not only had he accomplished the goal without a single casualty, he did not have to kill or wound any British soldiers. This alone made him happy, for Amnon never really enjoyed killing anyone and he always felt sorry for those young men who knew little or nothing about the battle they were under orders to wage against the Jews in Palestine.

Saturday, July 26, 1947

By that evening, Amnon's entire unit had reunited in Tiberias. He was notified that one of his commanding officers had arrived and wanted to see him right away. Amnon walked to the safe house the officer was, located not too far from where he and his men were staying.

"Amnon," the commanding officer began, "I was informed of the great job you did on Mount Carmel. You may not know this, because the British haven't announced it, but another of our units blew up one of their major deportation ships, outside Haifa Harbor."

"Sounds good to me," Amnon responded

The commander then laid a map of the Yarden Valley out on the table in front of them and pointed to a location on the Jordan River, a couple of kilometers from Kibbutz Maoz Chaim.

"The British built a makeshift bridge at this location so they can move military forces of the Arab Legion across the river any time they please. I want this bridge destroyed. When can you do it?" he demanded.

"Monday night," promised Amnon.

The commander hugged Amnon, saying, "Good luck, Amnon," as they walked to the door. "Call me, when you're done." He closed the door behind him.

Amnon would have liked to spend some time with him, just to sit and talk for a while. But knowing that he, like everyone else in the Haganah, worked day and night, Amnon strode back to his safe house, took out his map, and began to plan the operation.

It was past midnight when Amnon was through cudgeling his brain for a solution to a real difficulty he had discovered.

There was only one narrow road going south from Tiberias with no extensions into the few settlements in the area, only dirt roads. West of that road began the hills of Samaria, an almost entirely Arab area. This didn't bother him at all. In fact, it gave him an excellent escape route. However, lately the Arabs had become more militant, which meant additional precautions would be needed. There were two kibbutzim on the east side of the Jordan River, just past the tip of Lake Kineret.

Amnon decided to go there the next day to thoroughly explore the territory and plot the best course to follow.

Sunday, July 27, 1947

Early in the morning, Amnon and one of his men borrowed Lambretta scooters, and headed south. Turning eastward as the road circled the southern tip of the lake, they crossed the Jordan River, which was extremely narrow at that point and very shallow, and followed it north. After a short drive, Amnon noticed that there was no marked boundary with Trans-Jordan, and he could see a pretty good dirt road. Knowing that the Jordanians had some sort of a road there, which ran all the way south close to the river, his plan began to form. The combination of the terrain, the probability they could cross the Jordan River close to Tiberias, and the availability of transport outside of Palestine all contributed to his final plan of action.

"There couldn't be a better way to handle this operation than from behind enemy lines," Amnon told his men. He sent one of his men to their arms cache with a shopping list. Six Arab habits with all the trimmings, six British military uniforms, six standard British rifles and ammo, two cases of grenades, two cases of dynamite, detonators, wire, and battery. He also asked for tall rubber boots. All these items were to be placed in a stolen British Police armored car, to be ready to depart at 9:00pm.

Monday, July 28, 1947

Amnon selected five of his best men for the job, two that had by then become explosives experts. The armored car's plates were replaced with new matching plates used by the police. They put the British uniforms over their simple short-sleeved khaki shirts and trousers, and on signal drove out, the British flag waving from its usual place on the right front for everyone to see. In five minutes, driving at moderate speed, lights full on, they were out of Tiberias. Just before 9:30pm, they passed the tip of Lake Kineret, and about fifteen minutes later crossed the Jordan River. There was no traffic; they saw no one, and Amnon hoped no one saw them.

As they approached the spot where they were to cross over into Trans-Jordan, the driver turned the lights off and stopped the car for a few minutes to adjust his eyes to the darkness. High clouds scudding across the night sky partially blocked the moon that, from time to time, benevolently sent down thin slivers of moonlight to light their way.

Daniel Rosenfeld

Driving slowly, in total darkness, it took them just under an hour to cover the thirty kilometers to their targeted bridge. When Amnon saw the guard post on the Jordanian side, he found a good place to drive off the road. He found it on the west side, and the car was driven to the river and turned around, ready for a quick departure.

Amnon and his men got out, put on the rubber boots, loaded the bags of explosives on their backs and walked along the river bank until they were about 100 meters from the bridge. There were bushes and all kind of plants growing on both sides of the river. As Amnon expected, the British Corps of Engineers had chosen a very shallow location for the bridge.

Amnon paused to observe the bridge as well as the guard post and its surroundings. He could see two soldiers at the bridge, nothing else. He sent the two explosive experts with two other men downriver, and instructed them to walk in the water, crouching as best they could, while he and another man followed them closely along the bank. Thankful for the gathering clouds Amnon welcomed the greater darkness. He didn't expect rain since it never rained in Palestine during the summer. Having easily reached the bridge, the men tied the dynamite to the main support posts, and pulled the wire northward for about fifty meters before parking themselves on the Palestinian side of the river.

As soon as the dynamite was in place, Amnon and one of his men drove the car back to the road, turned south, and approached the bridge with their lights on. Seeing the British flag, the guards waved them to stop, which they did. Firing two shots, they quickly drove across as the guards fell to the ground, crossing the bridge at high speed. They drove west for a couple of minutes, then turned the car so its lights faced north, and turned them on and off three times; the signal for detonation. Two seconds later the bridge was blown to bits.

The four men ran toward them, got in, and they drove off to Samaria. A few minutes later two police cars came speeding toward them. Amnon slowed down as the oncoming car stopped.

"What happened?" someone asked. "We heard an explosion."

"I can't stop!" Amnon shouted. "I'm carrying two wounded soldiers to Ramallah hospital!" and off he drove.

No one followed them. The police cars continued towards the bridge. Within minutes Amnon lost sight of them. Of course they didn't go to Ramallah, but followed the road to Beit Shean, arriving twenty minutes later. They drove the car into a barn, as usual hid the arms and clothing, and settled in the local safe house.

At 5:30am, Amnon and his men joined the local farmers in the fields. Again, Amnon was elated he had accomplished his goal without casualties. It would take the British weeks to rebuild the bridge.

"*Next time,*" he thought, "*It won't be that easy. They will surely triple the guards, probably on both sides.*"

The British forces were left only with the Allenby Bridge, east of Jehrico.

Thursday, July 31, 1947

Amnon

The month of July came to an end with many unusual and disturbing occurrences. All the immigrants who arrived on the Exodus were returned to France. When the ships carrying them docked in a southern French port, they refused to disembark. Many demonstrations took place in Palestine and in Europe, and as of this date the immigrants were still on board, their fate as yet unknown. No other immigrant ship had drawn as much publicity as the Exodus, which was the point of the exercise. World attention was then firmly focused, as never before, on the plight of the Holocaust survivors who wanted only to be permitted to continue their journey to Palestine, their Jewish Homeland.

Destruction of the radar installation on Mount Carmel, as well as the British deportation ships was made public and became the focus of numerous articles in the world press that forced the world to realize Jewish forces had just cause for fighting their British overlords. The United Nations Commission on Palestine was still at work, and the Yishuv was increasingly confident that those events would influence the commission's decision in favor of a Jewish State.

The bad news was that the British executed three more Etzel members. In retaliation, Etzel hung two British sergeants they had abducted, which caused British soldiers to run amok in Tel Aviv, shooting anyone in sight. Six innocent people were killed and many wounded.

A few weeks ago, Amnon had thought tension in Palestine had risen to its highest level, only to learn it could reach new heights. Everyone's nerves were more on edge than ever before as Etzel and Lehi's attacks continued non-stop on British police stations, railroad stations, office buildings, and military barracks. The Haganah's forces worked on specific sites and locations, their main objective being to force the British to terminate the unjust ban on immigration of survivors, and influence world opinion towards the establishment of a Jewish State.

However the British, didn't seem to be changing either their inflexible negativity toward the Jews or their pro-Arab policies. In fact, in order to divert the Yishuv's attention from them, they incited the Arabs against the Jews more than ever before, which intensified Arab attacks by vigilantes and other organized groups. Arab attackers who were killed or captured by the Haganah's defense forces were found to be equipped with British arms and munitions.

The future, and the future of the Yishuv's cause looked pretty dim in those days. However, Amnon, like every other Haganah member, was filled with idealistic strength and commitment. Moreover, the entire Yishuv supported them without reservation, and along with all new arrivals, both legal and illegal, stood firmly together. They were like an immovable wall against the hostile Arabs and their British masters.

Friday, August 8, 1947

A few days after the successful demolition of the bridge, Amnon was called back to Kfar Gilaadi and the smuggling duties. Shipments of arms had resumed, which meant the nightly trips into Lebanon would also resume. In those days, Arabs were so accustomed to smuggling that Amnon doubted they either knew or cared what was inside the boxes the well-trained mules carried. They were well paid for their work, and so long as no one was caught, it seemed that was all they cared about.

The mule caravans labored night after night across the mountainous paths, and Amnon was thankful that mission went on without interference from the British authorities. Obviously, the British had no idea the smuggling operation existed. A lot of the arms that comprised their nightly loads were Second World War surplus weaponry purchased in Europe and shipped to the port of Beirut, an easy point of entry since custom officials were easily bribed. Lebanon was a French Mandate at the time. It was an open secret that the French never liked the British to begin with. That by itself helped the Haganah's cause. Amnon's understanding was that the French authorities had no knowledge of the arms that were shipped through Beirut.

Latest radio reports were that the British had decided to return the Exodus immigrants to their original ports of embarkation, and that ships carrying the Exodus immigrants had arrived in Hamburg, Germany, where its voyage had begun. British soldiers on board were using force to get the passengers to disembark, but the immigrants were putting up tremendous resistance.

Newspapermen from around the world were in Hamburg reporting on breaking developments in the situation. This particular event received more media coverage than any other in the short history of what the British termed "illegal immigration."

The British civilian police arrested the mayors of Tel Aviv, Ramat Gan and Natania along with their attorneys and many journalists whom they claimed were sympathetic to the Jewish Resistance movement. With every such move the British made, the Yishuv grew stronger and stronger in its support of the Resistance movement. The latest British moves began to show desperation, and Amnon began to feel that Palestine was headed toward some major changes.

If there was to be any kind of solution, the British had to leave Palestine. Even though the British were intent on inciting the Arabs, Amnon felt certain that not all Arabs were willing participants. The British focused on the radical Arab clergy through the Mufti's offices in Jerusalem. There were many Arabs who didn't like British rule, and sought independence. But having observed Arab history in Palestine, Amnon knew most Arab Palestinians were peasants living in small villages where their ancestors had lived for generations. Who was running the country was not on their minds if left alone to their habits and customs.

"People maimed by unheard of atrocities are seeking a future for themselves in Palestine, where they hope and dream they will finally have a homeland to call their own. It is long past time for the creation of a Jewish nation," Amnon was haunted by the plight of the survivors in Europe as well as the need for a Jewish State.

Their nightly activities continued. Caravan after caravan of mules arrived, and day after day the arms cache was emptied, awaiting the next arrival. For a few hours every day they also helped the kibbutz with its work. It was the peak time for vegetable and fruit harvest. Truckloads of produce were shipped straight to canning factories, and a few to produce terminals in Haifa and Tel Aviv. Every truck carried weapons too.

Amnon

Thursday, August 21, 1947

Arab attacks on Jewish settlements sharply increased, especially attacks on civilians working in the fields. Every man working the land carried a rifle and ammo. As of the previous week, attacks had also begun on the suburbs of Tel Aviv. Haganah forces were spread along the Jaffa-Tel Aviv line defending the Jewish city. A number of major attacks were repulsed. Neither British civilian police nor British military made any effort to intervene or try to stop those Arab attacks. In many cases, they appeared to be enjoying the show.

A final shipment of arms had arrived last Monday and Amnon and his men were dispatched to Hadera. They took positions around the city to guard against Arab attack, they weren't used to that kind of work. For some time, however, Haganah forces had engaged in limited action against British installations. Their primary objectives were anything that would reduce British ability to stop immigration, and their secondary objectives were to block, or delay, the movements of British military throughout the country. The security zones the British had established were surrounded with endless rows of barbed wire.

One of the most notorious hate cities in Palestine was the Arab city of Genin; a great number of the Arab attackers were known to have been citizens of Genin. British authorities in that city, as in any other, were chiefly represented by their police stations.

Genin was about an hour and a half away from Hadera. There was no direct road to it from Hadera. The only road went northeast about 40 kilometers, and then forked into two roads, one of which went southeast to Genin. The entire area was littered with dozens of small Arab villages, which had been there for generations.

Amnon's new instructions were to blow up the police station in Genin.

A quick study of the terrain showed Amnon that the city of Affula was much closer to Genin, and the route between those two cities was less populated. He instructed his men to proceed to Affula immediately; all of them took different buses and as usual met up in Affula two days later. For some reason, the Affula safe house was full, and Amnon was sure there were many other projects in the works. Immediately, he set out to make arrangements for clothing, weapons, ammunition, first aid, and transportation.

Amnon's main dilemma was how to penetrate the police station's compound. Checking with the intelligence officer in Affula, he learned the Genin police station was located in a single building on the main drag. He was also told there was no barbed wire in front of or around the building, and that the adjacent buildings on both sides were private residences.

With a half-formed plan in mind, and knowing the typical milk canister used in Palestine held about eight gallons of milk, Amnon called his two explosives experts.

"Can you fabricate time bombs in a milk canister?" he asked.

"Give us half an hour to think about it, and we'll call you back," they responded.

Twenty minutes later they came to him with a solution.

"Yes, we can make a very powerful bomb using a milk canister. What do you have to destroy?" asked one. "That will tell us how many canisters are needed."

"I need to demolish the police station in Genin. It's about the size of the building across the street," Amnon answered.

" That'll take eight. How soon would you need them?" they asked.

"By noon tomorrow," was his answer.

"How do you want the time clocks set?"

"Under the lids, inside the canisters."

"Be sure to rest tomorrow afternoon. We're going to have a long night."

By the time Amnon completed his plans, and had given out his instructions, it was long past midnight. He had only one day to prepare for the operation.

Saturday, August 23, 1947

Leaving early, Amnon walked over to the garage and auto repair shop the Haganah used and selected a truck and a four-seater car. It was the type of truck the Arabs used, and he made sure the license plate numbers matched the Arab territory he was going to be driving in. All the trucks the Haganah used had hidden bellies. Since the truck he wanted had an open bed, he had to make sure there was enough room for his materials. Then he walked across town to the house where clothing supplies were kept. When Amnon asked for eight Arab habits and four British civilian policemen uniforms with their special leather belts and straps, the woman in charge told him that she didn't have any policemen uniforms.

"Call Tiberias, " Amnon commanded. "I need these uniforms by 5:00pm today."

"Don't worry, you'll have everything you need by 5:00 this afternoon." she assured him.

It was close to noon. Not having had anything to eat or drink since he got up that morning, Amnon was starved. He went back to the safe house, and straight to the kitchen where he found some vegetables, eggs, and farmer's cheese. He cut up the vegetables, made himself a salad, a large omelet with farmer's cheese, and devoured the lot with a glass of tea.

Though he hadn't yet heard from his explosives experts, Amnon felt certain they'd deliver. He decided he could use a nap. He found an empty room and fell asleep. When he awoke, it was 3:00pm, and found a note saying his milk delivery was completed.

Needing to meet with his men who were resting somewhere else, Amnon sent a messenger instructing the twelve of them to meet him at the garage at 7:30pm. Amnon planned to leave at dusk; he wanted his party to look as authentic as possible, just a bunch of Arabs returning from work.

Arriving at the garage close to 6:00pm, he immediately checked that all his materiel and equipment were there. By 7:30pm the last man strolled into the garage. They sat down on the floor and Amnon explained the operation. They left at 8:00pm sharp. About three kilometers out of Affula Amnon and the driver put on a British civilian police sergeant's uniform, cap and all. Six others put on Arab cloaks and headdresses, and the party of four, which used the small passenger car, remained in their own shorts and shirts.

The hills of Samaria blocked the setting sun, and it quickly grew dark. 8 kilometers from Affula was a dirt road that connected the Affula-Genin road to a string of Jewish kibbutzim not more than five or six kilometers away. The small car was parked out of sight just beyond the intersection, and the four men formed two defense stations on both sides of the dirt road. Amnon's instructions were to block anyone who might be pursuing his truck on the way back from his mission.

Amnon ordered the men who were left in Affula to spread heavy nails outside the Affula police station at 9:30pm so no cars could leave town when radioed for help, which might happen since Affula was the closest police station to Genin. The only possible danger left was that one or more patrol cars might be on the road in the Affula area. But any military campaign had to face certain risks.

Driving past the first houses in Genin, Amnon noticed traffic was extremely light though a number of cars were still on the road. To look like any other Arab truck, his headlights were on as they passed by the police station. Two policemen were guarding the entrance.

In a nearby shopping district, Amnon found a quiet street and instructed his driver to park and turn off the lights. He got out of the truck and looked around. It was quiet, dark, not a soul in sight. He instructed his explosives guys to set three canisters to detonate in 15 minutes, 20 minutes, and 30 minutes.

The place where they'd parked the truck was less than five minutes away from the police station.

When all was ready, they drove past the police station and parked the truck in front of the house to its right. Amnon and his driver got out of the truck and walked over to the policemen standing at the entrance. They saw his rank and stiffened with a salute. Amnon and his assistant stuck revolvers at their bellies and instructed them to walk over to the truck where they were knocked out and pulled into the truck. Amnon and his driver then took positions at the entrance to the station.

The others took off the first three canisters and placed them the correct distance from each other along the wall of the police station. The canisters were covered with blankets. The truck then made a U-turn and stopped in front of the residence on the left. Three more canisters followed. The last two were carried into the police station exactly three minutes before the timer was set to blow, and placed one on each side of the main hallway. They ran out, jumped onto the truck, and drove off. Amnon was more than amazed at the lack of security in that police station. The British no doubt felt very secure in that hate-filled Arab town where they provided many incentives to its citizenry, and where much of their incitement against the Jews took place.

Two minutes later the first explosion shattered the quiet night, followed minutes later by additional explosions. Flames shot up to the skies as a series of mini-explosions ripped through the night. Amnon correctly assumed the mini-explosions meant the weapons storage room had also been destroyed. They sped

Daniel Rosenfeld

off to the north with full lights on. About ten kilometers out of Genin, they threw the two still unconscious policemen off the truck, and sped on.

A patrol car passed them driving fast towards Genin. Amnon's men were lying on the floor of the truck. As soon as they left Genin they removed and rolled up the Arab habits and headdresses, and Amnon removed and rolled up the policeman's uniform. He couldn't bother the driver, as they needed to get away as quickly as possible. A few minutes later Amnon noticed the patrol car that had passed them earlier was speeding behind them trying to catch up.

Their car was much faster than the truck, and as they got closer, the man sitting next to the driver began shooting at them. They didn't respond. Amnon noticed a second patrol car approaching in the distance. They kept driving as fast as the truck could handle. Soon they turned into the dirt road where Amnon had left his men in position and stopped for two seconds. Amnon jumped off the truck with two more of his men and joined the others who were already in position. He told the driver to proceed to kibbutz Ein Harod, where the usual procedure was followed.

Amnon and his men were spread out on both sides of the road, about five meters from each other. With grenades in both hands, pins out, they waited for the two patrol cars to arrive. The patrol cars showed up a minute later, making the sharp turn onto the dirt road. Twelve grenades greeted them. Tires blew out, one gas tank exploded, and a patrol car overturned, the British policemen in them either dead or wounded. Not a single bullet had been fired.

They drove the four-seater along the bank of the road, past the two demolished cars, hopped in one on top of the other, and returned to the Affula road. Once in Affula they drove slowly and without lights through a number of side streets and eventually reached the neighborhood of their safe house. They parked some distance away, and each of them went to his sleeping quarters with his weapons, which were hidden immediately upon arrival.

Another operation was over, and Amnon was wound up. He couldn't fall asleep. He got up, warmed a glass of milk, and downed it with some biscuits he found in the kitchen. All of this took place in the dark, of course. He sat in the kitchen for a while reflecting on the night's events.

"We showed the British we can hit them anywhere in the country. We showed them we're determined to continue our struggle. We showed them they don't have a chance in hell to win this battle. We showed them our determination and commitment to our cause."

His thoughts then carried him to the ease with which they switched clothes, looked and acted like someone else. Amnon knew he and his men weren't the only ones who pretended to be British policemen or soldiers when penetrating British installations. The Etzel and Lehi did the same.

"Blowing up the Genin police station is also meant as a message to Genin's Arab population," Amnon thought. *"We will get you anywhere, and any time."*

Friday, August 29, 1947

Amnon was so busy he didn't pay attention to some major developments in the world around him. Britain announced it had given India and Pakistan their independence. In fact, the Indian peninsula was divided between its Muslims and Hindu populations. Pakistan became the Muslim nation and India the Hindu one. Heavy fighting was reported taking place between the Muslims and the Hindus with scores of fatalities.

Both India and Pakistan were far from Palestine. Giving up India meant the United Kingdom no longer needed a land route to India, one of the reasons that had kept them attached to Palestine for so many years. The Sudan and Egypt had also gotten their independence. The time had come for the United Kingdom to finally give up Palestine.

The question was how to handle the British.

Leaders of the Yishuv had exchanged sharp words with the leaders of Lehi and the Irgun, which controlled Etzel. The Yishuv leaders felt international sentiment was moving strongly in favor of the Jews. They believed the United Nations Commission would recommend a solution which would benefit the Yishuv. They also felt that giving up India, a country the British had ruled for a hundred years suggested the United Kingdom was on the verge of relinquishing Palestine, as it had other parts of the old British Empire. The leaders felt that the time for restraint had arrived.

They claimed that the Exodus affair was the straw that broke the camel's back. But, believing the opposite, the leaders of the two radical resistance groups, Etzel and Lehi, refused to curtail their sabotage and terrorist activities. The rift grew wider between the Haganah, the main Jewish defense force, representing the majority of Jews in Palestine, and the other two organizations. It was feared that a serious confrontation between the Haganah and the two radical resistance organizations was about to take place.

The United Nations Commission on Palestine had left for New York, and its report was expected any day. The Jewish Agency for Palestine, the main Jewish Governmental body, headquartered in Jerusalem, was at a loss as how to handle the two radical groups.

During those days of high tension, the British incited the Arabs further, inducing them to attack Jewish settlements and towns, and almost overnight, the major Haganah forces became their defenders. All attacks were repulsed with heavy losses to the Arabs.

Tuesday, September 2, 1947

Yesterday was a great day for the Yishuv. The United Nations special commission on Palestine published its report. It recommended the partition of Palestine: 55% of the country to the Jews and 45% to the Arabs, with Jerusalem to become an International Zone.

Amnon was summoned to the Haganah's Affula safe house. Haganah intelligence reported that lately there had been too many Arabs brought into the British police station in that Jewish town; it was suspected the Arabs would mount an attack from within. Amnon's instructions were to blow up the police station in Affula ASAP.

He set out to tour the area around the police station. Very carefully,

Amnon studied its immediate neighborhood, all streets leading to the station and away from it, and all surrounding houses and businesses.

Amnon's mental notes indicated there were too many Jewish businesses on the same street. Carefully checking the back of the Police building, he found a large parking lot not visible from the street. He then visited the Municipal offices for information about the owner of the two-story house behind the police station. Within ten minutes he had the owner's name, address, and business telephone number.

A few hours later Amnon contacted the owner of the house, who had been told to expect his call. Amnon explained he had instructions to blow up the police station and needed his house as a base for the attack.

"Say nothing about this to anybody," Amnon warned him, " especially not to your wife and children, until after we've completed our job, maybe not even then. In fact, just to be on the safe side, so you won't know anything more, I suggest you take your wife and family away on a week's holiday. Go visit friends or relatives. That way, none of you will be implicated. You can return a week from Saturday."

Saturday, September 6, 1947

The man took Amnon's advice and left the next morning with his family. Amnon and four of his men entered the house the next day, and took a good look out from the rear window, mentally noting everything in his view.

The fence dividing the properties was wire mesh. On top were three layers of barbed wire one on top of the other. Inside the police station, four rows of barbed wire were attached to the fence on the ground. The police station building appeared to be concrete blocks covered with white stucco.

The back of the house had six windows on each floor with steel bars on the ground floor, but not on top. Based on traffic, in and out, Amnon determined there were approximately twenty-four policemen in that seemingly isolated station. Probably their isolation made them feel they needed a larger staff of police personnel.

Amnon suggested they cut through the fence at night, creating a large opening wide enough for them to slip through. Then they'd cut through the barbed wire. Everything cut, they'd attach all the wires together so they wouldn't look cut. The night of the attack, they'd simply push the fence and the barbed wires aside and enter. He also suggested they have a ladder ready so they could throw fire bombs into two upper windows, hopefully causing a blazing fire in some of the rooms.

At the same time, from a number of positions across the street, other unit members would start firing at the front of the police station, while more men positioned, one man per window would fire at the back of the station. This simultaneous firing at the front and back of the police station would provide cover for the two explosives experts as they placed two time bombs next to the rear wall and readied two more to be thrown in through the upper windows. These last two bombs would have to be carried up the ladder on the climber's shoulder, presenting the risk that throwing a time bomb into a room already ablaze might detonate the bomb before the man had a chance to escape.

Amnon concluded, "The police station would call the fire department for help, but the only fire truck won't be available because we've lured it elsewhere."

This was the first time Amnon had actually sat down with his men to discuss an operation. The comfort of the requisitioned house must have encouraged it. His first question was for the explosive experts. "Can you put together a time bomb to be thrown into a burning room, and have it explode three minutes after hitting the floor?" Amnon asked. "It will take exactly one minute to climb the ladder, drop the bomb through the window, and flee back down. "At this moment, the second man will go up with the second bomb, throw it in through the second window, and come back down. By then, the first man will have already rejoined us here, with the second man following within a minute or less."

"I can do it with ice," one of his experts responded, " and I suggest we use two ladders.

"If you noticed," he continued, " all the windows were open to let in fresh air. If the windows were covered by our men, all we would need are much shorter ladders, and both of us would throw the bombs in at the same time."

"Excellent observation," Amnon told him. "Go prepare the bombs. You'll do the ice part here two nights from now, shortly before the attack."

Turning to the others, Amnon instructed, "Tonight we cut the fence and the barbed wire. While we're busy cutting, I want full alert to cover the windows in case something goes wrong."

Taking a man with him, Amnon went to the garage. He picked up two cars which they drove back to the house they were using as their base, and parked on the street in front. Getaway cars were always needed. He then took a brief rest, and let his men do the same.

It was 2:30am when Amnon woke them. He figured it would take about an hour to cut the fence and barbed wire and reattach them. Two men were assigned to cover the windows while two men sneaked into the back yard and methodically started to cut the fence. From where Amnon was standing in the base house he couldn't hear the sound of wires being clipped, and was certain the police in the station couldn't hear anything either. Diligently, the men continued to cut through the rows of barbed wires.

In the silence of the night, Amnon could hear his own heartbeats as he waited for his men to finish. They were back in less than an hour, and reported they'd put all fence and barbed wire openings neatly back together. Amnon didn't think it was necessary to tell the men that cutting the wires a day in advance was his way of also testing British preparedness.

There was no movement whatsoever inside the police station, so Amnon assumed the darkened second floor was a dormitory and the men inside sleeping. On the first floor on the front side of the building, where the reception desk and guards were, some lights were on.

On the next morning's news broadcast, there was a brief announcement about the British governor's birthday, which gave Amnon a great idea. He arranged for a case of whiskey to be delivered late in the afternoon to the Captain in charge of the police station, with a note, inviting him and his men to celebrate the occasion.   The signature was totally illegible.   Knowing the British propensity for alcohol, Amnon figured they would drink the case dry in no time.

When the Ice cart passed by that morning, Amnon bought two blocks and stuffed them into the icebox. Then he called in the men who were to shoot at the station from the front, and discussed their positions and getaway tactics, stressing the need to cover the windows and main entrance.

Suddenly, Amnon got another idea, and sent a message asking his explosives experts to see him immediately. When they arrived, Amnon asked them to fabricate a fairly light bomb, which could be thrown into the main entrance from a moving car, and would explode on impact. For this maneuver, he decided to use one of the cars he had parked on the street in front of the house.

The operation got underway at exactly 1:00am.

Two men cleared the way through the fence and the barbed wire. The ladders were then pushed through to them, followed by four time bombs and two firebombs, all of which were placed against the back wall of the police building. At precisely 1:10am, two things happened simultaneously. Two firebombs were thrown into the building through two upper floor windows, and a small powerful bomb was thrown at the front entrance of the police station. The bomb went off before the guards at the entrance had a chance to pull their revolvers out of their holsters. They fell to the ground.

At that exact moment, the firing began from the front, covering the building and particularly its windows. A few minutes later the timed explosives were thrown in through the upper rear windows and also placed next to the outer walls. Minutes later, the entire second floor, which was in flames, collapsed onto the first floor when the explosives detonated. The fire then spread throughout the ground floor, which was also rocked by explosions. All the windows in the house from which the attack was launched blew to pieces, and part of the outside wall was damaged from flying debris.

Amnon and his men jumped into the two cars and drove north with no lights on. There were a number of kibbutzim north of Affula. Half of Amnon's men were dropped off at one kibbutz and the rest split into two groups, each going to a different kibbutz. Having first hidden their weapons as usual, the men were guided to their sleeping quarters. At 5:30am, they joined the kibbutz farm laborers in their work in the fields.

In case the British searched the kibbutz, it was standard operating procedure for Resistance members to blend in with the kibbutz work force. Every man at work was a member of the kibbutz, and the youngsters were city boys who volunteered to help fill the gaps left by the shortage of laborers.

Around noon the British authorities learned their Affula police station had been blown up. It seemed no patrol cars had been out that night, and the station blew up before anyone had a chance to call for help. Amnon was on the telephone with his main safe house in Affula, and when he was told no one showed up, he called the other two kibbutzim and told his men to take the first transport to Tiberias. Late that night, his entire unit was in Tiberias, and he so advised his command.

As always after an operation, Amnon gave himself time to reflect on events of the day as well as events of the world. Amnon's favorite school subjects had been geography and history, subjects that related well to each other. For news, he had to depend almost exclusively on the local British broadcasting system's somewhat slanted international news reports; sometimes he also managed to read local Hebrew newspapers. The Haganah's clandestine radio station also provided important information and commentaries. It wasn't long before he became adept at listening and reading between the lines.

However, Amnon couldn't understand why the Hindus and the Muslims were fighting their ferocious war. The Indian peninsula had been divided into two separate countries for their benefit, one for each. He found it worse than horrible that one hundred fifty thousand people, almost a third of the Yishuv, had died in the course of that devastating war.

"It's not only horrible, it's utterly insane!" Amnon proclaimed

Amnon found that letting his thoughts roam while his body relaxed helped him cool down after a tense period of planning, strategizing, and executing a military sabotage mission. Amnon often wondered how he'd gotten so good at this. As a child he hadn't been hyperactive like his younger brother, nor could his behavior have been described as aggressive. Amnon suspected he had the benefit of his mother's common sense and his father's logic. Doubtless from his having read so much, for he was an avid reader, he had developed his own cold and calculating military strategy, which along with the other two accounted for his successes to date.

Amnon was particularly pleased that his unit thus far had the fewest casualties during that period of Resistance. Were it not for his youth, Amnon might well have risen to a high position in the Haganah. But if asked if he wanted this, his answer would have been an emphatic NO! Truthfully, Amnon didn't like military life. But living during this most historic period, together with his strong commitment to the Jewish cause, meant he had to do whatever was needed, for as long as it took for this cause he believed in with his entire being.

Amnon's thoughts always returned to the same subjects that haunted him, particularly the suffering of his brethren.

But the more Amnon thought about it, the more it seemed the Allies, like Great Britain and even the United States, had forgotten where their hearts were. Their treasuries mattered more to them than the plight of a homeless people. Well, since nobody seemed willing to simply hand the Jews their freedom from the United Kingdom and its antiquated colonial policies, they would fight for it, and they would not quit until they had jolly well won!

Saturday, September 13, 1947

Amnon's unit wasn't allowed to relax for even one day. Intelligence reports continually described increased Arab activity in many villages, as well as across the Syrian border. Defenses had to be mounted in most kibbutzim and settlements across the Galilee and the eastern boundaries with Trans-Jordan and Syria.

Daniel Rosenfeld

Amnon's unit was dispatched from one kibbutz to another to review their defenses and weaponry. They needed to know which settlements were more vulnerable to attack, so the Haganah could prepare manpower and materiel. Amnon reported all findings to his headquarters, in particular the manpower needed to repulse any attacks.

Saturday, September 27, 1947
Finally, after years of resistance, the British Colonial Secretary announced Great Britain was ready to relinquish its Mandate over Palestine. When that day arrived, the survivors would be able to immigrate to Palestine without fear. Doubtless, thought Amnon, the United Nations would have to be involved. Though the news was good, final resolution was still far in the future. The Yishuv could certainly hope they'd ultimately win their independence. As the future looked brighter at one end, however, it was getting darker at the other.
Continuous British incitement of the Arabs resulted in increasing daily Arab violence against the Jews throughout the country. Neither British civilian police nor military made any move to intervene or try to stop the violence. This was similar to the behavior of British military personnel at the very beginning of British power in Palestine after the First World War, when they deliberately flouted orders from London.
When Great Britain received its Mandate in Palestine, British military considered the Jewish settlers to be Bolsheviks, meaning "communists". The British High Commissioner's very first Palestinian appointment was a violently anti-Jewish Muslim fanatic instead of a known-to-be-more-moderate Arab leader as the First Mufti, the leading Arab Muslim representative in Palestine. Moreover, though the British in Palestine appeared to follow the provisions of the Balfour Declaration, they actively provoked the schism between the Arabs and the Jews. Possibly the announcement of their departure was just another devious ploy among the many they had used before.

Friday, October 17, 1947
September came to an end with two major occurrences. Etzel blew up the British police station in Haifa, and an immigrant ship from Europe managed to break through the British blockade with all its passengers who landed safely and were quickly moved to their assigned destinations.
In their continued survey of all kibbutzim and settlements, Amnon and his men moved in a westward direction, south of the Lebanese border and along Palestine's long border with Lebanon and Syria. They were faced with a dual problem; possible attack from across those borders, as well as from Arab villages and towns inside Palestine. Every kibbutz and settlement had to be ready to defend itself from all sides.
The task was enormous, and Amnon sensed an impending conflict. His main hope was that despite British incitement, the Palestinian Arabs were not as organized as the Yishuv's people. However, Amnon didn't know the strength of neighboring countries' armies. That intelligence was left to Haganah intelligence services, which Amnon felt sure would share the information when the time was

right.

Thursday, October 30, 1947

October drew to a somewhat violent close with a number of disturbing incidents. A Syrian force penetrated Palestine, but British forces routed them and sent them back across the border. Amnon's feeling was that the Syrians were only "testing the waters," at the behest of the British. Very likely, the British felt they had to show their international responsibility under the Mandate, and had thus done their duty, so as to remain in good favor with the United Nations.

British actions inside Palestine were one thing, but permitting another country to invade Palestine was quite another and unacceptable. However, the incident sent a clear message to all the Jews in Palestine: If and when the British finally moved out of Palestine, the country would immediately become a no-holds-barred battleground.

"All of us must be fully prepared for the battle," Amnon announced.

Other serious concerns were that tensions had worsened between the Haganah and the Etzel-Lehi groups, and there were reports of numerous clashes between them. Far removed from the scene of confrontation, Amnon didn't know exactly what was happening. But he did know that like most radical groups, the Etzel and Lehi lacked sufficient planning or patience, and they wanted too much too fast.

To get the British to give up Palestine was an enormous task, both politically and militarily. Compared to the Haganah, the combined forces of the Etzel and Lehi comprised a small organization that did not represent the majority of the Jewish population. Moreover, being virtually without settlements of their own, the Etzel and the Lehi had almost nothing to do with the defense of the Palestinian Jews.

Saturday, November 15, 1947

Even though the British Army routed Syrian invaders, the Yishuv's leaders didn't trust the British, and figuring the Syrians might possibly attack again, a large Haganah force was sent to the Galilee region to trounce any possible invaders.

At the same time heavy lobbying was being done in New York at the United Nations, which was reviewing the recommendations of their Palestine Commission. A two-third-majority vote of the general assembly would carry the motion to partition Palestine.

Since it was known the Arab nations were planning to reject the partition proposition, the Yishuv's leaders also knew the resolution would need the favorable vote of numerous other member nations in the General Assembly. Interestingly enough, Russia favored, and in fact, had helped promote the idea of partition. Amnon wondered whether the Russian vote in favor of partition was because they cared about what happened to the Jews, or if they simply saw it as a way to oppose the United Kingdom.

It was believed the United Nations would bring the Palestine matter to a vote in the General Assembly by the end of November.

That situation in the United Nations was extremely unsettling for the Arabs. If not for continuing British incitement over the years and British support of the radical Arab leadership, the picture might have been entirely different. It took years to develop the prevailing level of Arab hatred.

Historically, when Palestine was under the rule of the Ottoman [Turkish] Empire, there was little, if any, Turkish incitement against the Jews, or other minorities such as the Christians. While occasionally there were clashes between Jews and nationalistic Arabs, Jews far outnumbered the Muslims in the Old City of Jerusalem, and for many years both enjoyed a peaceful co-existence with their neighbors of other religions. The great schism did not begin to develop until the British installed Haj Amin al Husseini as the Mufti of Jerusalem on Day Two of the Mandate, going against their own Balfour Declaration for their own devious and hypocritical reasons.

Amnon and his men had been in the upper Galilee for several days. With the onset of winter and the rainy season, the temperature had dropped and it was quite cold, especially at night, but there hadn't been any rain yet. They set up camp between two mountains to guard a possible route into Palestine by the Syrians, and were well dug in on both sides of the rough terrain. Other Haganah contingents were in other locations to ensure coverage of the entire area.

The clandestine radio operated by the Haganah reported that an immigrant ship had broken through the British blockade and released its passengers on a beach near Nahariah. Another important bit of news reported that the Yishuv leadership had set up a national council to prepare for recruitment in case of an emergency, signaling that the leadership was getting ready for whatever came next, for mounting Arab unrest was being felt throughout Palestine.

Sunday, November 30, 1947

Yesterday, the United Nations passed a Resolution accepting the recommendation of the special commission on Palestine to partition Palestine between the Jews and the Arabs, with Jerusalem to remain an International Zone. Though there was overwhelming joy in Jewish sectors of Palestine and the world, Palestinian Arabs and the Arab League countries were incensed by passage of that Resolution.

As history will one day corroborate, November 30, 1947, was Day One of the War of Independence. On that day, in retaliation for what the Arab League would later call "the injustice of the United Nations," Arabs fired at two buses on their way from the coast to Jerusalem, killing six passengers and wounding many others. Being stationed in northern Palestine, in the middle of nowhere, so to speak, Amnon was too far from the scene to assess the news. But he knew for sure that if the Arabs were going to shoot at anything that moved, the Haganah would retaliate wherever and whenever necessary.

Wednesday, December 10, 1947

Arabs declared a three-day strike to protest the decision of the United Nations, and Arab mobs descended upon and attacked numerous Jewish areas, but

Haganah forces repulsed all with the assistance of Etzel and Lehi. Though they continued to operate independently, the three Resistance organizations began planning a defense scheme. Amnon didn't have much information, but the news reported that all attacks had been repelled, which clearly indicated the defenses worked.

The British began to evacuate their personnel from the Tel Aviv area. That was good news. No one cared to have them in their midst. It also signaled that they were planning to depart Palestine.

During the past three years, the turmoil in Palestine had revolved mostly around the issue of immigration, and the need to save Jewish lives. The developing tension resulted from the Yishuv fighting the British, who not only refused entry to the survivors, but also had callously deviated from the conditions set forth in their own Balfour Declaration, which professed to support the creation of a Jewish homeland under their auspices. And then, owing to ongoing British incitement of the Arabs over the years, new battle lines were drawn, and the Yishuv moved from fighting the British to fighting the Arabs and the British.

Arab hostility had been nurtured by the British, and it seemed armed warfare was on its way. Who armed the Arabs? Why, the British, of course. While the Jews had to buy or steal their arms, Arabs were given arms by the supposedly withdrawing British overlords.

Arab attacks continued throughout Palestine. Tension was high, but so was the Yishuv's spirit. One thing was known for sure - the Arabs would not defeat the Jews. The Yishuv was highly organized; the Arabs were not. Although there was an Arab High Committee, and also a violently anti-Jewish Mufti in Jerusalem, they couldn't compare with the combined and highly determined Jewish defense forces.

Wednesday, December 31, 1947

Since last week Amnon's new assignment had been to guard convoys traveling from the coast to Jerusalem and back. All traveling took place in convoys, and Haganah fighters guarded them, not an easy task since Arab snipers fired at those convoys from the hills. On occasion convoy guards entered into heavy battles with attacking Arabs. All the cars were then armored with steel plates, and what was known as the "armor period" had begun.

Sometimes cars caught fire and had to be abandoned. Since these convoys were transporting needed supplies, everything had to be transferred from the disabled cars, under cover of firepower. There were fatalities and wounded on both sides. Guarding convoys was the most dangerous work Amnon had yet been involved in. It was never known where an attack would come from.

Yesterday, in the Har Tuv intersection at the foot of the Judean hills where the road begins to wind upward, Amnon's convoy was attacked. It consisted of an armored car in the lead, six trucks loaded with supplies, another armored car, four buses, and an armored car at the rear. Since the heavily laden trucks were unable to increase their speed, the Arabs had the advantage. Amnon decided to stop the convoy and engage the attackers in battle.

Unfortunately, the road was much lower than the banks on both sides, which made fighting difficult, and it took over an hour to route the attackers, most killed in their positions, and a few while fleeing up the mountain. Amnon's men suffered several fatalities and wounded. The bodies of the dead fighters and the wounded were placed on the floor of the buses, and the convoy continued on its way.

Having yet to develop the tough shell necessary to hide one's deepest feelings, it was extremely hard for Amnon to ride in the same car with his comrades lying dead on the floor. Someone attended to the wounded while the rest remained alert for anything else that might be lying in wait for them on the road up ahead. Some fifteen kilometers east of Har Tuv, where the road wound sharply upward, Amnon noticed some activity on the right side of the road no more than two hundred meters ahead.

The convoy was rolling at ten kilometers per hour, and Amnon knew that if they stopped on that sharp incline, they'd never get the vehicles moving up the mountain again. He instructed half his fighters to jump off the convoy and immediately mounted a frontal attack against the Arabs. Moving fast, two by two on both sides of the road with one group giving fire cover to the other, they soon wiped out the entire Arab squad. Since the Arabs were fighting directly with Amnon's men, they didn't pay attention to the convoy, but were busy defending themselves.

They suffered yet another fatality, and Amnon was shaken, having gone through so much with all of these wonderful young men. They had been friends before they became battle comrades. And suddenly, they were gone. Silently, Amnon mourned and wept bitter tears in his heart for all of them, wondering how he would be able to face their parents.

The last armored car stopped for the fighters, and they placed their dead comrade on the floor. Then, all of them having climbed onto the car and either standing on the running board or sitting on top of the vehicle, they again continued on the way to Jerusalem.

In Jerusalem, the convoy stopped along Jaffa Road, the main drag where ambulances always waited ready to take the wounded and the dead. Tears welled in Amnon's eyes at the somber sight, and he couldn't even say goodbye to his friends before they were taken away. Haganah officers immediately surrounded him, as well as others who wanted to know what had happened. Many people had been waiting for relatives who arrived on the buses, and Amnon hoped he wouldn't know anyone, but that would have been impossible.

He went home to his parents.

Restless and heart sore at the sudden loss of so many friends, Amnon asked endless questions about the latest news and how they perceived the situation. Amnon and his parents talked for hours. They felt the situation in Jerusalem was bound to get worse. Travel from the coast to Jerusalem became more difficult and scarce. The City was bound to run out of major necessities, especially food.

His father gave him some insight as to what the British government was planning.

Thursday, January 22, 1948

Arab forces attacked Jewish settlements and communities all over Palestine. All attacks were repulsed with heavy losses to the Arabs. The worst of those attacks were on the Jewish communities bordering Jaffa. Travel throughout the country became impossible.

It became obvious the Haganah had to develop a new plan of action to ensure that whole sections of Palestine became Arab-free, and two days ago Amnon had been asked to join a meeting in Jerusalem where that issue was to be the main topic.

At the meeting, it was made clear that as Jerusalem was quite isolated and surrounded by dozens of Arab towns and villages, there was little the Haganah could do. The creation of an Arab free zone in the Jerusalem area was out of the question. Outside of the City of Jerusalem there were only three settlements to the west, and three east of the city known as Gush Etzion. The Jewish settlements in the Jerusalem area were miniscule compared to the Arab presence. Therefore it was felt that the Jewish City of Jerusalem was entirely surrounded by Arabs.

They decided that cleaning out all surrounding areas of Jerusalem was not a job the Haganah could undertake. However, the picture was entirely different for Tel Aviv, Haifa, Tiberias, the Galilee, or the coastal areas. Thus the Jerusalem meeting was held mostly for informational purposes. Plans for serious action throughout Palestine, but excluding Jerusalem, were being prepared. As for Jerusalem, Haganah fighters were instructed to be prepared to hold the city to the last man.

During the past month, Amnon's only pleasure in life was seeing his parents more often, especially his mother and brother whom he most missed, plus occasionally being able to sleep in his own bed. Amnon's mother was overjoyed at seeing him. It always reduced his feelings of melancholy.

The situation in Palestine had become extremely unsettling. Every day there were announcements of the death of one person or another. While it was true Arab casualties were far greater than those of the Jews, what difference could that have made? Whether Jew or Arab, men were still dying because the British had reneged on their original obligations. Moreover, the British continued to lurk in the country, even though they had supposedly withdrawn from some major Jewish locations.

Their presence was felt everywhere. After all, they had trained the Arab militants, and armed the rest of them. Amnon knew that when the British finally did leave, the Haganah would be able to maneuver much more freely. In the meanwhile, however, it appeared they'd have to endure a most difficult period of time until the British departure became fact.

With no specific date for the long-awaited departure of the British, the Yishuv wondered precisely when it would be. The British Government had never given out that information, only that they intended to leave. It occurred to Amnon that quite possibly the British were deliberately delaying their departure so they could help the Arabs build a huge force of trained military men, just as they had done before. But for precisely what reason? He didn't know.

Amnon's restless mind was again absorbed in speculation. *"The United*

Daniel Rosenfeld

Nations gave the British a legitimate reason for quitting Palestine in the form of the Resolution to partition Palestine between the Arabs and the Jews. Why then did they promote the creation of an Arab military force, arm and train its men? There had to be a reason. A nation as imperialistic and colonistic as Britain did nothing without a reason."

After much considered thought, Amnon concluded Britain believed a well-trained Arab force that included men from all the Arab countries bordering on Palestine would capture all of Palestine and eliminate the Jews, creating a vacuum that would bring the British back into the picture. In the event of a major war in the area, they would be in a position to intervene and then present themselves to the world as the saviors of Jerusalem and the Holy Land.

But having become very familiar with the history of the British in the Middle East and detailed accounts of their numerous blunders, Amnon felt certain this was yet another British blunder in the making.

That was to be the last night Amnon would sleep in his own bed for months to come. Convoys, he was told, would no longer run every single day. Thus his free time would be devoted to defending the northern section of Jerusalem on its eastern boundary with the Arabs.   There were three main Jewish neighborhoods in that area -- Mea Shearim, Beit Israel, and Sanhedria. Mea Shearim and Beit Israel were strictly Jewish orthodox communities; Sanhedria was mixed. Carefully, Amnon toured that borderline, as he had done in the past, learning the territory extremely well. It would be his responsibility to ensure the defense of this entire line, from the edge of Sanhedria to the Italian hospital on the southern corner of the Mea Shearim intersection, where the Mea Shearim quarter ended.

The border was about three kilometers long; the Mea Shearim intersection was very important, because the road-leading north was the main route to Ramallah and Samaria. *"The Arabs will definitely want to control this road,"* Amnon said to himself.

The road running south from the intersection went to the Old City of Jerusalem. Much of the property west of that road housed the Russian Compound, where British Government offices were located.   The western edge of that compound bordered the Jaffa Road, the main Jerusalem Street.

Amnon began to make mental notes of that entire line, especially the parts that faced undeveloped land between Beit Israel quarter and Sanhedriah. The Mea Shearim area was right across from a wealthy Arab neighborhood, in front of which was a major British police station. Amnon pondered the best places for bunkers and trenches, and developed a detailed defense program; with that fixed in his mind, Amnon called on his commander and asked to discuss manpower issues and weapons.

However, this section of Jerusalem was only a small part of the whole picture. There was the borderline between the Italian hospital and the Old City, the section known as Yemin Moshe, which on the west faced the Old City, as well as the southern communities of Talpiot, Arnona and Kibbutz Ramat Rachel. There were very few Arab villages to the west of the new city because the terrain was too steep for farming, and the northwestern area was also extremely mountainous with too many deep gorges and valleys, a hostile topography of no benefit to any army.

Thus it was obvious the main lines of defense would have to be to the east and south of Jerusalem.

Friday, January 30, 1948

Amnon made a few more trips guarding the convoys, during which they were attacked more frequently than before. The number of fighters was increased on each trip to ensure their return fire became correspondingly heavier. Unfortunately, the road to Jerusalem was a constant uphill through very rugged country that was friendlier to the enemy than it was to the convoys, and the heavy loads of supplies made it impossible to speed up along the winding road.

Though Amnon carefully noted the locations the Arabs attacked from each time, his notes were useless; the Arabs were never in the same place twice. The mountainous terrain with its huge rocks and trees gave them a distinct advantage that allowed small groups to come seemingly out of nowhere along many kilometers of the road.

At one point, encountering a large contingent of Arab fighters, Amnon and his men mounted an attack and routed them with heavy casualties. From then on, knowing the supplies they carried to Jerusalem were desperately needed, and expecting more of the same, they kept alert with their weapons at the ready, and whenever they met up with a squad of Arab fighters, took care of the problem before continuing on their way.

Attacks on Jewish traffic were again being reported all over the country. By the end of January all traffic in Palestine moved in guarded convoys. Amnon was informed that planning was underway to eliminate this problem. He knew very well the only solution was to capture territory and expel its Arab population, thus creating entirely Jewish sections in Palestine. That was the only way the Yishuv could return to normal life.

This time, the Haganah had to work on many fronts. Immigration was still flowing to Palestine. Those intercepted were still sent to detention camps in Cyprus. Those who managed to get through the British blockade had to be housed and fed. All Jewish cities and settlements had to be defended against attacks by Arab fighters. The British were still around, and openly helping the Arabs. Attacks were increasing at an alarming rate. Jewish traffic was being disrupted everywhere, and life was becoming more uncertain than ever. Tension throughout Palestine reached new heights. Large battles were raging on the Tel Aviv boundary coming from Jaffa. All attacks were repulsed with tremendous losses to the Arabs.

January ended with the largest number of fatalities yet on both sides.

Monday, February 2, 1948

A large car bomb set off by British soldiers exploded in front of the Palestine Post building. A number of people were killed and many wounded. The official British Government report stated that British army deserters had worked jointly with Arabs on this bombing campaign. Amnon wondered why the British

Government made such an announcement. "British deserters! What a laugh. The British openly help the Arabs, so now these helpers are called "deserters". This is just another twist in British hypocrisy," Amnon declared.

The explosion did not disrupt publication of The Palestine Post, the only English language newspaper in Palestine.

There was another gory trip from Tel Aviv to Jerusalem following an Arab attack on a convoy. It began when a tire blew on one of the buses. There was no way that bus was going to make the uphill journey. Amnon had to transfer all its passengers to the bus behind it. Firing from the Arabs sent bullets flying down at them that bounced off the steel armor plates. Danger was twofold. "If I let the bus passengers out, they'll be shot as soon as they step out," Amnon thought. He stopped the convoy. He found they were being shot at from both sides of the road. Quickly, he turned the first armored car around, and mounted a ferocious fusillade against the Arabs on the north side simultaneously with three of his men who had jumped out and taken cover under a large rock. The Arabs couldn't see them as they raced down the road about fifty meters, and scrambled up the rocks, finding an opening to attack the Arab squad firing at them from the north.

As soon as firing at the convoy from the north side had stopped, Amnon sent two more men to help the first three. In the meanwhile, firing continued from the south side of the road, but not as intense. Amnon concluded that the Arabs on the south weren't sure what their next move would be. Suddenly, Amnon heard two grenade explosions, and through the tiny window in the steel plate he saw that his men had eliminated the northern squad of Arabs.

They took positions, and began sniping at the Arabs on the south side. Amnon instructed the passengers of the disabled bus to transfer to the one in back, letting them out one by one at ten-second intervals. Firing at the convoy, which had stopped, suddenly resumed; Amnon estimated only one Arab was shooting at them while his snipers engaged the others.

Three passengers were wounded, one seriously, before Amnon's men got them all into the second bus. He had the armored car push the disabled bus into the small ravine to make more room on the road. One of the trucks wouldn't move. Even revving the engine as hard as it could, its load was too heavy for an uphill start. Unable to remain at that location, they had to move on, since Amnon didn't know what to expect further on up the road as they drove toward Jerusalem.

Amnon also had to take into account the very limited amount of ammunition they had left. Not wishing to leave any of their supplies to the Arabs, he set the truck on fire before they slowly resumed their climb eastward. Just then, four of his men slid down to the road and he learned that another one of his fighters had been killed. With no way to carry him down, his men had had to leave their dead comrade where he fell. One of the Arab bullets also went right through the small window in the steel plate, killing one passenger. Apparently one Arab was left unnoticed and he sniped at the bus from the north side. Amnon didn't learn of this second casualty until he reached Jerusalem.

As usual, a large crowd awaited them in Jerusalem. There were ambulances, two journalists, soldiers, and officers of the Haganah. Suddenly, a British civilian police car arrived at the scene.

Six policemen got out and demanded that Amnon and his men surrender their weapons. Amnon told them to go to hell, and instructed his men to surround the policemen. A policeman drew his revolver and started firing at the crowd. In the next moment, he was dead on the ground. Amnon calculated that at least three of them shot him simultaneously.

Meanwhile the other policemen drew their revolvers, but Amnon's men were right behind them and stuck their guns in their backs. Their weapons were taken away, and Amnon instructed them to pick up the dead policeman and walk away. They wanted to use their car, but Amnon wouldn't let them, anticipating they'd be sneered at and spat upon, all the way down Jaffa Road. Amnon told them they could walk the two kilometers to their main station headquarters. They were lucky they weren't killed; the two shots fired by the dead policeman had killed one bystander and wounded another.

That day was a long and difficult one for Amnon. It felt like an entire year had gone by, with one horrible event after another, including the death of another of his precious friends, and a dead passenger's blood was all over the floor of the bus. All of it was just too much for him. Suddenly, he was too exhausted to face anything or anybody more. He just wanted to get away and be left alone.

Amnon headed for the nearest safe house, drank some water, and collapsed into a bed in one of the rooms. Not knowing or caring what time it was, Amnon forced himself to shut out the world and willed himself to sleep.

Thursday, February 5, 1948

Amnon was still mad at the world. Every single day, Jews, Arabs and British personnel were dying in this war, and he could see no end in sight, while the British continued to tantalize the Yishuv with their ongoing game regarding the date they would finally leave Palestine. According to the latest news, that would be May 15, 1948, fully three months ahead -- three full months they would continue to strengthen and support the Arabs.

Yesterday's convoy had met and overcame a new challenge. The Arabs had blocked the road with heavy rocks and Amnon wondered how much longer they'd be able to get supplies through to Jerusalem, and when Jerusalem might finally be cut off. Amnon knew Haganah engineers were working on plans to create a new route to Jerusalem, but those plans were only on paper, and before construction could begin, they had to clear away and conquer an enormous amount of land.

The Haganah had begun a massive operation in the Galilee to free it from Arabs and had racked up successful progress to date. As Amnon had learned, they would soon extend their operation to other areas throughout Palestine, necessary if they were to have some peace and be able to move and work freely so that life could resume in a normal manner.

"*But what about Jerusalem? If we're cut off from the rest of the country, what are our chances of survival?*" Amnon wondered.

Daniel Rosenfeld

Already there weren't enough food supplies in the city. Kerosene, the major fuel used in every household for cook stoves had run out. Bread, flour, eggs, meat and poultry were rationed. The rations were so small Amnon wondered if it was worth going after them. He soon found out that when you have no food, even the tiniest ration becomes absolutely vital.

Amnon had not eaten meat in days, nor had he seen fish or poultry. The main staple was bread and canned food. The Arab peasants who had formerly been the major suppliers of vegetables and fruit to Jerusalem had vanished. The few kibbutzim located near Jerusalem were only able to supply a tiny fraction of the city's needs, and they, too, would soon be cut off.

Though all of this reminded Amnon of the many sieges Jerusalem had suffered in the past, he knew deep in his heart that none of these enemies, British or Arab, would succeed in their efforts to defeat them, the Yishuv was fired by high idealism, and it meant to accomplish the greatest feat in its long history. They would fight to establish a Jewish Homeland, knowing they must ultimately win, for if, God forbid, they failed, then Hitler would have triumphed, and they would die before they let that happen!

Over two hundred thousand suffering survivors and other Jewish refugees from all over Europe were depending on them. They also had an obligation to the countless pioneers who had suffered and died to settle and develop this land of theirs. Nobody, not the British, and certainly not the Arabs would be permitted to keep them from their goals!

Sunday, February 15, 1948

There were fewer convoys from the coast. Amnon and his unit were moved to the front line with orders to defend the three-kilometer stretch of the boundary between Mea Shearim and Sanhedriah, with two other units placed under his command. The nights were cold, damp and very long; time seemed to stop moving. Sometimes it rained, which made things worse, for none of them had winter clothing. Luckily, Amnon had an old British battle jacket; it was beginning to show its age, but served its purpose.

Amnon's men were on day and night shifts, while he toured all positions. The most complex position was the one in Mea Shearim, for the buildings along the entire main street of this community, which led to the Mea Shearim intersection, had no doors to the street, just some high windows, and there was no place where he could set up a post, bunker, or any kind of trench.

Although Amnon couldn't recall a single fighter in the Haganah who was an ultra-Orthodox Jew, he walked across the alley in the back of the buildings where the apartment doors were, and knocking on the door of the only apartment facing the Mea Shearim intersection, politely introduced himself before asking, "Could we use one of your rooms as the Haganah's front post in this sector?"

The very sight of Amnon in his khaki uniform was repulsive to the tenants in that apartment, as it was to the entire community of ultra-orthodox Jews. Not surprisingly, therefore, the answer was an unequivocal "No!" And the door was slammed in his face.

Amnon

Perhaps he shouldn't have gotten so angry.

"Here we are set to fight for their lives, and there's no support from these people," Amnon fumed to himself.

Although he'd have liked to bash the man in the head, he restrained himself, and again toured every centimeter of the intersection without success, finally winding up thinking he'd just have to use one or two of the other corners of the intersection. But that was impossible; the British police station was on the eastern corner, facing Mea Shearim, and any movement could be easily observed from their building.

It was an impossible predicament. But Amnon had to come up with something -- he couldn't leave the street unguarded. The more he beat his brains over the problem, the further away it seemed from a solution. Then a light bulb went off. He looked at the street next door, which also forked into the intersection, and realized he could fend off any attack from the house on the corner. The corner house was oddly shaped, but its windows gave access to almost the entire intersection, and his men could guard from behind the block wall surrounding the building like a fence.

It wasn't the perfect solution, but it came pretty close, since that street also had to be defended. Thus he concluded he could defend two possible areas of penetration from one location. In the center of Mea Shearim was a narrow street that took him to Beit Israel. In that community, Amnon found it much easier to plan his defense since a large area, between Beit Israel and the Arabs, about 400 meters, was uninhabited, and his men could watch all enemy movement clearly.

The same type of no man's land continued all the way to Sanhedria. The closest structure to the easternmost building in that community, no more than 200 meters, was the British police academy building. The road to Ramallah could easily be seen from a number of locations in Beit Israel, as could Mount Scopus, the Hebrew University, and Hadassah Hospital buildings. Amnon couldn't help but wonder what would become of Mount Scopus in the event of a full-fledged war.

The Haganah's clandestine radio station reported that the last of the bridges crossing to Syria and Lebanon in the north had been blown up. That would definitely slow down any Arab force coming from the north. Upper Galilee was already in Jewish hands, and next to come would be central Galilee and the Tiberias region.

"Haganah men guided by our leadership seem to be making some progress in the midst of all this chaos," Amnon told his men. "It will be very difficult to do anything in the Jerusalem area because so many British forces are still here, however, operations in Haifa, Jaffa, and Safed are under way."

All Arab attacks around Jerusalem were concentrated in or near the Old City. The Jewish enclave inside the Old City was constantly under fire. The Yemin Moshe community facing the Jaffa Gate of the Old City was also under attack. Firing and sniping rarely stopped. In Amnon's sector, it was quiet. Sometimes Amnon felt bored, but then he thought of the hectic past few years, and became thankful for a quiet period. But despite the fact that his area seemed peaceful, he kept his men on constant alert, and used the time to enhance their knowledge by conducting a variety of training courses.

Tuesday, February 17, 1948

The radio announced that kibbutz Tirat Zvi had been attacked by a large Arab force. That kibbutz was the southernmost settlement along the Jordan River, south of Beit Shean. The attack was repelled, but Amnon found it interesting that these large Arab attacks, all outside large cities, appeared to concentrate on distant settlements only. To him, that showed the Arabs were not yet ready to mount a major war. But he had a strong feeling that when the British left, there would be a major confrontation with the Arabs.

It was easy to speculate, but Amnon couldn't figure out why the British had set their departure from Palestine for May, especially when they could have left almost immediately. The more he thought about it, the more convinced he became that their departure date coincided with a much larger scheme the British had for Palestine.

The British needed to help build the Arab militias, and they had to train their personnel. They also had to transfer arms and weapons, none of which could be accomplished in a rush. At this point, he remembered his father telling him about the British plan to hand over to the Arabs all their installations in Palestine. That would also take time, and meanwhile none of the British forces in Palestine were trying in any way, shape, or form, to foster peace between the Arabs and the Jews. They seemed to operate completely opposite of their obligations as a mandated territory under the former League of Nations, now the United Nations.

The last house in Sanhedriah was about 200 meters from the British Police Academy building. That building was surrounded by many rows of barbed wire. Amnon didn't see much activity there, and wondered what they might be up to in that building. To satisfy his curiosity, he decided that as soon as it got dark, he'd go and take a look. Leaving his building, the only vacant one in the area, he began crawling towards the police academy.

It was deadly quiet, and very dark; cloudy skies completely hid the moon and stars. He crawled to the far end, and cut through the fence so he could get closer to the building. Twenty minutes later, he was standing near one of the windows and could easily hear conversation inside. He didn't see any guards, and the building seemed to be empty except for a few rooms on the ground floor. All of the conversation he heard was in English, and related to the men's wish to be home by now.

They were fed up with the local situation, and wanted out. Amnon didn't learn much of anything and finally returned to his side of the fence, carefully connecting the torn wires so that no one would notice the opening. He set two men to watch the British police academy building in two-hour shifts. After chatting for a while with one of the men, Amnon decided to sleep there that night.

Tuesday, February 27, 1948

Today the British detonated three cars loaded with explosives in Ben Yehuda Street in Jerusalem. Over 50 innocent bystanders were killed. There was also major property damage. Amnon supposed that some of the British soldiers were trying to pay the Jews back for what they'd been doing to them for years. The British official radio station again accused British army deserters.

"What nonsense! Deserters!" Declared Amnon. "The British are helping the Arabs in the open. They don't have deserters. Liars and hypocrites, that's what they are! Let them leave already. We'll deal with the Arabs."

Tuesday, March 2, 1948

Rumors reached Amnon that a Haganah engineer had invented some kind of Cannon. Details were scant, but he was told he'd soon get more information. Amnon hoped the Haganah would get this new weapon in time to help the convoy situation. Convoys from Tel Aviv had great difficulty reaching Jerusalem because of the boulders the Arabs put in the road to block their way. When the latest convoys had been forced to stop at those rocky roadblocks, some of the men had to engage in heavy battles while others worked to clear the road. The number of casualties increased, and Amnon developed a bad feeling that Jerusalem would soon be completely cut off from the rest of the country.

Meanwhile, he continued to monitor the eastern line, checking on his men day and night; making sure everyone was on full alert.

"We can't afford to make a single mistake. The lives of tens of thousands of people depend on our readiness to repel any attack," he stated at every stop.

The news from other parts of Palestine was not good at all. Day after day, Arab forces, which were renamed the Liberation Armies, attacked one settlement after another. Attacks also continued on the two major cities, Tel Aviv and Haifa. Any movement of vehicles had to be done through convoys, and only the most important cargo was permitted to be shipped. Public transportation was reduced to absolute necessities.

In the midst of all of this, two new Hebrew newspapers made their debut, Maariv and Yediot Acharonot. Demand for news was so great that people would sit for hours and listen endlessly to news services, both official and clandestine. No wonder the two new evening newspapers were such a success. However, Amnon only got the two new newspapers a few days later, when a convoy managed to bring some copies from Tel-Aviv. Never in his life had he felt such a hunger for news.

Saturday, March 6, 1948

That morning, Amnon was called to the Jerusalem headquarters of the Haganah. "I want you to blow up the new Arab Command building in east Jerusalem," Yoav, Amnon's new Jerusalem commander, baldly stated. "I've heard a great deal about you. You possess an excellent strategic mind, and you will find a way to penetrate the Arab sector east of us. Just tell me what materials you need, and I'll have them ready for you," he assured Amnon.

"Give me one day, and I'll have the answer for you," Amnon promised, and left in a hurry. He sent a message to Yaacov, his deputy, and asked him to take charge until he returned the next day, then proceeded immediately to Jaffa

Road. He perused the western side toward the Barclays Bank building. From the intersection in front of the bank, Jaffa Road continued down toward the Jaffa Gate in the Old City. It was a narrow street with shops on both sides, most were owned by Arabs. Just before the Jaffa Gate, another narrow road led eastward toward East Jerusalem.

The Jerusalem municipal building was also located near this intersection. The Russian Compound, which housed most of the British Government's offices, was on the eastern side of Jaffa Road. The entire area was crawling with British military and civilian policemen. Guards stood in front of each building, and armored cars patrolled the streets all the way to the Old City.

Across from the Russian compound was the main Jerusalem Post Office, also guarded by many soldiers and policemen. Everywhere in that area Jews and Arabs mixed, going about their business. Everyone felt secure by the strong British presence. Amnon returned to the safe house where he obtained typical clothing worn by Arab youth. Pocketing a headdress [keffia], he headed back to Jaffa Road.

When he got there he entered the Main Post Office building and headed straight to the rest room. He emerged with his head covered, made a right turn outside and headed toward the Old City. He bought a couple of Arabic newspapers, and put them under his arm. As soon as he reached the road leading east, he turned left. Here there were no Jews at all.

The sidewalks were busy with shoppers going to or coming from the Old City markets; the streets were busy with Arab buses. Amnon kept walking until he reached the neighborhood of the Arab Command building. Most of the area was residential, with just a few shops.

He found a place to sit down not too far from the Arab Command, opened the newspaper, and pretended to be reading. Two cars were parked in front of the building. He took special notice because they had British military plates. Amnon didn't sit there more than fifteen minutes, as he didn't want to attract attention. As he stood up and folded the newspaper, he noticed five British military officers come out of the building, get into the two cars, and drive off. That gave him an idea.

Knowing that in Palestine all phone cables were above ground and supported by tall wooden posts, before he left he examined the phone lines that connected to the building. He noted where the wires connected, and how high above the ground. He walked down the road for a half hour or so, then returned, this time using the sidewalk along the side of the building. As he approached it he noticed a couple of Arabs standing, talking inside the front entrance. They seemed to be arguing, so he decided to slide in. He toured the first floor of the building, politely greeting a couple of men who passed by. No one else was there, and he didn't think the two men even noticed him.

As he explored the lobby area, he opened two doors to what he discovered were cloakrooms. Quickly, he left the building. Then, he retraced his steps to the Jewish side of the city, took off the headdress in the Post Office's men's room, and walked back to his safe house.

Tired from all that walking, Amnon decided to take a nap. When he woke up hungry around 10:00pm, he sat on a sofa and ate a sandwich and a glass of tea. With eyes closed, he concentrated on the operation, analyzing all the risks involved, and tried to devise the best plan of attack.

Luckily, few people were in the safe house that night, and Amnon could concentrate on his objective. Within the hour he had the entire plan of action in his mind, (nothing was ever committed to paper). Since the short nap he had allowed himself hadn't been enough by any means, he went back to bed and slept through the night.

The next day, Amnon got up early, washed, shaved, ate breakfast and was at the Haganah's headquarters a few minutes past eight. Yoav was waiting for him.

"How are you going to pull this off?" Yoav asked as soon as he saw Amnon.

" I have an idea which would help us kill two birds with one stone," Amnon stated. He explained, "I need four British military armored cars, all the same make and design. If you don't know where to get them, I could easily penetrate the military barracks near Talpiot, and borrow the vehicles. My men and supplies for this operation should be ready in Talpiot. When we're ready to start this operation, we'll seem to have come out of the barracks. The four armored cars will drive like a small convoy to the Old City where we'll turn toward east Jerusalem straight to the Arab High Command building. We'll park in front of the building. Our Irish major will walk in and ask for help he'd been promised to unload a delivery of weapons. Two cases will be filled with rifles and ammunition while the other two cases will be booby-trapped. Those two cases will contain enough explosives to blow up the building. Any Arabs who come out to help will be directed to the two cars containing these cases, thus getting them into the building. The cases containing the explosives will be placed on the bottom so that when the top cases are opened, rifles will be seen. They won't suspect anything. We'll then invite one or two of the highest-ranking Arabs to come check the latest weapons, just arrived. While the other Arabs will be directed back with thanks for their help, their bosses will be shoved into the third vehicle at gunpoint and silenced. Before departing we'll call on the Arabs to open the cases immediately and put the rifles away. On the way back I'm planning to shoot up anything that moves, just to create chaos on the Arab side. The British armored cars flying British flags will certainly confuse everyone," Amnon concluded his presentation.

"I never thought of capturing Arab officers. This is one hell of an idea," his commander told him. "Are you planning to wear British uniforms?"

"Absolutely. The Arabs would never suspect British armored cars delivering weapons."

"We have one problem, though." The commander's tone was somber. "What you refer to as the Irish major can't help anymore. He was killed in action a few weeks ago. You're the only one who speaks perfect English. That officer will have to be you..."

Wednesday, March 10, 1948

Daniel Rosenfeld

The day before yesterday Amnon had spied on the British military barracks on the outskirts of Talpiot. He found a great location completely hidden from view, yet from which he could see everything going on in the barracks. There was heavy traffic all day and well into the evening. Thus he decided the best way to enter the barracks would be to fake a flat tire and get a lift from the first truck that came along. Though there were many military police at the main entrance to the barracks, there was almost no checking as cars continuously went in and out.

Returning to his headquarters the next day, Amnon made sure he had all the uniforms ready, carefully explaining what he needed to the chief supplies officer and requesting everything be ready by this afternoon. Amnon detailed how he wanted the cases arranged, and how to have the booby-trapped ones marked, also requesting one command car, which he knew the Haganah had, to be ready at 5:00pm.

Amnon returned to his headquarters with eight of his men and spent some time meticulously going over the plan of attack. With his men thoroughly briefed, he told them it was imperative at least one of the Arab commanders be brought back alive, even if unconscious.

They left for Talpiot before sunset in one of their command cars with British plates and flag. During the trip, all of them put on British uniforms. Amnon's had the insignia of a major with a number of wartime medals attached to his officer's jacket. One of his men was a sergeant, one a corporal, and the others privates. All of them also wore the appropriate hats. About two kilometers before the barracks, they pulled over, stopped on the side of the road, and punctured a front tire.

With his men pretending to fix the problem, Amnon kept his eyes peeled for a truck. Soon one appeared. Stepping into the center of the road, Amnon waved the driver to stop. When he did, Amnon jumped in, and took the vacant seat next to the driver while his men jumped into the back.

Amnon chose well; it was a fully covered supply truck. When the driver stopped for a couple of seconds at the main entrance gate, the guard jumped to attention and saluted Amnon's rank before waving the truck in.

Amnon asked the driver to drop them off near the transportation shed so he could replace their disabled vehicle. As instructed, the driver dropped them off a few minutes later next to the transport shed. On the right side of the shed, were row after row of trucks, jeeps, armored cars, private cars, even some military buses. There were soldiers all over the place, going and coming from every direction. Nevertheless Amnon led his men straight to the line-up of armored cars and chose four. Within minutes, four fully gassed up and equipped armored cars rolled toward Talpiot. With usual British efficiency, each car had a Bren gun with six cases of loaded clips. They drove off the main road to the designated safe house. The cases were loaded onto the first two vehicles, and off they went. About forty-five minutes later, the four armored cars parked in front of the Arab Command building. Amnon got out of the car and walked straight into the building.

At that moment, the driver of the first car cut the telephone wires on the

208

Amnon

side of the building. Amnon asked the man standing at the front entrance, who probably was a guard, to call his chief and tell him he had a weapons delivery for them. Within a minute, five Arabs came out, and their chief introduced himself. Amnon asked if he'd be kind enough to have his men unload the four cases earmarked for them.

The delighted Arab never asked who or what, just yelled at his men to help. Leading them to the first armored car, Amnon had them take the booby-trapped case first. Two of them carried it into the building. The cases with the rifles followed, Amnon directing them to place it on top of the first case. Then, from the second car, came the second set of cases, which were placed next to the first two. When their chief asked Amnon if he was sure there weren't any more, Amnon assured him the four cases were all he'd been given.

He thanked Amnon dismissively and began walking back with his men when Amnon called him to come take a look at an interesting new weapon. As soon as the armored car opened, Amnon shoved him in, and he was silenced. They drove off in a hurry; about 200 meters away they slowed down and continued at a slow pace. As they reached the intersection near the Damascus Gate of the Old City, they started firing into doorways, windows, and at anything that moved. They even pitched some hand grenades.

The panic was on. British armored cars started shooting at Arabs. Amnon and his men continued firing the guns so kindly given them by the British military almost until they reached the Jaffa Gate.

During the course of the shooting spree, at least three police cars passed them by, but, not knowing what to make of what they saw, they did nothing. Since Amnon had specifically instructed his men not to fire at British cars to avoid being fired upon, they held their fire.

As they turned south, they quickly shed the British uniforms before parking the armored cars on a side road where Amnon had previously stashed a six-seater taxicab. Just before all of them piled into the cab, they heard the explosions.

"Goodbye, Command Building!" Amnon hooted.

Grinning victoriously at each other, they carried the Arab chief, who was still out, around to the trunk, locked him in, and sped off through a number of dirt roads and side streets until they reached their safe house in Jerusalem. Yoav was waiting for him. The Arab chief was taken out of the trunk; Amnon and his crew never saw him again. Doubtless, the intelligence machinery of the Haganah collected some valuable information from him. Their commander had warmed up some milk, which he personally served Amnon and his men along with fine English biscuits.

Wanting only to unwind from all the night's tension, Amnon mumbled his thanks, found a bed on which to collapse, and slept without interruption until 8:00am. He was certain his men did the same.

Saturday, March 13, 1948

Amnon sent his men back to their unit on the eastern frontline and returned to bed. He felt like continuing to rest, but as usual his mind was working.

209

Obviously, his psychological analysis was correct. Feeling overly secure with the British on their side, the Arabs didn't do much about security, especially inside their own territory. They took the bait of weapons delivery so nonchalantly it was almost a joke. Amnon was glad the explosions occurred after he'd cleared the area. The official broadcasting system announced that drunken soldiers had gone on a shooting spree, and the military police was investigating.

There wasn't one word about the Arab Command building having been blown up.

"*Damn*", Amnon thought, "*We didn't get credit for this action. The British propaganda experts were too sharp to announce to the world that Jews had penetrated Arab territory and blown up their command headquarters in Jerusalem. But with or without credit, we accomplished our objective.*"

Amnon was certain the Arabs knew quite well who blew up their building. The disappearance of one of their key men must certainly also have been a mystery.

Yoav, Amnon's commander, came to check up on him a while later, finding Amnon stretched out in bed on his back.

"I had the armored cars taken to western Jerusalem near Bait Vagan," he told Amnon. "We'll surely be able to use them in the future. I'd like to discuss with you the British military barracks near Talpiot. What other value might that barracks be to us? What would be the risks of penetrating it again?"

"Let me spy around the barracks for a day or two. I'll get back to you," Amnon responded.

"Get going. The eastern front line seems to be very quiet. Our intelligence noted no activity on their side. Your deputy can carry on for a few days without you."

Amnon got up, shaved, and showered, and had a tall glass of coffee with some cheese and a thick slice of black bread he cut from a loaf. Then he slipped over his khaki uniform the simple Arab habit generally worn by their young men, stuffed the headdress into his pocket, and left to swiftly walk all the way toward the Old City of Jerusalem. As he neared the Jaffa Gate, he slipped behind a tree, put on the headdress, and proceeded through the Gate and into the Jewish quarter.

For some reason he couldn't understand, Amnon found himself walking in the direction of the ancient Hurva synagogue, a magnificent house of prayer he'd always admired. Something drew him to the door of the synagogue, and finding it open, Amnon went in. He looked around, and stopped for a moment in front of the closed wall unit that housed the Torah Scrolls, softly whispering: "Shma Israel Adonai Elohanu Adonai Echad," and he added, "Am Echad," before he walked out.

Amnon never saw the synagogue he loved so much again. He hurried back to the path leading from the Old City, and was on his way to Talpiot. He decided to walk that long distance since walking provided a better chance of observing what was going and coming, taking special account of all British and Arab traffic.

As Amnon neared the barracks, he got off the road and made his way through the small woods on one side of the barracks. From there he could see the main entrance, but was too far away to see everything clearly. He looked around for some place he could station himself that would be closer without putting himself at risk of discovery.

He decided to walk around the entire barracks complex at a distance of at least 200 meters, where possible, and diligently circled the compound. The entire barracks was fenced in, with the added security of two rows of barbed wire topping the fence. There were also several rows of barbed wire inside the compound against the fence on the ground.

Amnon didn't spot any security patrols inside the complex proper. He did notice two large sheds with entrances guarded by military police. Those two sheds were different from all the others in the barracks because they were the only ones guarded. None of the other sheds were guarded. He also noticed heavy lifting equipment next to the guarded sheds. One of the sheds in the complex had a banner across its entrance: 'Military Police.' Other sheds bore a variety of signs, none of which could be clearly read from a distance. The biggest concentration of guards was at the front gate. However, most cars and pedestrians were waved through fairly quickly, and Amnon wondered if they'd even noticed four of their armored cars were missing.

"*If I had something stolen from me, I certainly would have increased security,*" Amnon thought, but he didn't notice or sense any change since the night he and his men went in. After circling the entire barracks, Amnon found where he'd watch the front gate. He identified an excellent location where a number of trees formed a tiny forest. One of the trees was oddly shaped. Amnon shimmied up it and sat on a heavy branch, well hidden from view while still able to observe his target.

It was beginning to get dark, but Amnon had been so preoccupied with his walk around the barracks, making mental notes of everything he observed, he hadn't thought to check the time. Bus service from Talpiot to Jerusalem stopped soon after sunset, so it was too late for him to go back, leaving him no alternative but to stay where he was. Though hungry and thirsty, with Talpiot just a few kilometers away, there was no point in taking a risk. Making himself as comfortable as possible on his tree, he spent the night there, but he certainly didn't sleep.

There was quite a bit of traffic, mostly entering the compound, with trucks far outnumbering all other types of vehicles. Arriving in convoys, the trucks were driven to an area north of the main entrance, and Amnon could see soldiers unloading the cargo, which looked like the typical cases used for transporting weapons and ammunition. Amnon asked himself, "*Why are the British bringing hundreds of cases of weapons and ammunition to this particular barracks when their major weapons storage had always been closer to the coast? And why bring in such huge quantities of weapons when they are planning to leave Palestine? Precisely why are these trucks arriving at night?*"

Amnon carefully noted the location of the sheds used to store the newly arrived weaponry. From Amnon's observation post on the front side of the barracks, it occurred to him that the sheds where all the unloading was taking place were the ones he'd spotted with lots of guards.

About an hour later, a private car arrived which was directed to the sheds where the cases had been unloaded and stored. He could clearly see four Arabs in their khaki uniforms, heads covered with their typical keffias, get out of the car. Two soldiers, by the look of their hats, both officers, greeted them. They went into one of the sheds and came out carrying one case, which they placed into their trunk. A few minutes later they departed.

. What a fortuitous coincidence! Amnon could barely wait for the next morning to report his findings to his commander. He couldn't have chosen a better night in the whole year to walk out to Talpiot. "*Any other night, I might not have witnessed such a large arms delivery intended for the Arabs,*" he thought.

Traffic slowed to a trickle as it neared midnight; then there was none. Lights went out in most of the sheds, only a few exterior lights remaining on. Amnon was just about to climb down from his tree when he noticed traffic inside the compound, indicating the British military police began patrolling their compound at midnight. A large searchlight could be seen moving from shed to shed as the patrol car passed, occasionally shining along the fence as well.

Amnon jumped off the tree and made himself comfortable on the ground. Absorbed as he'd been observing the compound, he hadn't noticed the temperature had dropped, the air getting colder by the minute. He tried curling up like an animal, but lacking an animal's furry coat, that didn't help. He tried to sleep, but the combination of the cold and his shivering body ruled that out also. He was also starving, and his mouth was as dry as the Negev Desert.

"Okay, so it's another Yom Kippur," Amnon told himself. "When the fasting is over it will be time to eat." Thankfully, he dozed off just before dawn, and awoke with the first warm beams of sunlight combined with the resumption of heavy traffic. In the distance, he saw the first daily bus from Talpiot heading toward Jerusalem, and instantly took off through the small wood, running like a deer to arrive just as the bus passed. Fortunately, the driver saw his frantic waving, and stopped the bus. After paying the fare, Amnon collapsed into a seat wishing the bus could fly him back to Jerusalem so that he could report all of his findings to his commander. Of course, being the first bus of the day, it made numerous stops on its way to Jerusalem.

Yoav wasn't in when he got to the Haganah's headquarters. Explaining to one of the secretaries it was a matter of life and death, Amnon left an urgent message for Yoav, asking that it be delivered without fail, immediately, no matter where he was.

Since Amnon hadn't eaten for almost twenty-four hours, he immediately found something to eat and drink in the kitchen and fell asleep while sitting and waiting. Yoav arrived a little over an hour after Amnon and woke him up. Taking Amnon into the nearest spare room, he closed the door and said, "You discovered the British were transporting arms to their Talpiot barracks, didn't you?"

Absolutely floored, Amnon asked, "How did you know?"

"It's simple. Our intelligence reported early this morning that large army trucks in convoys were heading for Jerusalem, and later seen passing through the city leading south. Then, with your urgent message I put two and two together, and there you have it."

"We need to do something about this, right away," Amnon insisted. "Otherwise, the Arabs will receive, or inherit, a phenomenal amount of weaponry. Plus who knows what else might be in those sheds."

Before Yoav could open his mouth, Amnon added, "I know how to penetrate this barracks easily. Let me have the four armored cars we swiped the other day. If I can get started as soon as it's dark, I'll have all these sheds blown up tonight. I'll also need the armored cars to be armed, as they usually are, with extra ammo and grenades."

"I need six jerricans of gasoline, six small time bombs, each attached to a can, and six pieces of strong string or rope, each about three meters long. Also, I want a dozen men from my unit, the veterans, please."

"I take it you're not going to tell me your plans, are you?" Yoav guessed.

" We don't have time," Amnon declared. "I want my men right away so I can prepare them for this mission."

Within minutes, a replacement unit was dispatched to the eastern line and a messenger on his way, with instructions for twelve of Amnon's key men to be at the safe house by noon. When he arrived at the safe house, and returned to the room he'd slept in, he drew a picture of his plans in his mind.

Amnon's men arrived, as ordered. He'd made arrangements for sandwiches and drinks, which were delivered at noon. They sat in the large living room, in the absence of many chairs mostly on the floor, and Amnon explained the plan of attack.

With instructions to leave as soon as the sun had set, four men were sent to Bait Vagan to drive the armored cars back to the safe house vicinity. The cans filled with gasoline, the small time bombs, and the strings had already been delivered by the time the men returned with the armored cars.

Leaving as soon as it was dark, they drove in convoy style, the way British police or military always did toward the Talpiot barracks, stopping five hundred meters away. Six men got out with two Bren guns, four rifles, and plenty of ammunition. They positioned themselves in the area where Amnon had spent the previous night. Within minutes, the rest of them, with Amnon in the lead armored car, were back on the road. As the first of the four armored cars reached the gate, Amnon's four men started firing at the gate and the guards, including the armored cars their comrades were driving.

The four armored cars immediately drove through the gate while the British soldiers took cover and began firing. The first two armored cars proceeded to their destination while the last two turned and started firing at the attackers, (except that the firing was aimed way above their comrades' heads) so that they appeared to be British soldiers defending the barracks. Amnon in one armored vehicle arrived at the first shed while the second car pulled up to the second shed.

The guards thought nothing of seeing British armored cars stop in front of the sheds, and Amnon and his men took them out quickly. Breaking the center window in each of the sheds with the butts of their revolvers, they gently dropped in the cans of gasoline to which a ten-minute time bomb was attached. The noise of the firing and the calls from the front gate immediately set off an alarm in the barracks, and sirens started wailing throughout the compound. Within minutes Amnon had all the bombs inside the sheds, and they took off back toward the front gate. As soon as Amnon and the second armored car arrived, they joined the two other cars that were ahead of them and all four lunged towards the attackers, always firing way over their heads. The soldiers at the gate and whatever British officers were there cheered them on; certain someone had sent armored cars to fight off the attackers.

As they drove straight into the line of fire, Amnon's men shifted to the right away from it. Only two men stayed where they were, and as soon as the last car came abreast, in they jumped. The others were picked up within a minute or two. When everybody was accounted for, they threw a number of grenades, which exploded way behind them. They kept firing a few minutes longer while driving away as fast as they could.

Several times blocked traffic foiled them off the road. Before they reached the city outskirts, explosions could be heard, and they slowed down. No one followed them. Once inside the city, Amnon's instructions were to keep a reasonable distance between each of the armored cars. They arrived at their safe house, and the cars were immediately taken over by others and removed to a secure location. Many friends and comrades joined Amnon and his men inside the house.

At least a hundred explosions were heard all over Jerusalem. The sky was red from all the fires. Amnon's hand and his back hurt from all the hearty congratulatory handshakes and thumps. Someone brought a bottle of wine, and each one of them took a sip. Exhausted from the high tension of battle, they sat on the floor trying to unwind. Amnon didn't believe anyone ever learned how many weapons and cases of ammunition were destroyed.

Amnon's commander came over and sat down beside him.

"Do you mind telling me how you did this?" Yoav asked.

"It was easy," Amnon smiled. "We attacked our own men, and defended the barracks. The British should give us a medal," he added. Yoav laughed, and punched Amnon's shoulder.

Mentally and physically exhausted, Amnon took the best bed he could find in the house and collapsed, hoping to sleep. But he was too wound up, and sleep did not come. So he got up and walked back into the living room where he found a few men and women talking, and joined the conversation. They were discussing the new weapon invented by a member of the Haganah.

Apparently, it had been tried in Jaffa during a recent attack by the Arabs and been pronounced a huge success. They said it was named Davidka, after the name of its inventor; it was a small short-barreled cannon that could be used in close range fighting. Amnon couldn't wait to see one.

Wednesday, March 31, 1948

After the successful attack on the Talpiot barracks, Amnon returned to his previous assignment. The eastern section of the front where he was posted was still quiet with not much more than occasional sniper fire. The Arabs had some artillery pieces, and from time to time cannon shots could be heard. Bombshells landed in various parts of Jewish Jerusalem. The Jewish quarter inside the Old City was under constant firing. The brave men and women in the quarter repelled many attacks, but it was not known how much longer they'd be able to hold on.

Amnon got word that the last Jewish convoy from the coast couldn't get through, and had to return to Tel Aviv. Jerusalem was completely cut off from the world. To offset the bad, there was the great news that the government of Czechoslovakia had agreed to sell the Haganah arms that were being clandestinely airlifted to a Haganah airport. Amnon never knew that the Haganah had an airport, nor where it was. Actually, Czech weaponry continued to flow to the Haganah for many months to come.

As soon as the British announced their firm departure date from Palestine, the leaders of the Yishuv decided to form a provisional government. The date set was May 15, 1948, and the Arabs would make that "Day One" of their intensified attacks on Jewish neighborhoods and settlements throughout Palestine. They also increased their firing on public buses, homes, and apartment buildings. As the violence grew, Amnon felt certain a much larger Arab scheme was brewing.

As the date of the British departure became known, and Arab intentions clearer, the leaders of the Yishuv had to accomplish one of their main objectives, which was to clean out Arab enclaves from predominantly Jewish areas. As the grand British scheme moved into clear focus, the entire Yishuv began to sense an impending siege. Previously, the British had tried hard to camouflage their support of the Arabs, although their every move and their policies clearly provided an entirely different picture.

Amnon couldn't stop thinking of what would happen when the British had finally gone. "In six weeks they'll officially leave Palestine. The declaration by our leaders to create a provisional government makes a lot of sense. A country without a government, without authority would become an anarchy; along with the Arab war mood, our entire region would turn into a blood bath," Amnon said to his men. "I can't see how we'll deal with the Arabs when they openly reject the partition of Palestine. It's quite obvious now that they've begun to mount a war against us."

There was so much to think and worry about, but Amnon was certain the Yishuv's leadership was handling the affairs of a nation-to-be with much care and courage.

Monday, April 5, 1948

Haganah forces began a sweeping military campaign to open the road to Jerusalem. That operation was known as the Nachshon Campaign. Amnon wanted so much to be part of it, but other units were called in. In fact, Haganah forces managed to clear most of the countryside, and new convoys were arriving in Jerusalem bringing much needed food and military supplies. However, news of the battle for the Castel Mountain was inconclusive. Mount Castel, as it was called, was situated at the point where the main road to Jerusalem reached its highest point. From that mountain top Arabs could still shoot and attack passing convoys. It was imperative for the Haganah to capture it. Amnon was sure that eventually Mount Castel would be captured no matter how fierce the battles.

News of the mountain changing hands annoyed Amnon a great deal as it did the rest of Jerusalem. A few days later Amnon received information that his cousin had been killed in that battle. There was also news that Arab forces had attacked kibbutz Mishmar Haemek, but were repulsed.

All was still quiet on his section of the front. As always, the units under Amnon's command were on constant alert, and he toured all of his positions, ceaselessly, day and night. "One mistake anywhere on this line would be critical if the Arabs attacked us. This is a very long front line and we're spread too thin," he kept telling his men. But no such attack occurred, and he was puzzled that the Arabs should apparently ignore that section of Jerusalem, which was wide open on at least a two-kilometer stretch. He listened with envy to the Haganah's clandestine radio station describing the fighting to open the road to Jerusalem. Amnon desperately wanted to be there, though he realized the responsibility given him to guard the city against attack was just as important.

Friday, April 9, 1948

A major battle had been won. The Arab supreme military chief was killed at Mount Castel, which was in the hands of the Haganah, and the upper section of the road to Jerusalem was under its control. The lower section of the road, however, which stretched over twenty-five kilometers, was still in hostile territory. Another incident occurred today that left a dreadful mark on all of the Yishuv. The combined forces of the Etzel and Lehi attacked the Arab village of Deir Yassin, near Jerusalem, and massacred its entire population. The Yishuv was absolutely appalled at that news.

War was one thing, but massacre of civilians was totally unacceptable. The Etzel and Lehi organizations were always radical, certainly too radical for the general Yishuv, and particularly the Haganah. While there was never an actual count, Amnon believed that less than fifteen percent of the population approved of those radical organizations and their deeds.

The Yishuv was fighting what Amnon thought of as a very unusual war, principally because the Arabs weren't organized. There was also no battlefront or zone that the Arabs were concentrating on. In most cases, attacks were sporadic, and in dozens of locations not strategically connected in any way. Every action seemed more like terrorist, sabotage, or harassment rather than a real battle with a military plan or purpose in mind. Actually, the Arabs' general purpose was to disrupt the partition of Palestine. They wanted to create a hostile atmosphere, which they believed would stop further Jewish immigration to Palestine.

"In both cases, they will be roundly defeated," Amnon pronounced.

So long as the British remained in Palestine, the Arabs couldn't mount a full-scale war. They also surely knew that by themselves they would never defeat the Jews. Rumors abounded that the leaders of the Arab League, which had been formed under the aegis of Great Britain, was making a lot of noise about the war of the near future. The League, and some of its member countries that had benefited from British assistance and military training, would meet as soon as the British left to discuss their further plans for Palestine.

Amnon's territory was still quiet. He got permission from his commanding officer to infiltrate the Arab territory east of his units and check it out. Amnon didn't like the calm. All the main roads in the Arab area to the east and particularly the main road between Jerusalem and Ramallah could be observed from many of Amnon's positions. There was no major civilian or military traffic. St. George's, the school Amnon attended, was on the east side of that key road, and the Police Academy on the west side about two kilometers to the north.

Amnon picked up two Arab habits, and called one of his men who was more fluent than him in Arabic. Taking food and water, as darkness fell they walked down Shmuel Hanavi Street, and at an appropriate moment, crossed over to the other side. Each also carried a revolver with plenty of ammunition and four grenades.

They walked alongside the road until they reached the bend, which turned east, and then continued parallel to the road, but to the south, a long way behind the main road. Most houses were dark. They encountered no one, and Amnon was certain that no one saw them. There were no signs of any military preparations, military posts, observation posts, or bunkers.

Walking for hours, they covered the entire area including the residential neighborhood behind the Mea Shearim police station. From there they could look into Mea Shearim, which was also dark. However, Amnon noticed a lot of activity south of his line, closer to the Old City. He decided the following night he'd pay a visit to that area. The Haganah line in that section was under the command of another officer. Amnon wondered whether he should be forewarned of his infiltration mission

Monday, April 12, 1948

The Arab League, meeting in Cairo, declared that it approved a plan to invade Palestine after the British departure. The countries involved were Egypt, Trans-Jordan, Syria, Lebanon, and Iraq. This news item was overwhelming to the entire Yishuv, for it provided an idea of what could develop, and what to expect. It also put the Yishuv and its leadership on alert, giving it time to plan the defenses. It became clear that all Arab communities located in predominantly Jewish rural areas, as well as Arab quarters in predominantly Jewish cities, had to be evacuated.

This was not going to be easy. But it had to be done fast, for the Yishuv had only one month to accomplish this goal. If not, the Jews would have to fight on two constant fronts -- one, facing an external Arab enemy, and the other, facing the Arab enemy within their midst.

Fortunately, Arab nations surrounding Palestine helped the Yishuv meet its objective. Arab radio stations from neighboring countries were broadcasting announcements to the Arab population in Palestine; "Leave your homes and find safe refuge in neighboring countries. Soon the British will leave Palestine and we shall capture the entire country from our enemies. You shall return with great triumph to your land. The Jews will be eliminated."

Amnon called on his commander, told him of his findings, and asked permission to infiltrate the lower section of the eastern frontline.

That section ran from the Italian hospital on the southwestern corner of the Mea Shearim intersection, all the way to the Old City, and specifically to the Damascus Gate, which was a relatively short distance from the Jaffa Gate. Gates were named after the cities to which the roads from the gate led. The entire lower eastern section, which included two major Christian Arab schools, was heavily inhabited by well to do Arabs. This road also cut through the center of the area, which was the eastern boundary of the Russian compound where the majority of British governmental offices were located.

Doubtless, their British buddies had told the Arabs that that territory would be handed over to them when the British finally departed from Palestine. That area was overwhelmingly populated with Arabs. Since the Haganah's defense line didn't run all the way to the Old City, but only a short distance from Mea Shearim, it was obvious something had to be done to ensure that they wouldn't have a thorn in their side. Amnon received Yoav's blessings.

Before leaving, Amnon expressed concern about the area of the Russian compound and suggested the Haganah make arrangements to conquer it as soon as the British left. Amnon also shared with Yoav his conclusion that the Arabs deliberately kept the northeastern line quiet because the only road to Jerusalem from Ramallah and the West Bank ran parallel to it not more than three hundred meters away. That made a great deal of sense to Yoav, and he promised to bring it up at the higher command meeting. Yoav and Amnon, arranged to get together the following day.

That night Amnon slipped into the Italian hospital with his companion from the night before. Behind the outer walls they put on the usual Arab gear, and covered their heads with the red and white checked headdresses. They quickly found their way to the hospital's main entrance, walked out to the street, and turned south. They didn't have to go very far.

No more than five hundred meters away was a great deal of activity. Arab soldiers, all dressed in khakis, were building bunkers facing the main girls' school across an open yard about the size of a soccer field. As they continued to walk slowly down the street they noticed additional similar building preparations and soldiers everywhere. Many Arab civilians were walking the sidewalk, and a few cars also went by.

Retracing their steps, they returned to the hospital. From the main entrance they easily observed a lot of activity at the large police station across from the Mea Shearim intersection. Men talking and pointing at Mandelbaum Street, which was the street next to Mea Shearim Street. Mandelbaum Street also adjoined that intersection. The very house on the corner was where Amnon had set up his major guard post for the Mea Shearim intersection.

In the small garden on the north side of the hospital building they found a good spot to keep an eye on the police station. Four different cars stopped in front of the station during the next two hours. Arab officers went into the station and spent about fifteen minutes before coming out and driving off towards the

218

Old City. What bothered Amnon most was that those officers wore the caps of the Arab Legion, which was based in Trans-Jordan. The British Government established the Arab Legion. Its chief of staff and most of its officers were British military career men.

"What the hell are Arab Legion men doing here?" Amnon whispered.

On the following day, Amnon joined his commander and the deputy commander for the Jerusalem area for a meeting. Several other area commanders were also present. They discussed at length the defense of Jerusalem and examined every possibility of Arab attack. Amnon learned that forces of the Arab Legion were already in Palestine, particularly the area east of Jerusalem. The Yishuv had four Jewish settlements southeast of Jerusalem known as Gush Etzion.

Those settlements had already been attacked, and the feeling was the Arab Legion would soon try to conquer that entire area. The top command felt, as did Amnon, that the northern section of the front was left out of conflict because the Arabs were planning to enter the Jewish side of Jerusalem through the lower eastern area where a number of roads existed. They also probably believed if the Russian compound were in their hands, the main battle for Jerusalem would have to start as close to that compound as possible.

From the point of view of a frontal assault they were right. However, knowing the Haganah would put up a bloody defense, it would be so much easier to attack Jerusalem from the north. They discussed all possibilities and Arab options, and concluded the Mea Shearim police station was bound to become their area headquarters and they were building a defense line along the lower eastern line, just in case they were pushed back, they also concluded the Arabs would try to capture the Russian compound if they couldn't hold it after they got it from the British. Capturing the Russian compound would put the Arabs in the center of Jerusalem. To mount a major assault an army needs space to maneuver. The compound's eastern area was densely populated. The only open area was the girl's school. Another area of possible attack was the great divide between the Old City and the Jewish quarter of Yemin Moshe; however, access to that area was limited to one single narrow road.

The girl's school was the largest structure on that side. It had a large yard on its eastern side with homes to the right and left. Amnon was convinced, that logistically the school's huge backyard would be the best area for an Arab assault. If the assault came from any other place in that entirely residential area, the attackers would be faced with house to house combat, which would hamper a swift advance and cause the attackers to lose their momentum.

The Haganah would have to meet two main objectives at the same time – the first, a swift takeover of the Russian compound from the Arabs, who'd almost certainly be given the complex when the British left, the second, to stop Arab forces advancing from the east, a territory which would doubtless be handed over to Arab civilians just to round out the complete territorial package the British gave the Arabs.

The United Nations would frown on the British delivering government offices to Arab military forces. Hence, it was agreed the British would probably deliver the Russian compound to Arab civilians. At this point the Arabs would mount their ground assault. The concept of the situation had been established. The deputy chief left, assuring Yoav and Amnon that a final decision would be rendered by evening.

Amnon asked his commander why the Haganah didn't evacuate Gush Etzion. "What's the point of holding on to a piece of land in the middle of such hostile territory, particularly since it's so far from us, and our ability to help almost nil?"

Amnon reminded Yoav of the thirty-five Palmach unit ambushed and killed in that area. Yoav said that members of Gush Etzion had been asked to evacuate, but flatly refused. They decided to make a stand, which Amnon thought ridiculous. Arab Legion forces had already attacked those settlements. The Gush would easily be surrounded and cut off, and the Arab Legion wouldn't need to fire a shot. In due course the Gush's members would have no alternative but to surrender.

"*Sheer madness,*" Amnon thought.

Amnon returned to his headquarters at 8:00pm, when he was notified he had been put in charge of the entire line of defense, including the portion of the line to the south of Mea Shearim. He was told to prepare the defenses to ensure his forces could stop any Arab advance at any cost. The Haganah's chief Jerusalem commander recognized that if the Arabs broke through, they would easily capture the entire business sector of Jerusalem, including the Russian compound. Should that happen, it was going to be anyone's guess as to the fate of Jerusalem and its Jewish population.

The Haganah was spread too thinly in Jerusalem, no question about it. Its major forces had been shifted to the Galilee, Haifa, and Jaffa areas. The clean up had begun, and had to be completed within less than a month. The constant Arab radio announcements certainly helped; Arabs by the thousands were on the move, especially from densely populated areas adjacent to Jewish neighborhoods as well as from many villages in general Jewish areas. By May 15th, all Haganah forces had to be poised to defend the country against the five neighboring nations.

The message Amnon received was loud and clear. But as far as he was concerned, the battle for Jerusalem had begun a long time ago.

Amnon immediately called his deputy and four of his deputy commanders to a meeting, where he explained the circumstances. He outlined the entire length of the eastern frontline, and divided it into four sections. Each deputy commander was to be responsible for one section. The strongest and most experienced unit, Amnon's own, would take charge of the southernmost section, where he believed the Arabs would mount their main assault. Amnon instructed Yaakov, his deputy, that he was now in charge of Amnon's unit. The discussion then turned to how to coordinate action between the four sections, as well as communications in general.

Since they did not have wireless radios, Amnon had to find a way to communicate in the event an attack by Arabs on any one of the sections. They did have a lot of flare guns. Amnon could never understand where they got the flares -- they were just there. That led them to decide on colors. Each section was designated a color. Amnon made everyone learn the colors and sections by heart. If a section were being attacked one flare would be shot up. If the attackers number more than 100, two flares would be shot up. Two of the northern sections, the Beit Israel and Sanhedriah quarters were fairly close, and men in any of those sections could observe each other. Should an assault take place during the daytime, which was more typical of the Arabs, it could be observed from at least three sections. The two southern sections were in densely populated areas, and one section couldn't see the other, despite the relatively short distance between them.

Amnon also instructed each section to send one man as soon as it was dark to crawl across the no man's land as close as possible to the Ramallah road, and take notes of anything that moved; vehicles, men, artillery, police, etc. That man was to return to his base before sunrise, and report to Amnon in person if he detected any questionable movement. During the day, the men on duty were to take notes of any military or police movement on the road, as well as the entire territory east of the road, as far as they could see.

When all matters pertaining to the three northern sections were concluded Amnon turned the discussion to the new addition to his command, namely, the southern section. He drew the streets, the surrounding buildings, the Russian compound, and the schools on a piece of paper and marked the locations of known Arab bunkers.

"The girl's school complex will be the enemy's route of attack," Amnon told them. "It's the only place that makes sense from a strategic point of view. British officers command the Arabs forces. We know that a large no-man's-land lies between the Old City and Yemin Moshe, which is like a fortress. We also know that moving military forces through the Old City is entirely impossible. If they do use such a route, our forces would annihilate any such attacking force from a distance. An assault at that location would be suicidal."

"The Arabs need to capture the Russian compound and downtown Jerusalem to be able to declare victory. Therefore, they'll first choose a route that won't be seen by us, and second, one that is the shortest distance to the Russian compound. If they break through our lines at the girl's school, they'll be inside the Russian compound in less than thirty minutes. The school grounds are the most logical area for an assault."

"The rest of the area is densely residential, and attacking through residential buildings would turn the battle into house to house combat, which would slow down their assault and not meet with their objective of a swift capture. Furthermore, the Arabs have been building attack bunkers where they can easily install short-range artillery. Once they captured the school, they'd be on the road to the Russian compound. Therefore, we must prepare our plan for defense of this section, as their failure would be our success."

"Here's what we'll do. We'll take over the two houses immediately to the right and left of the school. The residents of these two houses will have to be abducted and taken elsewhere if they don't leave on their own. We'll fly Arab flags on them so hopefully they won't be bombarded. We'll put up minimal defense on the school grounds proper, and after a heavy softening bombardment, when their infantry attacks, we'll trap them in the middle, in the open school yard. We'll build up our defense in such a way that the Arabs will suspect nothing. Once their infantry is inside the rear yard of the school, which I call the ambush zone, we won't stop our heavy firing from both sides until their entire attacking force has been eliminated."

"Realizing what has happened, the British officers commanding the Arab forces will then focus their artillery on both houses. By then we'll be attacking their bunkers. In fact, as soon as the ambush has been completed, one of our units will pursue the rest of the retreating Arabs. As soon as these men have reached the end of the yard, they'll drop to the ground and prepare for a new Arab offensive. When it comes, which in my estimation will occur within an hour or less, our men will cut them down before they even start."

"During that time, some of our men will have climbed to the second floor of the school, most of which will probably be destroyed during the first bombardment, and fire from above at the second wave of attackers. It's going to be a bloody battle, but we must destroy their morale and we must win."

"Above all, we will have stopped their advance on Jerusalem." Amnon concluded.

Amnon was then asked for a timetable, if he had any; he responded that they still had some time. No major attack would occur before the British left Jerusalem. He also reiterated that much spying was still needed and that he himself would attend to some of the more complicated spy work.

Wednesday, April 14, 1948

The road that led to the school could still be traveled by anyone. Dressed in plain clothing that any Arab youth might wear, Amnon strolled along the street toward Barclays Bank, located on one side of the square from which the road continued downward toward the Jaffa Gate in the Old City of Jerusalem. Other streets connected to that square, one of them was the street the girl's school was on. Amnon walked into the bank, and sought a neighbor of his parents who actually lived above his parents' apartment in Rehavia. He had worked for Barclays Bank for many years. He was very happy to see Amnon, and they chatted for a while. Amnon asked him to tell his parents he was OK, but had no time to visit.

Amnon pretended to make a banking transaction, walked out of the bank, and retraced his steps back to Mea Shearim. He took keen note of every house, corner, yard, telephone and electric wires, as well as street signs. Amnon noticed a lot of activity at the school. As he passed by the houses next door to it, he paused, and looked in as best he could. Those were the private residences of wealthy Christian Arabs. There were few people walking on the sidewalks. An occasional public bus or taxi passed by, and very few cars.

Not too far away was an Abyssinian Church and an Abyssinian vendor was standing at the corner selling hot peanuts over a portable stove. Stopping for a moment, Amnon bought a bag of peanuts and chatted with that poor salesman for a minute. Thinking the Abyssinian Church would be a great place to operate from at night, Amnon returned to his unit, found a place to rest, and took a nap.

Amnon

He needed to be fresh, as that night he planned to take another stroll through Arab territory.

Taking his fluent Arabic-speaking man with him, both of them dressed casually but holding the headdresses in their hands, they began their stroll just as the sun set. A few people were walking home from work. As they neared the girls' school, they ducked into a small alley and put on their headdresses. Emerging about five minutes later, and seeing no one, they walked casually with a few short stops here and there straight to the school entrance where the gate stood invitingly open.

An old caretaker was cleaning the backyard, and Amnon's comrade engaged him in brief conversation. The backyard was quite long with a large soccer field and other games facilities. At the very end was a fence, and numerous trees ringed the property. Beyond the fence, they could see the narrow street through which Amnon had recently passed. There was no activity; obviously the Arabs did all their preparation work at night. Deciding to leave his comrade there to observe what happened later on at night, Amnon returned to the street, where he once again walked in the direction of the Old City.

The sun had set, and darkness was fast descending; few stars were in the sky, and the moon hadn't yet risen, which pleased him, for he'd hoped for a dark night. After ascertaining no one was around, Amnon jumped one of the residential homes' fences, and quietly slipped eastward to begin his stroll in a strictly Arab neighborhood. This narrow street was just a little lower than the one he'd come from, and Amnon doubted he could be seen from the street above.

"*If the Arabs were to use short-range cannons from that location, they would mostly hit the second floor of the school building,*" Amnon concluded.

When Amnon passed by, work was already in progress. A small truck delivered hundreds of jute bags filled with dirt or sand, and men were placing the bags in bunker forms. Another group of men were covering the bunkers with camouflage netting. It looked to Amnon like the bunkers were completed. He continued walking south until he reached Damascus Gate, seeing no military preparations except for those in the area behind the school, nor any other suspicious activity.

Amnon walked back, and by the time he reached the bunkers, all the working men had gone. Looking around, he noticed a few people who had passed him earlier were walking up on one of the narrow sidewalks. As soon as Amnon was sure nobody saw him, he crossed over and ducked into the compound behind the bunkers. No one was there.

There were six bunkers altogether about ten meters apart. He entered the center one, and took a good look at the darkened school; the dark night didn't help. But forcing his eyes to focus in better, he finally saw the second floor of the school building, and the very upper portion of the first floor. That, he calculated, meant no more than one meter from the bottom of the second floor would be a likely target for cannon or gunfire.

Amnon was just about to leave when two command cars pulled to a stop on the street near a bunker. Quickly, he jumped out and hid behind a tree in the back, from which he saw three Arab officers and two civilians approaching one of the bunkers. The civilians spoke German. The Arabs apparently understood them, and Amnon was dumbfounded, to say the least.

They took measurements of the bunker, particularly its depth, and the Germans told the Arabs they needed to make it longer so that cannons would be able to work properly. They made markings in one bunker, and told the Arabs to repeat the enlargement in all of them. The moment they left, Amnon crawled out of hiding, and swiftly retraced his steps away from there.

He was now; more strongly convinced than ever that the Arabs planned to attack Jerusalem from here. Before leaving the area to meet with his commander, Amnon met with the man he'd left talking with the caretaker of the schoolyard. He'd seen exactly what Amnon saw, though obviously hadn't heard anything.

Apart from Amnon's short visit to the Arab sector, there was no other activity. Amnon's men who had gone to spy in all other sectors had nothing to report. Amnon instructed them to continue spying nightly until further notice.

Amnon reported last night's discoveries to his commander, emphasizing the German-speaking civilians. Yoav told Amnon the Haganah had amassed evidence that some German Nazis who had escaped from Europe at the end of the war were helping the Arabs.

"*Just great*," Amnon thought. "*The British, who with the other Allies defeated the Nazis, are now working together with renegade Nazis to eliminate the Jews in Palestine.*"

Yoav asked Amnon whether he'd formulated a plan of defense, to which he responded by outlining his plan. Yoav liked it a lot, and said he'd support it all the way. They concluded Amnon should continue his espionage until as close as possible to May 15th unless the British left Jerusalem sooner. Amnon also shared his plan to abduct the Arab Christian families who lived in the houses adjoining the school a few days before hostilities broke out, for he didn't want them to be hurt. Yoav assured Amnon they would be transferred to a safe place and held until the end of the war.

Friday, April 16, 1948

The last two nights were almost identical. When it got dark, Amnon crossed the line and hid behind the bunkers. However, he discovered a better route to his hiding place, where he spent over six hours. Every night, as it got darker, two teams of Arab soldiers led by one of the officers Amnon had seen a few nights ago arrived and were put to work. The bunkers were made longer, and heavy bags of dirt were used to reinforce the already existing walls. Several trucks brought in more bags, the work was completed by 3:00am, and the soldiers left with the last truck. Since they hadn't left anyone to guard the bunkers, Amnon walked over and took a good look at what had been done. Basically, they had lengthened walls in each bunker, and fortified them with two rows of dirt bags. Thinking, that they must be feeling very secure to leave this place unguarded, Amnon left and headed back to base.

It took him much longer to return to base that night because British military traffic was heavy towards the small hours of the morning. One convoy after another passed by, and Amnon wondered why they chose that particular narrow road to drive through. Had he been wearing a British uniform, Amnon would have jumped on one of the trucks, for he was very curious to learn what sort of cargo they were moving.

The reports Amnon received from his other sectors revealed that the convoys came down from Ramallah, followed the route to the Old City, and then must have turned east to Trans-Jordan, for there had been no report of British convoys from any other source.

Sunday, April 18, 1948

Amnon was informed that two battalions, one Arab and the other Druz, had attacked Kibbutz Ramat Yohanan. The attack was repulsed with heavy losses to the attacking forces. The leadership of the Haganah met with top Druz men, and a pact was signed whereby the Druz agreed not to fight alongside the Arabs. That was a major victory for the Yishuv, insofar as the Druz had never before displayed any hostility toward the Jews. The Arabs who promised the Druz a lot of booty must have motivated this attack. But they had quickly learned the hard way that it wasn't easy to fight the Jews.

The Haganah mounted a new operation to open the road to Jerusalem successfully enough to permit several supply convoys to get through to Jerusalem. But it was anyone's guess how long the luxury of having an open road would last, for it was extremely difficult to guard a thirty kilometer stretch of road when the Haganah's forces were so thinly spread across the country. Operation Tiberias was successfully completed. All Arab residents had fled, and all sectors of the city were in Jewish hands. Heavy fighting was reported in Jaffa and Haifa.

Tuesday, April 20, 1948

The road to Jerusalem was again blocked, and convoys had to turn back. But great news was reported from Haifa. Arab forces were defeated, and the entire city was in Jewish hands.

Night after night, after dark, Amnon slipped through the lines to his hiding place. Finally, last night, there had been different action in the bunkers. Numerous trucks arrived, and soldiers began to unload cannon shells, which they laid neatly in rows, one row on top of another, at some distance behind each bunker. When the entire delivery was completed, the piles of shells were covered with netting, and two guards were left at each bunker.

Because of the guards, Amnon had to find another return route to his base. Zigzagging between houses, he jumped fences, hiding behind a stone wall whenever he saw someone, and finally made it back to base. In the morning meeting with his commander both agreed the original concept of the probable Arab plan of attack was correct.

"I think you should blow up the entire area," Yoav suggested.

"Not a good idea," Amnon objected. "I can blow up these bunkers and their supplies, but if we do, the Arabs will rebuild elsewhere, and we won't know in time where. Here, we know exactly where they are, and pretty much what they plan to do. The more we know about their plan of action, the better our chance of preparing ourselves and defeating them."

"I'll have to discuss this with the chief Jerusalem commander," Yoav said. "There are other issues that must be considered. Let's meet again tomorrow morning, same time, same place, and I'll let you know what he says. "

Thursday, April 22, 1948

Apparently, the chief Jerusalem commander agreed with Amnon -- no action to be taken against the bunkers, just preparation, readiness for the attack, and a concise defense plan accompanied by an equally concise offensive.

"If the attacking forces are defeated and humiliated, not only will Jerusalem be saved, but we'll also have sufficient time and energy to deal with other problem areas around the City," was the message given Amnon.

Obviously, Amnon was not familiar with the total defense plan for Jerusalem, but knew his own territory inside and out. And, he thought, "*If every section commander around the City of Jerusalem knows his sector as well as I do, we will do well.*"

Last night, at the bunkers, more trucks arrived. Hundreds of two and six-pounder cannon shells capable of piercing steel and concrete were unloaded. It was abundantly clear that the Arab command planned to minimize damage to nearby Arab buildings by using those cannons. Two and six-pounder shells, shot from a short distance, would devastate their targets, and the frightful noise level would demoralize any soldier.

There were more pressing developments to which Amnon had to attend, and as he didn't plan to return to his hiding place after that night, Amnon took a man with him to show him the way, and told him to continue spying on the bunker activity in his stead. Much greater activity was reported at the Mea Shearim police station, and a number of tanks were seen parked around the streets behind the station.

Amnon immediately recognized these to be British-made Sherman tanks that had successfully routed the Germans during the final phase of the Second World War. Knowing his side had nothing more powerful or strong than armored cars, he knew he'd need to rethink his defense strategy for that area. Unfortunately for the Haganah, armored cars were not built to fend off assaults by Sherman tanks.

Only three streets in the Mea Shearim sector were wide enough to accommodate the tanks, and those three streets faced the Mea Shearim police station, so Amnon called the man in charge of the Mea Shearim sector to a meeting in which they fully discussed the matter. Amnon's instructions were explicit and concise.

"Molotov cocktails are the most devastatingly effective weapon we have, especially when used in specific circumstances and from short distances. Therefore, dozens must be prepared, and held in readiness at every guard post at every corner of these three streets."

"I also want all residents of those corner buildings removed by May 10th, quietly, at night, and in total darkness, to avoid alerting either the Arabs or the police force across the street."

"Families may take one suitcase each, no furniture or other possessions. All power and water in the buildings must be turned off. Anyone who refuses to leave must be forcefully removed. The last thing we need is civilians around during a battle."

So far, the only signs of activity behind the scenes were at the girls' school and the police station. The sectors north of the police station were quiet, and Amnon hoped they'd remain that way.

He arranged to meet with all sector commanders at 8:30pm at the Beit Israel synagogue, updating them on their position, and issued explicit instructions for the impending battle.

"The road to Jerusalem is again cut off, and the City is under siege. Our supplies are limited, and we must make do with what we have," Amnon bluntly advised. "We must fight and repel the enemy, no matter what. From now on you and your men must stay on the fullest alert day and night."

"I've also learned we'll have to fight tanks. Our intelligence service has reported the Arabs have fewer than a dozen tanks. Considering the length of the frontline, a dozen tanks will neither make nor break the war. However, streets are narrow, and a tank will take up the entire width of the street, and there will also be men marching behind the tanks."

"We're used to fighting from close range. So when a tank is no more than two meters away, you will throw Molotov cocktails at it while also throwing hand grenades at the soldiers marching behind it."

"In a sense, we'll have the advantage, because we'll be operating through windows in lower and upper floors. As a tank passes by, one man should throw Molotov cocktails under the body of the tank, and another on top of it from the building stairway entrance or from behind the fence-wall. As soon as the tank is disabled, start firing at the Arab soldiers behind it, and they'll run for their lives. If you're unable to disable the tank, start firing at the enemy as soon as you see their soldiers."

A great deal of nerve was required to attack a passing tank from such a short distance, and Amnon strongly repeated some of his previous orders. "You must have nerves of steel to sit and wait until the tank is right under your nose, or next to your position. However, should a tank manage to pass through, you must immediately ambush the infantry behind it with hand grenades and fire. You'll have the advantage – you'll be inside the building and the enemy will be visible on the street. However, the main thing you have to concentrate on is to make sure the enemy doesn't see any of you at any time during the day. I want the Arabs to think we've fled the area or that we have no defenses here. If you must move, then do so only at night when it's dark, and absolutely don't use the streets. Walk through the back yards until where you cross the street is completely out of their sights.

"The doorways and street-level windows must be locked and guarded at all times, except those you're operating from. Clear?"

"Yes Sir," They said in unison, and Amnon let them return to their own sectors.

Walking back to his men at the school, Amnon considered the possibilities. "If a tank did pass by itself in a narrow street or even in an open space, it couldn't do much good, especially if the men marching behind it were killed."

In the daily meetings Amnon held with his sector commanders, they worked together to ensure no stone was left unturned. Carefully, they covered every centimeter of territory, every path, road, and street. They drew lines of defense and locations for defense in case they had to retreat. But so far the only enemy activities were at the same two known locations. The Arab Legion was still busy at Gush Etzion, which was outside the City boundary.

The nightly spying missions continued unabated. By then Amnon had all the information he needed about the families who lived next door to the school, including their daily habits. Due to local conditions, everyone was home by the time the sun had set.

Friday, April 30, 1948

Palestine's atmosphere seemed to be heating up as the British Government began to prepare for their big exodus. A great deal of activity could be seen throughout the Russian Compound complex. Most surprisingly, very little was actually being taken out of the buildings. Civilians, policemen, and soldiers ran back and forth, but there didn't appear to be any transfer of archives, nor were any trucks seen loading anything except for an occasional box or two. Surely the British Government had buildings filled with archives, files, and all sorts of documents by the thousands. Amnon thought it most peculiar that none appeared to be moving out.

Having been alerted that the British would leave all their installations in Palestine to the Arabs, Amnon posted a man to watch the compound from the eastern side, since the compound was so close to his southern sector. Yoav posted a team to watch the western side. Despite all the moving preparations, the Yishuv's leadership received not a single communication whatsoever regarding the impending transfer of offices, military barracks, water and power installations, or anything else under British control.

Through their Arab contacts, the Haganah's intelligence service found out the British planned to deliver all of their Palestine possessions to Arab civilians. It was infuriatingly obvious that, as far as the British were concerned, the Jews in Palestine did not exist. That helped firm Amnon's standing belief that the British didn't really plan to leave Palestine. They just planned to make an official departure for the United Nations' sake and for the world to see. Then, on that day, the armies of the Arab Legion as well as of all countries surrounding Palestine would attack and capture the country. At that point, British military forces stationed in Egypt would rush in to save the day, thus bringing the British back into the picture.

Doubtless, the British figured the Arabs would massacre most of the Jews and those left would be too weak to amount to anything. Immigration of survivors would stop, and those detained in Cyprus and elsewhere would be shipped back to Europe. As hard as Amnon tried to find another scenario, he

Amnon

failed. The British must have been convinced that the Arab armies, standing ready to invade Palestine after the British departed, would invade what they believed to be an unwary country, and win the war against the Jews.

"How little they know of our resolve to create a Jewish Homeland." Amnon mused. *"How little they know of our strong idealism, and the determined spirit we're all imbued with. They neither know or care that all of us carry in our very souls the pain and suffering of six million Jewish men, women, and children who were tortured, killed and burned by the Nazis."*

"Obviously, the British knew nothing of the idealism and spirit of the ancient Maccabees. That same strength and spirit makes us today one nation fiercely united in thought and aspiration. Without such knowledge, they can't know that deep in all our hearts and souls, we are all the modern reincarnation of those historical warriors, determined that the British and the Arabs will fail, and us win, and we will have our own Jewish Homeland right here in the Land of Israel, the land that is rightfully ours because it is the land of our ancestors."

His thoughts having gotten the best of him, Amnon once again focused on the present situation. He was so involved with only a small part of the defense of the City of Jerusalem that he lacked first-hand information of what was happening in the rest of Palestine. Though he wanted so much to know everything and be everywhere, obviously this wasn't possible. He listened avidly to the Haganah's radio broadcasts whenever he could, as well as those of the official radio station. He had to be content that he received most of his information when he met with his commanding officers.

Latest reports said British military forces had tried unsuccessfully to stop the Haganah forces' determined advance into Jaffa, and that the Haganah had forcefully captured all Arab villages that surrounded Jaffa. Thus Jaffa was completely cut off, and the Arabs living in Jaffa were allowed to evacuate if they wanted to. But most had fled following announcements made by neighboring Arab radio stations. That meant two major cities, Jaffa and Haifa, were in the hands of Jews.

Amnon's inspection tour of the positions along his entire line of responsibility, particularly those guard posts and buildings on the corners of each street joining the Mea Shearim intersection as well as the buildings along the streets, disclosed that dozens of Molotov cocktails and grenades were already on hand. All windows were locked, some curtained, and during the day, from a distance, nobody could see anything. From time to time, a tenant went shopping, or someone else either went out to or returned from work. Very few civilians could be seen; most residents in the area had already left. Only a few stubborn residents remained. Most buildings in the general area appeared to be normally quiet and peaceful.

One building at a time, Amnon called a meeting of the tenants in the corner buildings who hadn't left, and advised them of the need for them to vacate their apartments at a moment's notice, and that it would be best for them to leave by the 10th of May, for he would not risk their lives, nor risk having civilians running around when hostilities erupted. Fortunately, most of the tenants understood, but a few refused to leave. To these, Amnon bluntly stated they

229

either left of their own free will, or they'd be forcefully removed. He also advised everybody to take one or two suitcases, which should be packed and ready, since there might not be time for him to give them any advance notice.

The nightly spy reports from the front line continued without change. There had been no Arab activity, except for that seen east of the school. Amnon met with his appointed school spy, who was fluent in Arabic and looked every inch an Arab, and instructed him to penetrate deeper into Arab territory; he needed to know what was going on to the east of the known site, which they couldn't see.

"Go further east. Circle as much territory as you can, but be sure to return after midnight," Amnon instructed him.

"It might be better if I spend the day there too to get a better feel for things," he suggested.

"Very good idea," Amnon agreed. Knowing the Arab headdress would obscure the man's features, Amnon made sure he had enough money for food, and sent him on his way with his blessing.

Amnon's next stop was Sanhedriah, the last post to the north, beyond which there were only high hills, many fields, and deep valleys. That entire area was uninhabited. While in Sanhedriah, Amnon instructed one of the men on night duty to crawl north, in addition to the man who was spying on the eastern front. He instructed him to follow the same routine every night until further notice. Amnon also left instructions that he should be advised immediately of any activity in the Police Academy building, because that was the largest British installation of its kind in the country and in the immediate vicinity of Sanhedriah.

Amnon was too wired with everything at stake. His responsibilities were far greater than himself. *"We are such a small force,"* he thought, *"While in every assault the Arabs have mounted against Jewish settlements and towns the attackers numbered in the hundreds. Moreover, we lack a normal supply line and enough supplies."*

But despite their having so little, and needing to count virtually every spent bullet, Amnon had confidence in himself and his men, knowing they were better trained. Besides, Amnon knew in his heart they had the strength of their sworn mission in life, a mission that had eluded the Jews for 2000 years. Unconsciously, Amnon's shoulders squared and he walked a little taller as he told himself, *"Not only will we fight, but we must and shall win this war! Two more weeks, and the British will leave Palestine, which means two more weeks of unmitigated anxiety for the entire Yishuv and our fighting men in particular."*

Sunday, May 2, 1948

Amnon was informed the Haganah had conquered the entire upper Galilee, and was marching on Safed. This great news made him feel very good.

"Slowly but surely we're consolidating our hold on territories where we have major settlements. When Safed is cleared of Arabs, most of the Galilee will be ours and free. The major enemy to watch is the Syrian army, as it would descend upon us from the heights of the Golan," Amnon told his men.

He also learned that at their request, many Arabs were evacuated from

Haifa, though many others chose to stay, but those would pose no problem. Jaffa's Arab population had completely abandoned the city, the British had also left, and the city was in the hands of the Haganah. The Arabs had also evacuated a number of sectors in Jerusalem, particularly of interest, the suburban community of Katamon.

Because Haganah forces were spread so thinly, a long meeting at Haganah headquarters discussed extensively the need to recruit men and women of 50 years and older to serve as guards. Those projected recruits, to be called 'Mishmar Haam' [guardians of the nation] would serve as back-up men, messengers, deliver supplies, drive cars requisitioned by the Haganah, and guard all the buildings expected to be captured from the Arabs. The moment those properties were turned over to the Arabs by the British, it was planned that two active units would storm the Russian compound complex, as well as all other British Government offices and installations and capture them. The men and women of Mishmar Haam would then take over, freeing the fighting men to return to the front.

Units were assigned to each building, and every person knew in advance exactly where he or she would go. The Haganah planned to capture the entire area up to the Barclays Bank Square, and the command learned that members of Lehi would liberate the street and surrounding buildings all the way to Jaffa Gate.

"If this can be achieved, we'll control the entire line from Sanhedriah in the north all the way to Jaffa Gate at the Old City," the commander in chief stated.

As of that date, the Haganah's intelligence service had no information about any attack on Jewish Jerusalem, other than the girls' school where Amnon's units were already planted. Anxiously, Amnon thought of his Arab-look-alike spy who had gone deep into Arab territory. *"Just what sort of information has he learned,"* Amnon wondered, *"And how quickly will he bring it back? Our intelligence service and I need to know as much as possible about what's going on deep inside Arab territory, and as soon as possible."*

The armies of the Arab Legion were pounding away at Gush Etzion. This distant group of three settlements, way east of Jerusalem, was a thorn in the Arabs' sides, and it was very important to them to capture the Gush. Unfortunately, being so deep in Arab territory, they were out of the reach of the Haganah, which couldn't send any help. The Gush was under total siege, and sooner or later, they'd have to give up. Amnon always believed it was a senseless mistake to establish Jewish settlements in that area. But, sad as it was, the prolonged fighting and final fall of Gush Etzion to the Arab Legion would help delay the Legion's advance on Jerusalem.

That night Amnon again visited all the posts at the corners of Mea Shearim intersection, chatted with the men, and made sure they all had food and enough supplies. Amnon always reviewed every possible means of Arab attack and how best to defend his positions. Though he hated to discuss possible retreat, it was absolutely necessary, for a disorganized retreat would be disastrous.

Having marked out rows of buildings behind each post and other locations, he outlined each step of a retreat. Knowing every building, every door and every window throughout the area, he also planned counter-attacks, and how to conduct house-to-house combat that would give them an edge. Satisfied that every unit was fully prepared, Amnon went on to inspect the other northern sectors.

Tuesday, May 4, 1948

After two days and two nights deep in Arab territory, Amnon's Arab-look-alike spy returned with a load of vitally important information. Just outside the rear residential area east of the girls' school and out of their sight, several armored jeeps, each with a two or six-pounder cannon in tow, were parked on a dirt road. It was obvious there was one cannon for each of the bunkers. But even more disturbing was his report of heavy artillery cannons in the valley below.

The Haganah didn't possess any artillery to speak of, and its latest invention, the Davidka, was no match for any artillery in existence. Furthermore, the Haganah had no more than one or two Davidkas available for use in Jerusalem, none available on Amnon's frontline. The heavy artillery cannons, which were long-range and poised about one kilometer away from the girl's school, would have no appreciable affect on the front. It was obvious, however, that the British had given the Arabs long-range artillery and the Arabs planned to bombard the City of Jerusalem.

Amnon reported the existence and location of the artillery to his commanding officers, and was informed that there had been reports of heavy artillery as far as Ramallah to the north. The command, however, did not make much of the artillery problem, for they believed it would have little or no affect on the frontline fighting. Unfortunately, the general population would suffer most when shells land. It was later learned that most of the Arab heavy artillery were British-made product that fired 25-pounder shells.

It was decided not to do anything about the artillery, because the main objective was to repel and crush the Arabs' great offensive on Jerusalem. It was, therefore, of the utmost importance that they believe the Haganah had no knowledge of their plans.

As always, Amnon toured all positions in the area almost every day. His men reported that many Arab residents were already on the move.

Whole families were seen walking away, or driving away with a lot of luggage. Amnon had his men make an inventory of houses that were vacated. He was sure that when hostilities erupted, whoever was left would run for their lives. The families in the houses on both sides of the school were still there.

Jerusalem was completely cut off, and had been without a single supply convoy for days. The main road from Tel Aviv was blocked by massive amounts of rocks. Haganah engineers were already busy planning the alternate route to Jerusalem. But nobody knew how, where, or precisely when the manpower for such a project would be found, although the Yishuv did have lots of men and women over 50 who'd willingly become involved. Amnon was glad to hear such a project was on the Haganah drawing board.

The Yishuv's leadership knew Jerusalem must survive, no matter what;

Amnon

if Jerusalem were to fall to the Arabs, such a catastrophe would devastate the entire Yishuv, and all the world's Jewry. The Haganah, and Amnon in particular, knew the fight for Jerusalem was unquestionably the most critical of the entire impending war, and they were determined that the battle for Jerusalem must be won.

Friday, May 7, 1948

One of the Arab families who lived next to the school left yesterday. Two Arab cabs arrived about noon, and picked up the entire family with many suitcases and boxes. Both cabs were packed to the brim. Having decided he could wait no longer for the other family to move on its own, Amnon noted the cab company's telephone number and called for two cabs to come to the second house at 5:00pm. Then, dressed in Arab clothing with headdresses covering their heads, Amnon and two of his men waited on the sidewalk just a few meters from the house.

As soon as the cabs arrived, Amnon approached the drivers and asked them to come in and help with the luggage. They rang the doorbell, and the man of the house, who opened the door, tried to ask what they wanted. But before he could say much, Amnon and his men pointed their guns at him, and got the entire family out into the entry foyer. They were seven in all, husband, wife, four children of different ages, and an old maid. After tying the taxi drivers and the maid together on the floor, Amnon explained they were taking them away for their own safety, and they had no intention of harming them.

Then, they piled the family into the two cabs and they were driven off to one of the Haganah's safe houses. From there they were taken to a Haganah prison where they would be safely held until the end of the war. Amnon quickly returned to the house where he'd left one of his men to watch the two cabdrivers and the maid. When Amnon walked in, he found his man sitting on a stool with his gun drawn. Taking the two drivers and the maid, the cabs made another trip. These three were placed in another location. The cars were taken to a Haganah garage where they got a face-lift and new plates. Amnon wasn't in the least concerned about the disappearance of the cabdrivers. In those days a great number of people, particularly Arabs, were evacuating their homes and running away to join the heavy traffic into Trans-Jordan.

Two of Amnon's elite units moved into the newly vacated houses in the dark of night. The layout of the houses was studied carefully, particularly those windows facing on the schoolyard. Using the furniture, they built up the needed support and cover. And since all windows had curtains, they made sure there was some light in the houses so they wouldn't appear abandoned. Amnon brought in two Haganah women fighters who posed as Arab women. They went shopping for groceries, and hung laundered linen and shirts on the line so that both houses looked absolutely normal.

Monday, May 10, 1948

Amnon couldn't have been more delighted when he received word from his commander that the entire Galilee was in the hands of the Haganah. The city of Safed as well was cleared of its Arab inhabitants. The Arab city of Beisan was also captured. Jaffa and Haifa were already under Jewish control. The plan was being well implemented, and though the Haganah would have more than enough frontlines in the war which was about to break, at least they didn't have to worry about being stabbed in the back. On the other hand, news from Gush Etzion was bleak. The Gush would not be able to hold out much longer against the Arab Legion's merciless attacks.

Additionally, the Jewish sector inside the Old City was under heavy fire and completely surrounded by the Arab Legion. They, too, had no chance of surviving. Haganah intelligence reported that Egyptian, Syrian, Lebanese and Iraqi troops were on the move toward Palestinian borders. The Jordanian Arab Legion was already inside Palestine and fighting. The British Government didn't bother to advise the United Nations of those massive invading armies waiting for May 15th to pounce on Palestine.

Friday, May 14, 1948

The British left Jerusalem, and Haganah forces captured the entire Russian Compound, as well as all other office buildings and installations from the Arabs. In fact, the British had barely left when artillery bombardment of Jerusalem began, with shells falling all over the city. Amnon, on the front line, could hear the firing and then the whistling of every flying shell followed by its impact explosion.

Heavy firing was directed at Mea Shearim and the Mandlebaum Street areas. Moderate firing also began on the school building. Amnon's men could see Arab soldiers firing from every window in the police station. As long as the Arabs were just firing, Amnon's instructions to his men were not to fire a single shot back, because in the absence of return fire, not knowing where the opponent was, or indeed if he was there at all would keep the enemy off guard. A large Arab force, which Amnon estimated to be over a hundred men, began moving forward under heavy cover toward Mea Shearim.

Amnon's men let them run through the intersection until they were no more than ten meters away at which point they mounted a barrage of gunfire. Dozens fell, dead or wounded, and the enemy's rear lines retreated in panic. They continued to fire at them until the last man was out of sight. The intersection was littered with bodies. Some of the fallen soldiers were screaming with pain. No one was let through to help. Someone raised a Red Cross flag, obviously with a blind request to allow them to pick up their wounded. Not wanting to take any risks, they too were shot down.

Night fell, and Amnon's men could see bodies being picked up in the darkness. Amnon calculated that while the Arabs were picking up their dead and wounded, he could safely check on his units next to the girls' school. The school and the entire neighborhood were under steady, but, not too heavy-gunfire. Again, the defenders didn't return a single shot. Amnon ran back to the Mea Shearim positions. He could see tanks on the move, but was unable to tell how many soldiers walked behind them.

Turning into Mandlebaum Street, the first of the tanks passed the corner, and was showered from above and underneath with Molotov cocktails. A few grenades were also thrown under its body. A minute later, the tank's gas tank exploded, stopping it in its tracks, and completely blocking the street, all of which Amnon thought made a magnificent view.

Arab soldiers walking behind the tank didn't know what had hit them; most were hit by the fire, some by grenades, and some by the defending gunfire. None survived. Mandelbaum Street was very narrow, and the disabled tank took up all the space, making it the best roadblock Amnon ever saw. It was absolutely perfect! Immediately, the tanks in the rear turned back and disappeared from view. When Amnon climbed to the top of the apartment house and looked north, he saw no action and was glad that at least the northern section was quiet.

Firing on the schoolhouse intensified, but as yet there was no movement of any kind. Amnon desperately wanted to know what was happening elsewhere in the country, but obviously there was no way to find out, as he couldn't leave his area.

"*I'll have to wait until one of my commanders shows up,*" he thought, but knew that was not likely to happen for a few days.

Saturday, May 15, 1948

The British High Commissioner for Palestine left after a small ceremonial party at Haifa harbor. He was taken by a small navy craft to a battleship, which would take him to England. With his official departure, it was said that the British had left the country. That evening, David Ben Gurion, the head of the provisional government set up by the leaders of the Yishuv, declared independence in a general meeting held at the Tel Aviv Museum, and proclaimed the establishment of the State of Israel.

The United States government was the first to recognize the new state. Russia soon followed, as did many other nations.

On May 15th, the armies of four Arab countries invaded the newly established State of Israel: Egypt from the south, Syria and Lebanon from the north, and Iraq from the east. The Jordanian Arab Legion was already fighting inside Palestine. Egyptian warplanes bombarded Tel Aviv, and Jerusalem was under artillery fire night and day.

The Jordanian Arab Legion and other Arab forces fought in the Jerusalem area, and got as far as Latrun, which was on the way to Tel Aviv. It appeared their intention was to block off Jerusalem, as well as give the Arabs an advantage over the territory from the coast to the Jordan River. Syrian and Lebanese forces attacked Jewish settlements in the north, while Egyptian armies captured most of the Negev desert and advanced on two fronts, toward Jerusalem and Tel Aviv from the south.

The Haganah defenders held back the Jordanian, Iraqi, and Syrian forces, while the Egyptians moved rapidly through the desert and southeastern Arab villages and towns toward Jerusalem. In fact, the Egyptian army reached Kibbutz Ramat Rachel, on the outskirts of southern Jerusalem. The kibbutz changed hands a number of times, but finally the Egyptian army was repulsed.

Daniel Rosenfeld

Monday, May 17, 1948

Having captured the Gush Etzion settlements, the Arab Legion armies turned on Jerusalem, and just as Amnon predicted, enormous firepower rained on the girls' school. Two and six pounders came flying in like bees seeking pollen. Heavy machine gun fire didn't stop for a second. Almost all the cannon shells hit the upper floor, and there wasn't a single second without fifty to a hundred shots fired at the building.

It was 5:00pm when the bombardment stopped, and enemy troops began pouring in, firing as they advanced. Amnon and his men didn't fire one shot. Instead, they let them advance as close as ten meters from both houses, then dropped about two dozen grenades on the attackers, followed by a massive barrage of gunfire. The results were stunning. About two hundred Arab soldiers were killed or wounded, and the rest retreated in such panic that many soldiers dropped their guns while running away.

Amnon's men kept peppering the retreating soldiers with fire, and began giving chase until they were almost at the enemy's starting point. Amnon quickly moved one unit into the ground floor of the school building, while two of his units took positions on the ground, right under the enemy's noses. Amnon knew their British officers would mount a counter attack before dark, because he could hear their shouted orders. In less than twenty minutes, there was a new barrage of fire, mostly aimed at the two houses flanking the school as the Legions' officers realized their troops were ambushed. Shells flew right over their heads, and the noise was unbearable. Machine gun fire began at a pace Amnon had never heard or seen before. Their officers didn't realize Amnon and his units were dug in, or half dug in, just a stone's throw away. The barrage continued for over an hour, and then came the renewed infantry assault. As before, Amnon and his men rained grenades on the attacking force and fired at very close range. There was no way to count Arab casualties. This time, however, when they retreated in panic, Amnon's men gave a much longer chase than before, and ran them wild until the last of them were killed, or out of sight.

As soon as they reached their cannon bunkers, they damaged the cannons and blew up the shells, which obviously they couldn't move. Amnon and his men collected every piece of weaponry laying on the ground, as well as every case of ammunition. His biggest take was two powerful machine guns along with dozens of cases of ammunition. Amnon didn't possess a single machine gun of his own, and his most sophisticated automatic rifle was one Bren gun. When silence finally descended on the area, Amnon found it wonderful that he could almost hear himself think. His men suffered two fatalities and a number of wounded, mostly from flying stones hit by shells.

Anticipating the next step, Amnon instructed his men to dig trenches in a zigzag pattern at the far east side of the school grounds. His men used most of the sand bags so conveniently filled and supplied by the Arabs. As soon as they dug the first row of trenches, they proceeded to dig another zigzagged row ten to fifteen meters behind the first, connected to the front trenches at each end. Amnon decided on zigzagged trenches so that in the event of a new assault they'd incur the least number of casualties from hand grenades. Placing a unit of men in

236

each row, Amnon split a unit between the two houses, or rather, what remained of them. The school itself was virtually obliterated.

Though Amnon wondered how long before the Arabs reorganized, and when he could expect another assault, he left his deputy in charge and dashed to the Mea Shearim front. Sniper fire from distant buildings was obviously building up as he streaked through the dangerous openings between houses. His men at the Mea Shearim intersection had repelled two attacks, though they were not under the same intense fire his units had encountered at the girls' school. Their attackers numbered no more than two to three dozen Arabs at a time, and beyond Mea Shearim all the way to Sanhedriah, not one bullet had been fired.

Amnon returned to the girl's school front. The night passed with constant sniper fire. Amnon told his men half of each unit could sleep while the other half stood on watch. But there was no way anyone could sleep. The noise of firing was beginning to intensify as the night went on. Amnon decided not to waste any time, tired or not; he began to set up two locations for the machine guns they'd captured.

Amnon had them set up in the farthest southern and northern corners of the school grounds behind no more than a few dirt filled bags. To camouflage the machine guns, he covered the bags with tree branches which were laying on the ground everywhere, and instructed his men to start firing as soon as the enemy started advancing. Unlike before, they were not to wait until the Arabs were closing in on them.

Dawn was about to break, and firing intensified by the minute. In the distance, Amnon could see a number of armored cars and one tank approaching. A salvo of bullets and shells came flying in. The tank spit its shells directly at the houses and what was left of the school building as fast as its cannon could be loaded while Arab soldiers fired from neighboring housetops. Amnon's men didn't respond, and he told his men in the houses to snipe at the soldiers on rooftops, or soldiers firing at them from windows of nearby buildings. This cat and mouse game continued for a couple of hours. The Arabs had undoubtedly moved some of their artillery pieces located in the eastern valley further east to enable them to shell the school grounds, for their artillery fire began to descend in the area. Fortunately, they didn't score a single direct hit, and their shells landed in a wide area behind their target.

While the battle was going on, unbeknownst to Amnon, four members of Lehi mounted an incredible attack on the Arab section of Jerusalem running down Jaffa Road from Barclays Bank Square all the way to the Jaffa Gate in the Old City of Jerusalem, mainly a business district with shops and businesses on both sides of the street. The four Lehi fighters fought house to house until the entire balance of Jaffa road was cleared of all Arab forces. As the area was cleared, older Haganah men and Mishmar Haam men and women took positions to guard the new territory. As Amnon and his men were holding the eastern perimeter on his front line, so were all other Haganah units holding their lines all around the other Jerusalem frontlines.

Firepower against Amnon's men began to increase at an alarming rate. It was almost impossible to raise your head off the ground, or peek out any opening in the neighboring houses. Amnon knew another assault was due any minute. All this time, the machine guns hadn't fired a single shot, and their location was still unknown to the Arabs. The barrage kept intensifying, and once more the noise level grew so intense that Amnon thought his eardrums would explode.

Minutes later, a new assault rang in the new day. The newly acquired machine guns sprayed the oncoming infantry relentlessly. Amnon and his men fired from every single trench they had dug in the schoolyard, as did his men from behind windows or any opening in the remnants of destroyed walls. His men in the front trenches threw grenades, as well as fielding them.

Screaming and shouting as they advanced, the Arabs poured in only to be felled left and right, yet on they kept coming. When they passed the first row of trenches, Amnon could see hand-to-hand fighting as a number of Arab soldiers jumped into the trenches. The second row and the rest of his men were responding with everything they had. The Arab soldiers were approaching the second row with one of them getting ready to throw a hand grenade. He was killed before his arm flew up, and the grenade exploded in his hand, seriously wounding a number of his comrades. A few Arabs leaped into the trenches and brief bayonet-to-bayonet fights ensued as they were killed one by one.

Amnon could see their lines thinning out, and the Arab commanding officer must have realized it, too. When an attacking force realizes its attack has fizzled is the most important and vital moment for the defending side. Amnon seized that moment, and shouted at his men to jump out of the trenches and attack the remaining Arabs face to face. The sight of so many corpses from the previous night and following morning added to the fear of the last Arab attackers as they turned tail and ran in every direction.

A wild and disorganized retreat is the best sight a defending army can watch. Amnon and his men kept firing at the escaping Arabs until none could be seen. Amnon hated shooting people in the back; it seemed so ungentlemanly. But that was war, and it was a war he had not initiated. They had to defend themselves and their homeland in that war, which he absolutely had to win.

Amnon had barely shouted instructions to remove his small number dead and wounded comrades, when one of his men from the Mea Shearim unit came running up urgently asking him to hurry to Mea Shearim Street. Hundreds of Hasidim, (ultra orthodox Jews) had begun a march from the other side of Mea Shearim, and were vociferously denouncing the State of Israel as they marched on toward the Arab front.

They had to have been barking mad, the lot of them!

Mea Shearim was a narrow street, just about 5 meters wide. He shouted final instructions to his men to move the machine guns to different locations, get medical help for the wounded and remove the fallen fighters, then ran between buildings as Arab artillery continued to rain down on the city. The moment he arrived at the center of Mea Shearim Street, via an even narrower side street, he saw that incredible phalanx of hundreds of Hassidim marching toward the Mea Shearim intersection, all cursing the newly established Jewish State and shouting such blatant insanities as, "We're better off with the Arabs!"

Amnon couldn't believe his eyes. But knowing the Messiah had not yet come, nor was likely to in the next ten minutes; if those insane Hassidim were not to be massacred by the Arabs some extraordinary quick thinking was a vital necessity. Somehow Amnon had to stop them in their tracks, but his lone voice couldn't possibly overpower their multitudinous voices.

First Amnon instructed two of his men to fire over their heads and into the ground in front of them. When they continued to march on, Amnon instructed his men to fire at the walls on both sides of the street immediately next to them. When ricocheting bullets and concrete chips showered down on them, they realized Amnon was dead serious, and stopped their march.

An odd, somewhat shocked, silence ensued as that yarmulked multitude in their long black coats over black trousers finally stood listening to what Amnon quite literally screamed at them.

"If you do not instantly retreat from this street, in the next moment we will direct our fire at you!" Amnon shouted furiously. Without giving them a chance to think, knowing some of them must have been injured by flying pieces of concrete or possibly by bullets, he plowed on, "I want you to get back, now, and vanish from my sight! Or, so help me, our next bullets are going to hit you!"

Deliberately, Amnon fired again, and this time they retreated, and started walking back where they'd come from. It was a somber sight. Hundreds of men in black moving away in total silence broken only by distant gun fire from the frontline, artillery shots fired at the city, and explosions coming from every direction. Had Amnon not gotten there in time, the Arabs would have mowed down those hundreds of lunatics in cold blood as soon as they arrived at the open intersection.

The fighting was so intense that all the residents of Mea Shearim and Beit Israel fled. Amnon instructed the Mea Shearim unit to attack and capture the police station that night. He also told them to use the endless packages of barbed wire he could see from his side to cover the streets on both sides of the station. Behind the police station, as well as on both sides were many beautiful homes owned by wealthy Arabs. Amnon was certain that by then they had fled too.

Amnon returned to his girl's school sector to find a sort of temporary cease-fire. While he was gone, the firing had stopped suddenly, and a British army officer came forward carrying two flags, a white flag in one hand, a red cross flag in the other. He requested the Arabs be allowed to take their dead and wounded. Amnon's deputy told him that would be acceptable as long as no more than two pairs of men carrying stretchers were on the scene at any one time. He accepted that condition, and returned to his position.

Soon enough, four Arab soldiers appeared with two stretchers, and the removal of their fallen men began. It took about six hours to complete that nasty task. As soon as the last body was removed, the firing began again with a vengeance. Amnon and his men didn't return fire. The enemy's two assaults had ended in total defeat, and Amnon didn't think they'd be foolish enough to try another. However, he instructed his men to remain on full alert.

Bombardment of what was left of the girl's school and neighboring houses continued throughout the night, with not one second that Amnon could have said his eardrums rested. As dawn began to break, that non-stop firing began to relax a bit.

Tuesday, May 18, 1948
The United Nations asked the invading Arab countries to stop the war on the newly established State of Israel. The request was arbitrarily rejected, and the Arab League informed the United Nations it was their intention to dismantle the new State, and the only way they would accept a cease-fire was if the Jews would accept living under Arab control. The leadership of the young state rejected that idea. The American Consul in Jerusalem was killed by an Arab sniper when leaving the offices of the French Consul. Both he and the French Consul had been working on trying to arrange a cease-fire. The news also reported that Russia had recognized the new State of Israel, and that a huge rally in support of Israel was held at Madison Square Garden in New York City.

In and around Israel, fighting was fierce everywhere. Haganah men were fighting the Syrian and Lebanese armies in the north, the Arab Legion and other Arab militias in the center of the country, as well as the Egyptians in the south. The Haganah attacked Latrun, held by the Arab Legion, trying to free the road to Jerusalem, but failed. It was reported the attacking force suffered over 500 casualties.

Recognition of the new State of Israel by the United States and Russia was quickly followed by many European and Latin American member nations. The United Kingdom [Great Britain] was the only nation that kept silent. However, despite the general silence, there were many British politicians who voiced the opinion that the Arab invaders had the right to invade Palestine, and that their action was not an act of aggression.

Another important news item was that the city of Akko, also known as Acre, had surrendered to the Haganah. With that surrender, the entire western Galilee was in Jewish hands.

It was the first time in days that Amnon managed to listen to the radio for a few minutes. The former British broadcasting station in Jerusalem was in the hands of the Yishuv, and it was the most wonderful feeling to listen to the Hebrew news broadcast on that station. In fact, the radio station was no more than a few blocks from where Amnon and his units were holding the line. It was an incredible feeling to hear the female newscaster say: "This is Kol Israel." (This is the Voice of Israel.) Amnon felt his insides jumping with joy. His eyes were tearing.

"Kol Israel. Let the Arabs know that we're here to stay. This City, and this land, is ours. This is our home, to which we have at last returned," Amnon declared.

As reality sank in, Amnon realized the war was far from over. He began hearing explosions and firing to which he'd been oblivious for a few moments. Immediately, he reviewed his position, and decided that very night he'd attack the Arabs who were digging and building all kinds of fortifications.

As soon as night had fallen, while Arab forces were still firing at all houses on the Haganah's side of the front, two of Amnon's units, with newly arrived replacements, began crawling across the small remainder of the school yard. One unit crawled straight ahead, while the other was split into two groups, each inching diagonally to the northern and southern ends of the enemy encampment. Precisely at the scheduled attack time of 10:00pm, Amnon's men attacked the Arabs, who were digging in from all sides.

It was clear the Arab command hadn't anticipated an assault. Amnon and his attacking force dropped two-dozen hand grenades on their newly built bunkers and attacked them head-on in a direct assault lasting about ten minutes. When it was over, the entire area across from the school was in the hands of the Haganah. There wasn't an Arab soldier left there.

Amnon ordered his men to move the machine guns forward to their new location, from which he could see the entire Arab Legion's artillery encampment below in the valley. The artillery was still firing at the city of Jerusalem at large. Apparently they didn't know their front position had been conquered. With the machine guns in place, Amnon lined all his men up on the ground, and at his signal they barraged the artillery post with gunfire.

Not only was the firing heavy, it was a big shocking surprise; the Arab artillerymen didn't know what hit them so suddenly. Leaving a few men to watch his new position, Amnon and the rest of his men cautiously advanced to the enemy artillery post, not knowing if anyone had survived. No one had. Amnon wanted to destroy the cannons, but had no explosives. He asked some of his men to find something sharp to open some of the shells. When they did, they poured the powder next to the pile of unused shells, ran a thin line, and ignited it, then streaked towards their position and dropped to the ground just as thunderous explosions rocked the ground under them. They had the satisfaction of destroying the Arabs' entire supply of shells. Certain their cannons were damaged beyond repair, Amnon sent a few men to check whether there were Arab residents left in any of the surrounding houses.

When they returned with the report that all the houses were abandoned, Amnon rushed a messenger to Haganah headquarters with the news of his success in destroying the artillery post in east Jerusalem, and also that the Arab residents had abandoned the entire area and he needed more men to take charge of the empty houses and stand watch.

The attack on the police station went well too. At precisely 10:00pm, the exact same time as Amnon's assault, the Mea Shearim units attacked the police station. Well over an hour later, while Amnon's men were waging a fierce battle, they captured the police building. Since it stood at the eastern side of the large Mea Shearim intersection, and the entire space between the Haganah's posts and the station was a blacktopped road, there was nowhere to hide, no way to advance unseen. One unit advanced under heavy fire cover by the other unit until the first one penetrated the building. From then on, it was room-to-room, door-to-door fighting until the building was in their hands.

Numerous Arab soldiers surrendered, and since that building was a police station, they locked the captured soldiers into the station's prison cells. Barbed wire packages were opened immediately and row after row of wire stretched across the two roads on either side of the building, until they ran out. In that area, too, Arab residents had abandoned all surrounding houses.

Following the capture of that important building, Amnon's men started to dig in and prepare defenses against a possible counter-attack. Amnon ordered one of his machine guns shifted to the police station building, and it was placed at a second-floor window overlooking the entire back side. During that attack Amnon's units suffered numerous fatalities, and two seriously wounded men, one a father of four children. Amnon passed the news of the capture of the Mea Shearim police station to his headquarters. A short while later a car arrived to take the dead and the wounded. Unfortunately, it was too late for one of them.

Wednesday, May 19, 1948

Kol Israel's news broadcast told of the bitter defense battle at kibbutz Degania, which was almost over. All the Syrian army's assaults had been repulsed, and the men in the kibbutz had managed to destroy all Syrian tanks. It looked as though Syria was reconsidering its position. Meanwhile, the Egyptian armies were advancing in the south. The Haganah didn't have enough men to fight all the invading armies at once. But at that stage, it was more important to defeat the Syrians and Jordanians than the Egyptians. There didn't appear to be any coordination between the different invading Arab armies. One army didn't know what the other was doing.

Since the Haganah controlled almost the entire territory north of the Old City, Amnon wondered what the Arab Legion might do next. Apart from heavy sniper fire, day and night, he didn't notice any other action. The battle against the Jewish enclave inside the Old City was still continuing. How much longer before it fell to the enemy was the question. Egyptian armies were getting close to kibbutz Ramat Rachel, south of Jerusalem. Heavy defenses were being built there while the Egyptians were advancing through Arab territory. The Haganah planned to make a stand at Ramat Rachel while its main forces were eliminating the Syrians, Lebanese and Iraqis in the north and northeast regions of the country.

The situation in Jerusalem got worse. There was no food, not even for rationed items. There was no kerosene for cooking. There was no meat, fish, or poultry. Bread was extremely scarce. At the front they got packages of Matza left over from last Passover. For days, all they had was one matza per person per day, along with a tablespoon of cocoa powder. For some unknown reason there were bags and bags of cocoa powder.

Amnon and his men were hungry, but very cheerful. The early news of the war against the invading armies began to swing to the Israeli side. To Amnon and his men that was more important than food. The news also reported that shiploads of detained immigrants in Cyprus and Europe would soon be released and permitted to travel to Israel. That kind of news was very encouraging.

"Isn't this what we're fighting for? To bring our brethren home!" Amnon declared.

Thursday, May 20, 1948

Great news from the north. The Syrian armies were retreating. It wasn't known whether they were out of the picture yet. Kibbutz Degania, which took the brunt of the battle, remained intact and held firmly by its residents. The United

Nations appointed a Swedish politician, Count Folke Bernadotte, as the mediator for Palestine. It wasn't clear at that time what he would do. The Arabs were still rejecting any compromise, and were aiming at the destruction of Israel.

Amnon's battle zone remained relatively quiet, nothing except constant sniper fire. There were no new attacks on his positions. The fiercest gunfire continued at Yemin Moshe, situated across from the Old City. That old Jewish neighborhood had been evacuated long before the war began, as there was no way anyone could live there. Gunfire was exchanged nonstop.

The situation inside the Old City got much worse. The Jewish quarter was completely surrounded by the Arab Legion. There was no way in or out. Their days were numbered.

Egyptian forces were nearing Ramat Rachel. They would probably reach it within a few days. Amnon heard that Haganah men were ready for them. The oddest piece of news was that British aircraft downed four Egyptian planes on a bombardment mission to Tel Aviv. Amnon couldn't figure that news item at all. It remained a mystery to him for days.

Saturday, May 23, 1948

Egyptian forces didn't waste any time. They attacked kibbutz Ramat Rachel as soon as they arrived. The kibbutz changed hands several times before the Egyptians were repulsed for good. They also attempted to penetrate Jerusalem from the south, but failed. They suffered heavy casualties.

Firing at Amnon's area from distant buildings had increased substantially. It was getting much worse at night. Amnon guessed Arab soldiers felt chances of us detecting their positions was nil during the dark of night. During the day, Amnon's snipers managed to hit many of them. Amnon's men didn't shoot at large, as the Arabs did. Only his trained snipers were at work.

Amnon decided to visit his parents, whom he hadn't seen in quite some time. He advised his deputy that he'd be away for a few hours, and began his long walk toward Rehavia.

On the way, Amnon passed through Mahne Yehuda market, which was mostly isolated. A few shops were open, little or no merchandise on their shelves. One shop had a small line of shoppers and Amnon walked over to see what was being sold. There were only women on line, and Amnon told them he was from the front, on a couple of hours leave, and would they mind if he went to the front of the line. One of the women approached him, slapped his face, and told him to go to the back of the line. Amnon could feel that slap for days. He was stunned. He wanted to say something, but thought the better of it, and walked away. Amnon couldn't help wondering why that woman was so aggressive. He knew many families in Jerusalem and elsewhere had lost sons and daughters to the war of independence. "*Who am I to judge that woman,*" he thought. Ten minutes later he was at his parents' apartment.

Amnon could feel his mother's embrace for days and days. His body was suddenly filled with love. He hadn't had such a feeling for a long time. All of his feelings had gone numb. The war, the constant analyzing of every risk, the need to avoid a single mistake, the concern for his men, the broken heart when a friend and comrade laid dead or bleeding to death in front of him, had turned his blood cold.

Amnon hadn't realized how dead his feelings were until his mother hugged and kissed him. His father came out of the living room to greet him when he heard his voice. Amnon's mother began to cry: "I can't make you a glass of tea," she said. "We have no kerosene to light the primus, and I can't boil water." Then, taking a good look at him, she said, "You're so thin. Don't they feed you in the army?"

"I have enough to eat," Amnon lied. "It's just that I work so hard, and that keeps me thin."

She wanted to know where he was, what he was doing. Amnon told her and his father of the battles, the defense of Jerusalem, and then they talked a little about the future. His father, who hadn't had a chance to put in a word, finally got into the conversation.

"As of May 15, 1948," he told Amnon, "I am retired from service in His Majesty's Government. I shall be receiving a monthly pension from London, and shall have no other means of support. However, when the Israeli government is set up, I expect to be permitted to join it, and offer my wide range of experience and service. For the time being, I am just sitting home. The provisional Israeli government is still in Tel Aviv, but there doesn't seem to be a way to reach anybody because of the blockade. Do you know when the blockade of the city will end?"

"No, I'm sorry, I know as little as you do in the matter."

They discussed the Arab artillery still firing at the city with no specific target in mind. Bombs landed here or there, causing some damage, and occasionally killing or injuring innocent bystanders. There was some sort of a basement at the side of the house, and Amnon's parents assured him they spent their nights and days there. They, like everyone else in the city, kept their radio on all day long and tuned to the news station, trying to learn the latest developments.

But from what little Amnon heard, it occurred to him most of the news concerned other areas of the country rather than Jerusalem itself. Amnon thought it wouldn't have been a good idea to tell the citizens of Jerusalem about every battle along its borders. It was bad enough they had little or no food.

Surprisingly, the city still had running water and electricity, which they used sparsely. They had no way to heat water, and they had to wash themselves by using towels soaked in cold water. That was better than what they had at the front. At that moment Amnon realized just how bad he smelled, and how badly he needed to wash himself.

Amnon's father asked him if it were possible to use DDT to fire the primus, and Amnon said it definitely was. Amnon's parents had several large containers of DDT, used to control mosquitoes during the summer. After pouring some into the primus, Amnon lit it, and it worked like a charm. He then heated water and washed himself. He took fresh underwear and a shirt from his drawer at home, but had to reuse his khaki pants.

His mother then brewed some tea. It was like being in paradise to have a

Amnon

hot glass of tea. There was no sugar, milk or lemon, but Amnon drank it anyway; he hadn't had tea in ages. Amnon thought of his men in the field, and wished he could bring them some, too. It was hard to leave, but he had no alternative. He had to return to his units. It was good, though, a breath of fresh air in the middle of a stinking war.

Tuesday, May 25, 1948

Amnon was called to his Mea Shearim units. He rushed over to find they were under heavy fire, usually a prelude to an assault. He was told that some activity had been noticed on the Arab side, but not enough to panic. The firing consisted mostly of machine gun and rifle fire. Amnon's assumption was that the Arabs didn't want to damage or destroy more Arab houses. Their fire was concentrated on the police station building and the Jewish buildings across the intersection. Hardly a bullet was fired at the Italian hospital. As always, they didn't respond. Only Amnon's snipers were at work, picking their targets, one at a time. It was amazing how many hits a good sniper can make. As there were many vacant houses in the area, Amnon had his snipers change positions constantly in order to avoid detection.

Two assaults were repelled, one after the other. The barbed wire, which his men had so neatly laid, caused the attackers endless difficulties. Arab soldiers thought they could jump over the wire, only to find in many cases that their trousers or awkward dresses got caught in the barbs, from which they couldn't untangle themselves. That, of course, made them easy targets for the defenders. Then the Arabs began sending one man at a time with a rope to tie the barbed wire so they could pull it away. But as each man came running out toward the rows of wire, he was shot, until finally that lunacy stopped.

As the day neared its end, Amnon sent one of his men to the girls' school sector, and he soon returned with a message that all was quiet, except for the endless firing. On the other hand, at the police station area, enemy fire sharply increased. Deciding to stay at the police station, Amnon planned an assault on the Arab line, which was way ahead of them, just to give the enemy something to worry about. He also thought that the further out they were, the more room for him to maneuver in case of renewed assaults.

As soon as it got dark, Amnon's men advanced cautiously to the east, following the street, entering one house after another. They found them all to be abandoned. They then followed the parallel street, south of the station, and there too they discovered all houses were abandoned. He immediately decided to move to the last row of houses, from which the ground sloped steeply towards a valley. Amnon sent a man to headquarters, asking that his commander, or any available senior commander come immediately to examine that new situation.

It was close to midnight when Itzhak, one of the most senior Haganah officers, arrived. They discussed this unusual situation. Firing was still heavy at the girl's school, which was less than a kilometer away, but firing at the police station, which obviously came from a great distance, was beginning to decrease. It was decided to make the last easternmost row of houses the front line. As soon as Itzhak left, Amnon called his men, and they shifted the barbed wire to new

245

locations surrounding that section of houses. They also dug new trenches wherever possible and spent the rest of the night developing a strategic defense plan. Amnon left some men at the old posts and all street corners.

Friday, May 28, 1948
Kol Israel reported a variety of forces were working behind the scenes at the United Nations. They were hoping to bring about a cease-fire in the Arab-Israeli war. The leadership of the new government of Israel welcomed such a cease-fire. The Arabs refused it. The bad and extremely sad news of the day, however, was the report that the fighting community in the Jewish quarter of the Old City had surrendered to the Arab Legion.

This didn't surprise Amnon at all. With no food or water, and running out of ammunition, what else could have been expected? Despite the rational analysis, it was a very sad day for all of them. Somehow, the Old City of Jerusalem, where the historic Temple used to stand, was the heart of their love. When Jews around the world ended their prayers with: "Next year in Jerusalem, please God!" they meant the Old City. They meant the Temple.

"*I shall never see the beautiful Hurva synagogue again*," Amnon thought. He loved that synagogue with all his heart.

Suddenly, he felt very tired. He had not felt tired in weeks despite such hectic activity. Finding a lovely spot near the gate of the house his men occupied, he sat down on a step, leaning his back against the wall. Amnon asked his deputy to continue to monitor the work; he wanted to relax a little. It was the news of the loss of the Jewish quarter in the Old City that hit him so hard. His heart was with those who had surrendered.

"*What will become of them? Will the Arab Legion treat them as prisoners of war per the Geneva Convention? How badly defeated they must be after weeks of standing up to a powerful military siege*," Amnon thought.

Amnon began to review the entire situation in the country. Obviously, he didn't have all the information relating to current events on the other fronts, but he couldn't stop thinking nonetheless. The bits of news, rumors, and information helped a little, but definitely not enough to create a complete picture. He shut his eyes, and tried to relax his mind, trying very hard not to think, but failing miserably. His thoughts were racing. It had been some time since he could sit down and spend a few minutes relaxing.

Monday, May 31, 1948
The country, the State of Israel, was two weeks old. Normally, people think of annual birthdays. But here in Jerusalem, every day was a birthday for the newly established country. There were still so many enemies, so many risks, and so many unknowns. And the greatest of the concerns was that the leadership had no clear idea how much manpower their enemies could muster. The Israeli defense forces were so few by comparison. Amnon used to say that Arab attackers outnumbered them twenty to one, but he knew his assumption was wrong. The population of Arab countries surrounding Israel was close to fifty million. The population of Israel was about six hundred thousand, which included

a great number of old and tired people.

That crucial month of May came to an end with a heavy load of news events. The British civilian and military authorities left Palestine. The leadership of the Yishuv, after proclaiming independence and officially creating the State of Israel, established a provisional government. With the declaration of the State of Israel, the armies of five Arab countries invaded Palestine with hopes of capturing it and destroying the hopes and aspirations of the Jews. There were battles for survival in every direction and every part of the country. Many member nations of the United Nations recognized the newly established State of Israel. The recognition of the State of Israel reflected a world change in attitude as well as a positive approach to the Jewish problem. The only major nation that didn't recognize the State of Israel was Great Britain.

A great deal of activity was reported at the United Nations, which was trying to arrange some kind of a cease-fire. The Syrian and Lebanese armies were contained. The Arab Legion was beginning to take more of a defensive position; no new attacks were made. The Egyptian army was the only one still too close to Jerusalem, even though it was repelled at Ramat Rachel. Its armies were also getting closer to the southern Jewish settlements bordering the northern Negev desert. Random firing and sniping from the Old City continued unabated. The entire area facing the Old City was completely abandoned, but kept out of Arab hands. On the eastern front, Amnon's territory, firing and sniping continued in some sections, but not with the previous vigor.

Amnon's southernmost territory, although much quieter, was still being shot and sniped at heavily from time to time, but from a great distance. Amnon had his men moved most of their weapons, supplies, and other requirements at night to avoid sniper fire. Arab artillery was still bombarding Jerusalem from artillery stationed to the north of the city, but at a lesser pace. This seemed strange because only two weeks ago the Arab Legion was determined to capture Jerusalem, while now suddenly showing restraint, they were just sitting in their seats, not doing much of anything. Amnon used the time to fortify their bunkers, trenches, and posts. They dug new trenches, investigated every type of activity across the line, and were ready for any surprise attack.

Tuesday, June 1, 1948

The government of the State of Israel declared the creation of the Israel Defense Forces. Basically, it was the establishment of the Israeli military system, of which the Haganah and its various organizations was the main core. The first of the other resistance movements against the British, the Lehi group, decided to join the Israel Defense Forces and ceased independent operations. No sooner had Lehi made its announcement than the Etzel organization followed suit. The State of Israel finally had one military force, united under one command. Amnon hadn't known the details of that amalgamation, but some rumors persisted that the Etzel wanted separate units and separate arms within the newly created Israel Defense forces.

"If any of the rumors are true, I can't comprehend the need to have one army inside the other," Amnon brooded. He was very annoyed at the lack of desire for total integration by the Irgun.

The most important news of the day was that Haganah engineers opened a dirt road through the mountains circumventing the Latrun area, which controlled the road to Jerusalem. The first trucks were to arrive soon with food supplies. It seemed that doing the impossible was the Haganah's trademark during those times. Knowing the mountainous stretch west of Jerusalem, Amnon applauded the men who managed to build a road through it. The road was nicknamed the "Burma Road," for its resemblance to the famous dirt road in the Far East during the war in the South Pacific. In Amnon's personal opinion, capturing territory and clearing it of Arab fighters was one of the most crucial accomplishments of the Haganah. If not for that, the Haganah would have had to battle Arab forces from within as well as from without Palestine.

Frantic efforts were being made by the provincial government of Israel to acquire some airplanes which could be converted to a fighting force. With the help of Jewish pilots who flew for the Allies during the Second World War, and contributions from wealthy individuals, a number of planes were bought and brought to Israel. The first city to be attacked by the tiny new air force was the city of Amman in Trans-Jordan. All the news about air force and air battle was entirely new to Amnon, as it surely was to every other member of the fighting organization. Amnon knew the Haganah had a clandestine airport somewhere in Palestine, but had no idea of its size or value. All he knew at the time was that shipments of arms from Czechoslovakia had been arriving there.

More talks of a cease-fire were reported. The United Nations was sponsoring an armistice so that the warring parties could discuss and come to some agreement about the future. The original partition plan was still acceptable to the Jews. The Arabs wouldn't hear of it. There must have been significant pressure created by so many fleeing Arabs flooding Trans- Jordan, and other Arab countries. It was estimated at the time that over 100,000 Arabs had fled Palestine.

Battle zones continued to be relatively free of attacks. Firing and sniping from the Arab sectors continued endlessly, as usual, heavier at night. At times, the firing was so heavy Amnon expected ground assaults, which never came. His men continued to monitor the Arab side at night by crawling across the no man's land. The only report Amnon wanted to explore concerned increased activity at the old Police Academy building across from Sanhedriah, and he decided to do some sleuthing.

Taking along one of his men more fluent in Arabic, they set out at 9:00pm, walked half a kilometer then headed southeast. From that point on they began their crawl, advancing twenty steps at a time, then stopping to watch and listen. A few lights, probably candlelight, flickered through some of the ground floor windows. As they approached the spot Amnon had entered at a few weeks earlier, he decided they should remain motionless on the ground for a while.

They stayed there for about an hour before they made their next move. The barbed wire Amnon had cut and tied neatly together the last time, was in the same exact position. Two soldiers patrolled the grounds every half hour. As soon as they passed, Amnon opened the barbed wire, crawled through, and retied the wires. They ran to the outer wall of the building, and slowed down just before reaching the first of the windows, all of which were open to let in fresh air.

People were talking in the room in English, but the talking soon escalated into an argument. At first Amnon couldn't understand the subject of the discussion, because it made no sense to him. It seemed the argument was about the orders Arab Legion officers had received to stop attacking Jewish targets. Apparently, the orders were very clear about continuing the barrage of gunfire, but without ground assaults anywhere. The Arab Legion was to defend against any Jewish assaults, but that was all. They were definitely not to capture any additional territory from the Jews.

It took Amnon a while to understand that heated discussion. The arguing British officers didn't understand why such orders had been given, and Amnon, on the outside, didn't understand it either. The two-man-patrol was getting nearer. Amnon and his comrade lay on the ground by the wall until they passed. Fortunately, the patrol was walking closer to the fence than the building. The two guards were talking, and in the still of the night, Amnon could hear them quite well.

First, Amnon thought, "*If any of my men dared talk while on patrol, I would have had their heads.*" And secondly, he was astounded by the discussion inside.

"Can you believe this nonsense, that a member of the Jewish Government of Israel visited with King Abdullah?" a British officer asked.

"How many times are you going to repeat this question?" the second officer blasted. "It's absolutely absurd!"

"Then, why have we stopped the war?" the first man asked.

"I don't know, so let's just change the subject. I'm sick and tired of this Palestine, anyhow. I want to go home," the officer said.

The discussion finally began making sense. Amnon and his comrade looked at each other with amazement, but didn't utter a word. The next three windows yielded nothing, but the fourth did; here too the language spoken was English. Most of the conversation related to the men's families back home and their hopes of being sent back to England soon. They were saying that the possibility of a cease-fire was real. Amnon was afraid to peek through the window, but finally decided to take the risk.

Moving his head very slowly, to avoid making even the slightest noise, he waited until he had a one-eyed view of the room. Three British officers were sitting around a table drinking scotch. On the table, Amnon saw a half-full bottle of scotch, and a plate with sandwiches. He was so hungry he could taste those sandwiches.

"*These bastards have all the bread in the world, while we haven't seen bread in days,*" Amnon thought.

He listened, and learned from the conversation that certain British personnel were being transferred from battle zones to this building until their passage to England was arranged.

"*So this was the increased activity my spy reported,*" Amnon decided.

Silently, Amnon and his comrade turned around, and retraced their steps to their point of entry. They waited next to the outer wall, lying on the ground until the patrolling guards completed their tour and were out of sight, before bolting for the fence, and out they went. The fence and barbed wire were put in place neatly so as not to attract any attention, and they actually ran directly back to the outpost. As tired as Amnon was, he decided to walk back to his center units.

Amnon had a hard time making sense of what he'd heard.

"A member of our government met with King Abdullah of Trans-Jordan? This is more far-fetched than a trip to the moon," Amnon thought.

"There's no question a change has taken place in the war with the Arab Legion. But how am I to know what's going on?" Amnon muttered to himself. He always had a deep sense of appreciation and respect for the Yishuv's leaders.

"They surely knew what's best for us. Almost all of their decisions so far have been satisfactory and on target."

It wasn't easy for the Jewish governing body to make decisions under the difficult circumstances they were confronted with. And it took a great deal of courage, strength, and stamina to stand up to the British Empire. The fighting men and women of the Haganah were also standing up to the very hostile Arab countries surrounding them. Walking on, Amnon finally reached his own unit, found a cot, and was asleep within minutes.

Wednesday, June 2, 1948

The head of the Irgun, Menachem Begin, decided to join the Israeli Defense Forces with some conditions. That was good news, for Amnon liked teamwork.

"After all, we're one country, one nation, one race - we should be one united army," Amnon declared. "We have enough political differences within the Yishuv. At least, let our military be one."

But despite their decision to join the newly created Israeli Defense Forces, the Irgun wanted a number of matters to remain separate, which didn't sit well with the provisional government. The Haganah elders had a lot of ill feelings about the Irgun. Amnon hoped that within a few weeks the two opposing organizations would see the light, and truly become one force.

News of supply trucks arriving in Jerusalem after cutting through the mountains was wonderful music to everyone's ears.

"Perhaps we'll have a decent meal soon," Amnon hoped. The entire population of Jerusalem was not just hungry, but close to starvation. And though the men on the front lines were sick and tired of matzot, they thanked God for it, for without matzot, they would have had no food at all, and Amnon always wondered where all the matzot had come from.

Amnon went to his headquarters, and told his commander of his visit to the Police Academy building, and what he'd heard.

"Did you mention what you heard to anyone?" Yoav asked.

"Not a soul," Amnon assured him.

"I know I can count on you," he said, before sternly adding, "Absolutely no one is to know what you heard. That's all I can tell you at the present moment." Not having mentioned he'd taken someone with him, Amnon hurried back to his unit, found the man who'd accompanied him that night and sternly warned to keep his mouth shut. But Amnon wasn't really concerned; they'd grown up learning to keep their mouths shut.

Before Amnon left, his commander told him it looked like the United Nations was going to be successful in arranging a temporary cease-fire. He didn't have complete details yet, but believed it would be accomplished soon, perhaps within days.

"Enough fighting," Amnon thought. *"Don't the Arabs see the futility of fighting us?"*

The fact was that the Arabs were losing the battle on every front. The Syrians and Lebanese were repelled in the north. The Arab Legion and Arab militias were unable to capture Jerusalem, their major goal. The only army, which hadn't yet faced defeat, was the Egyptian army, but that was on deliberate. However, the Egyptian armies were contained in such locations as south Jerusalem and the Negev, and couldn't advance any further.

The Haganah couldn't fight all the invading armies at once. But the most vital areas, such as the Galilee, Jerusalem, the coast line with its major cities, as well as the center of the country leading to Jerusalem, were free and in the hands of the Israelis. Amnon was certain the Egyptians would be next on the agenda. He was positive the Israeli government wouldn't let them stay inside the land of Israel.

The neighboring Arab countries were disagreeably overwhelmed by the arrival of so many thousands of unexpected Arab refugees fleeing Palestine. They neither expected nor appreciated having the tables turned. Believing they would easily capture Palestine and kick the Jews out when the British left, they were neither prepared nor wished to provide any kind of help to their fleeing Arab brethren whom they'd coaxed to leave.

"We have a great deal to thank the British for," thought Amnon, *"Thanks to their antiquated colonialist mind-set and imperialistic way of life they created the inhumane policies leading to this juncture."*

"How many lives have to be lost, and how much more suffering has to be endured by survivors of the Nazi holocaust?"

The British couldn't have been more wrong, and there were absolutely no extenuating circumstances to condone their cynical anti-Jewish behavior in this matter.

Thursday, June 3, 1948

Today Amnon and his men received their first slice of bread, and it tasted incredibly delicious. It had been weeks since they'd seen bread, much less tasted it. Amnon brought it up to his nose, and inhaled its aroma for the longest time before eating. He felt sure he was in paradise. The effect of one slice of bread! With the bread, each of them received half a tomato, one cucumber, and two slices of cheese, which comprised a veritable feast. Every man's contentment was clearly evident in the expression on his face. Amnon wondered what his own face reflected, but imagined the same contentment as everyone else.

Daniel Rosenfeld

"Hunger and thirst are two of man's worst enemies," Amnon declared. "Hopefully, this will be the last time we will need to cope with hunger." With the opening of the new road to Jerusalem, which was no more than a dirt road that zigzagged through the mountains of Judea, vital supplies began to flow to Jerusalem, including food for the hungry population. Opening this road was a major engineering coup. The Judean mountains were extremely rocky. Amnon gathered that all kinds of heavy equipment were used to break through. At least the new road was out of the sight of their Arab neighbors.

As Amnon thought about the breakthrough, and hoping not to go hungry again, it occurred to him that Napoleon was wrong. Napoleon said that a war was won when soldiers fought on full stomachs. But, in their case, he couldn't have been more wrong. The Israeli army won its war with sheer guts that were strengthened by an empty stomach.

There wasn't much happening on the Jerusalem front. Arabs fired across the lines day and night. But everyone knew where to walk, and how to hide, and also how to dodge enemy fire. A few sections of the city had been vacated or abandoned, while others were out of reach. The deadly unknown was where and when an artillery shell might fall. Shells killed a number of civilians, and wounded many. There was also damage to property, which could not be repaired because every man and woman was busy with the war effort.

As if nothing had changed, Amnon continued his daily inspections along the eastern sector, insuring all units continued on full alert, day and night. As far as he was concerned, the war was not yet over, and he wanted to make sure his men were ready for whatever might happen. His men kept going deep into Arab territory every night. There were no reports of any unusual activity. Amnon's visits at the headquarters seemed to have become routine. Most of the action was still taking place in those parts of the country where Israel had to make territorial gains.

United Nations mediators were working around the clock trying to arrange a cease-fire. There was talk of a temporary cease-fire, but it wasn't clear to anyone, at least not to Amnon, exactly what a temporary cease-fire meant. Perhaps the mediators hoped to start with a temporary cessation of hostilities, and later work it into a permanent one. But the Arabs were as unpredictable as they were disorganized, and it would be a mammoth job to get all five warring countries to agree to anything. Syrian, Lebanese, and Iraqi forces had suffered heavy losses and accomplished nothing. The Trans-Jordanian Arab Legion was holding the central part of Palestine and eastern Jerusalem, including the Old City. And though the Egyptian armies had suffered setbacks, they had not yet suffered real defeat.

Saturday, June 5, 1948

A messenger arrived early in the morning asking Amnon to come to his headquarters immediately. Soon after his arrival, Yoav, his commander, accompanied by two other officers Amnon had not seen before, began to confer about an area where Amnon had worked before. Just west of Jerusalem were three kibbutzim, Motza, Kiriat Anavim, and Maale Hachamisha. The mountainous area surrounding those kibbutzim was in uninhabited Arab territory. Amnon was told to take a few men from his unit and explore the mountains lying between those kibbutzim and Jerusalem, as well as how far north Israel could go in order to claim the land and what manpower would be necessary to occupy it.

Amnon was told there wasn't much time; he had to leave immediately, and only had three days at most to complete the study. Amnon left as soon as the meeting was over, and actually got a car ride to Mea Shearim. Amnon had not been in a car for what seemed an eternity. There was something romantic about being driven, and he felt really good. Amnon asked the driver to wait while he fetched his men.

He picked three men who'd been with him before in the mountains, and they were driven to kibbutz Motza. There, in the dining room, Amnon stretched a large map of the area on a table, and the four of them began to explore it. He summoned the old Haganah commander of the kibbutz, and conferred with him about security matters in the area; he confirmed they hadn't seen any Arab activity near the surrounding mountains. In fact, they'd neither been fired at, nor had they fired a single shot.

Amnon took note of the closest Arab village, and decided to explore the mountain area to the north of the kibbutz. He borrowed four mules and set out without delay. The kibbutz kitchen had meager food supplies, but managed to give them something for an overnight trip.

As they got started, Amnon scoped out the mountains, and created their own path as they went. In four hours they'd crossed two mountaintops, and Amnon could see a few kilometers beyond with the aid of powerful binoculars. There was no one in sight; the territory was much too mountainous and rocky for any settlement. Thinking the Jews must be the only people on earth who knew how to accomplish the impossible, Amnon marked the map, and they turned west toward Kiriat Anavim.

They rode the mules until nightfall, found a reasonably decent place to camp between two large rocks, and settled in for the night. Each had a bite to eat, and drank a little water from a canteen. With no need to keep watch, they stretched out as close to each other as possible to generate some natural heat. It was cold, and though they covered themselves with all the blankets they had, they couldn't get warm. Exhaustion helped them finally fall asleep. When they awoke the next morning, the sun was already up.

Amnon couldn't believe how well they'd slept; the combination of low temperature and dry mountain air must have done the job. Realizing how late it was, past 8:00am, Amnon jumped up and got everyone else going. The mules were grazing nearby, and he stood by affectionately watching them for a moment. The mule population was a magnificent group of animals that had served them well. He'd brought along a special container of water for them, and gave them each a drink.

They continued to criss-cross the mountains, and at each summit Amnon stopped and checked the entire territory in front of him, making notes on the map. As he did, he drew a line which he felt could be the dividing line between the Israeli and Arab territories. It was past 9:00pm when they reached Kiriat Anavim.

Daniel Rosenfeld

They identified themselves to the night watchman, who'd been advised they were enroute, but hadn't known when they'd show up.

As always, the kibbutz dining room was its central meeting place. It was the older members who greeted visitors, and Amnon's little group in particular. All the young men had been drafted years ago by the Haganah, and must have been elsewhere in service. Asking about the area, particularly the northern mountains, he learned the city of Ramallah was about thirty kilometers to the north with a small number of Arab villages around it, but none close to the kibbutz. Again, Amnon marked the map, and decided to take a short trip the next morning to investigate the northern mountains.

Sleeping in a real bed made all the difference in the world. Amnon couldn't remember when he'd last slept in a real bed. It was always a military cot without a mattress or pillow. He sunk his head in the pillow, and for a moment felt like he was floating on air. Amnon felt mentally and physically tired, and couldn't help wondering when he would return to normal living.

Being physically tired was nothing new, for he had often felt exhausted during his endless campaigns. But mental fatigue was new to him. It was the bed that made him feel like a normal human being again. Amnon stretched and tried to sink as far down into it as he could. It felt so good he wished he could stay there for at least a month. But when morning arrived, his sense of responsibility resurfaced along with reality, and he knew he had to leave this small corner of paradise. After an early breakfast, they proceeded on their short trip to Maale Hachamisha.

Amnon was happy the Arabs hadn't occupied all the surrounding mountains. They didn't have the same needs the Yishuv had. It was vital for Israel to capture as much territory as possible. After completing the tour at Maale Hachamisha, Amnon finished drawing the dividing line on the map as he saw it. In this kibbutz as well, only seniors were on hand. Amnon and his men were received with much hospitality and asked many questions about the war of defense in Jerusalem. After a dinner of fried eggs and two slices of bread, they went to bed. He slept like a log, and woke only when one of his men shook him the next morning. It was late; they had to return to Jerusalem.

Thursday, June 10, 1948

The United Nations declared a four-week cease-fire. The Arabs had accepted all conditions, and signed a formal agreement. Four weeks of peace. That was more than Amnon expected. The United Nations was hoping to bring about a permanent peace, and felt it needed the time to achieve its goal. It was impossible to assess the situation. The general command of the Israeli Defense Forces decided to use those four weeks to shore up its strength, and train its soldiers in the latest weaponry that had been arriving from Czechoslovakia. Large shipments of armaments had been shipped directly to Haifa. There was no longer any need for clandestine shipments. The only thing that remained clandestine was that these shipments were being kept secret from the general public.

The cease-fire was to become effective on June 11, 1948. Amnon was notified members of the elders corps (Mishmar Haam) would replace his units at

254

the front, and all units under his command were to report immediately for training to a camp near Ein Karem, a small Arab village hidden among beautiful valleys in the Judean mountains west of Jerusalem. All its Arab residents had left at the onset of hostilities.

It sounded funny -- training after all the battle experience anyone could wish for.

"Exactly how different," Amnon wondered, *"Can this new equipment and weaponry be?"*

To him, four weeks of training would be like a vacation. The location was perfect, summer in the mountains, cool dry air, no rain, and no hard work.

Despite his feelings about the four weeks ahead, Amnon was concerned about the future.

"The Arabs won't abandon their dream of destroying us so quickly. They previously refused the partition of Palestine except on their own terms, brazenly announced that when the British left they would invade Palestine, and did just that. The United Nations is far too optimistic, if not dangerously naive, to believe they will accept defeat after only the first few battles, and be ready to talk cease-fire or lasting peace," Amnon thought.

Amnon knew Arabs had never functioned that way. Given their revenge-oriented mentality, they would be seeking revenge even as they talked cease-fire with a forked tongue. No way could Amnon visualize a permanent peace after only four weeks of pitched battles. The Arabs needed to suffer a much greater defeat than they had thus far before Israel could expect any real and lasting peace. And the United Nations needed to learn much more about Arab mentality.

Amnon made a few inquiries within his senior ranks, and found many shared his feelings. The Israel Defense Forces would use those four weeks to build up its capabilities, and as soon as hostilities broke, would deliver a major blow to the remaining Arab armies. In fact, the cease-fire was an unexpected gift that would permit the Israel Defense forces to do just that.

Saturday, June 12, 1948

Amnon and his units arrived at Ein Karem in the early afternoon and began setting up camp. The main tent for the officers and trainers was already set up and a field kitchen in operation. There was also a large pickup truck holding a water tank. Amnon's men cleared stones and rocks from behind the kitchen and set up their tents. Very soon, more units arrived and followed suit. They were told training would start the next morning at 8:00 am, by which time everyone was expected to have washed and breakfasted.

Before the first session began, a truckload of 30 young men arrived. As soon as they alighted, a sergeant lined them up and started searching for Amnon. When he found him, he handed to Amnon a short note signed by his commander:

"Dear Amnon, the thirty young men who were brought to our Ein Karem camp have just arrived from British detention in Cyprus. These young men are Jewish orphans, survivors from Europe. The whereabouts of their parents or the circumstances of their death are unknown. All of them volunteered to join the army. Please take charge of this unit until further notice. Also, make sure they're ready for action after the four-week ceasefire.

Signed; Y."

Amnon went over and introduced himself. The young men were fluent in Russian, Polish, and different degrees of Yiddish. Not one spoke Hebrew or any other language. From that moment on, Yiddish became this unit's official language. Amnon didn't have a problem, as all of them understood his Yiddish-German. Even those who didn't speak it well got along. Amnon selected a small number of his men who knew some Yiddish, and split the men into three groups of ten.

The mountains and valleys surrounding Ein Karem provided a variety of excellent terrain for training. Amnon laid out a basic training program, and told his men to have those young men battle-ready within four weeks. He told them to work day and night, and to prepare them especially for night action. Amnon then attended his own classes, since he was there to learn about the latest weapons from Czechoslovakia.

He was assigned to a group of unit commanders who were being introduced to the Beza machine gun, the design for which was actually completed after the end of the Second World War at the Skoda Munitions Works outside Prague. Weighing 45 kilos, half the tripod, half the machine gun proper, it had a range of almost four kilometers, and could spray bullets with formidable accuracy at great distances. It was an intensive three-day course, after which Amnon and the other commanders were to train their men. All of them required special training to maximize this weapon's efficiency in battle.

The cease-fire brokered by the United Nations worked quite well in most parts of the country. In Jerusalem, sporadic fire came from Arab snipers somewhere in the Old City; however, since the Yemin Moshe quarter facing the Old City had been abandoned, it harmed no one. People began to move around, visit friends and families. Food supplies were arriving faster and distributed.

Friday, June 18, 1948

Sitting on a rock about a hundred meters away, Amnon watched his men train the new arrivals. The young trainees were very enthusiastic, and worked hard. Though Amnon detected an occasional language barrier, on the whole they seemed to understand each other well. Satisfied, Amnon returned to his own training session, which was winding down.

With the help of two other men, Amnon took one of the Bezas to a nearby cliff, and practiced.

"How many lives could have been saved if we'd had these machine guns at the beginning of the war," Amnon asked. He practiced a couple of hours, and was extremely impressed with the machine gun's capabilities. He returned to the main camp, and decided to visit his parents that evening before starting the Beza training for his units.

Since neither his parents nor any of their neighbors had a telephone, Amnon was never able to let them know he was coming. Their surprise at seeing him standing at their front door was always instant enchantment. They hugged and kissed him endlessly.

Amnon's mother proudly announced she managed to buy Bakala. Since he'd never heard of Bakala, Amnon had no idea it was a dried fish imported from Brazil. The dried fish was placed in a container half filled with water, and left to soak. Within an hour or so the dried fish absorbed the water and expanded into its original shape, and was ready to cook. The meal was heavenly. Amnon hadn't had a salad of fish or potatoes in months. His father opened an old bottle of wine he was hiding, and they had a feast. Amnon felt like a thirsty man finding an oasis in the middle of the desert.

They sat around the dining room table for hours, reviewing and discussing the situation, as well as the future of the newly created State. Amnon's father said he was planning to take the first bus to Tel Aviv when it became available to the general public, and offer his services to the Israeli Government. He felt sure they would need persons with his kind of background and experience to run the government. Amnon's father was a great administrator, and his decision to take early retirement from the British Government and stay in Israel was going to be his contribution to the newly established State. Amnon guessed he was caught in the crossfire of the times, the return of Jews from the Diaspora, and the creation of the State of Israel, their homeland. Amnon spent the night in his own bed and left early the next day.

When he got back to his camp, Amnon heard news of a freighter loaded with weapons that had arrived somewhere in the north of Israel. It was said the ship belonged to the Etzel organization, and that they would take its contents. That story was mind-boggling.

"If true," Amnon thought, *"Why does the Etzel need to have its own separate weaponry once the Irgun had joined the Israeli Defense Forces?"* Jewish politics were never to Amnon's liking.

"In this tiny country of ours, we have too many political parties. Was it because we're blessed with an over supply of intellectuals? If so, their intellectualism is full of stupidity."

The training session was already in progress when he arrived, and he watched his new men from the side, thinking they showed great enthusiasm. "They're just as enthusiastic as I am, and the entire youth of our country," he said. He loved watching the men work or train. There was never a complaint, never an argument, and they were always full of energy and idealism. Every one knew that the four-week honeymoon would be over soon, and they'd be going back to war.

Deep in their hearts all of them wanted peace and normalcy, but reality told them war would resume. Reality also told them that if war were to resume, they would need to deliver the Arabs a crushing blow in the form of a devastating defeat that would bring them to their knees and make them seek a lasting peace.

The newly arrived weaponry and the quantities of ammunition with it was something they'd never seen or had before. The Israel Defense Forces had artillery, some tanks, and aircraft for the first time. That month long cease-fire surely was of great benefit to Israel.

Daniel Rosenfeld

Tuesday, June 22, 1948

A very sad day indeed for Amnon and for Israel. The Altelena, a weapons ship brought in by the Irgun, was shelled by the Israeli Defense Forces and was in flames off the shores of Tel Aviv. This freight ship, sponsored by the Irguns' friends abroad, carried a huge load of weapons. First this freighter anchored off an isolated shore somewhere in the north of the country and members of the Irgun organization began unloading it. The Irgun insisted the weapons be placed in their own warehouses. The new Israeli Government refused and stated that all weapons belonged to the Israel Defense Forces.

"Israel has one army and one command, and there will be no weapons under any other organization's authority," the official statement read.

The freighter suddenly departed, only to be found later anchored off the beaches of Tel Aviv. Talks with the leaders of the Irgun failed and the government decided to blow up the ship.

What saddened Amnon so much was the division between the Haganah, then the Israeli Defense Forces, and the Etzel could not be resolved. This hurtful situation was totally unacceptable.

"How can the Etzel ignore or refuse to recognize that Israel has one government, one army, and one command? How can another body, no matter how noble its cause, want a separate army of its own, with its own separate cache of weapons?" Amnon couldn't figure it out.

Destroying precious weapons and armaments was the only answer to such a dilemma. The Etzel, together with its leaders, lost most of the respect they'd earned during the earlier struggle. If they refused to recognize that Israel was a democratic State, run by an elected body, they had no business having a separate union, and had to be eliminated. The destruction of the Altelena was a clear message to the leaders of the Irgun; "We are one country, one government, one military force, and no one will work or function outside of a united Israel."

Amnon couldn't easily get over that affair, for he was greatly bothered by the distinct division among the people. While some were more radical in their thinking than others, the people of Israel were at least united in their objective - to get the British out of Palestine and create a Jewish homeland. The people of Israel were also united in their determination to bring home the hundreds of thousands of Holocaust survivors who were stranded in the limbo of Displaced Persons camps and British detention camps.

The Yishuv had accomplished its main goal. It had gotten the British out at a tremendous cost in lives and sacrifice, and established its own State. Having accomplished those two major objectives, the doors were opened to the waiting survivors and all Jews who wished to come home. They had been united in fighting a bloody war, which was not yet over; they would, almost certainly, be fighting an even more bloody war before they saw its end.

"*Why now had the Etzel decided to put their personal egos over the good of our country, by demanding their own army and their own cache of weapons after having agreed to join the Israel Defense Forces? What was their explanation for their unacceptable behavior?*" Amnon continued to question those issues in his own mind.

Amnon

"More than 80% of the Yishuv fully backs the Haganah and the policy making, democratically elected bodies of the Jewish Agency, which later became the provisional government of the newly established State of Israel. The Irgun organization was supported by less than 10% of the population. No one denied their role in the making of the State. They agreed that their men join the Israel Defense Forces, so why wouldn't they bring in their arsenal of weapons or those they were receiving? If Etzel members and supporters wanted to have their own political party, which they had, no one in the entire country would stop them."

Amnon felt hurt by their attitude, and he also felt the Yishuv had a deadly cancer in their midst.

The Irgun's dream was that the State of Israel should cover the same territory it covered in the days of the Kings, three thousand years ago. To Amnon, as to the great majority of the Jews, that was ridiculous. Thousands of years had passed since those ancient times of Kings. All those lands were, and had more recently been occupied by other people, including millions of Arabs.

What would be the point of anyone expecting millions of Arabs to suddenly become part of a Jewish state? Moreover, most Etzel members are secular Jews rather than Orthodox, Amnon found it difficult to understand their totally unrealistic stance that the site of the brand new State of Israel must encompass all of the territory of the ancient Land of Israel.

Amnon concentrated with greater fervor on the training of his men and the new members of his unit, deriving special satisfaction from those Polish/Russian youngsters. They worked hard, without a single complaint, for they wanted to be soldiers, and help gain peace and tranquility. Those young men were a different breed of immigrants. While they, too, had many stories to tell about their ordeals throughout the war, and particularly the loss or disappearance of their parents, brothers and sisters, they did not seem to be as broken as other immigrants Amnon had seen.

At night, after a hard day in the fields and mountains, they lit a fire and sat around it teaching the Sabras some of their songs. Amnon's men taught them Hebrew, and they taught some Russian in return, and together they sang their hearts out. They had great fun, as they forgot their troubles in music.

Wednesday, June 30, 1948

Called to his command center, Amnon was informed the training period would be over by the end of the week. His enlarged unit was to return to the Mea Shearim district, to replace the elders. Amnon was also asked to check with his commanding officer as soon as he got back as there were new intelligence reports regarding his territory. That night, as they sat around the fire, Amnon notified his group they should be packed and ready to move at 7:00am Saturday morning. Having decided to grant the men a day off, he arranged for their transportation to Jerusalem. Amnon decided to stay behind, and spent part of the day with the camp's commander, then just relaxed and enjoyed the scenery.

Sunday, July 4, 1948

Amnon found Mea Shearim buzzing with people. All the residents had returned to their homes after the cease-fire was announced. If war broke out again, it could be disastrous. Five more days were left of the official cease-fire. Amnon rushed to the command center, and met with his superior officer who was waiting for him.

"Arab militias are amassing in the valleys east of Mea Shearim," he reported. "There are also major Arab forces in Ramallah. We believe they will attack from both directions at the same time."

"Number one, we need to get the population out of Mea Shearim and Beit Israel, and number two, I need you to find the right location for one Beza so that you can block all traffic on the Ramallah road. If you block traffic from the north, you'll only have to deal with an attack from the east."

"There is one building, five stories high, on Mea Shearim Street, just a few blocks from the Mea Shearim intersection, and I believe that the road to Ramallah is quite clearly visible from it," Amnon responded. "I'll check on it right away. As far as a ground attack is concerned, I have complete confidence in my men," Amnon assured him, "and I'll ascertain an appropriate line of defense. But why wait for them to attack us? Why not attack them first?"

"My instructions are quite clear on the subject," he advised. "We don't want to seem to be the ones who restarted the war. We must show the world that we're not the aggressors. If the United Nations sees the Arabs restart the war, we'll gain significant political points with the world body."

"And what about the cost in lives?" Amnon asked.

"You know, and I know, that to us, every man counts. We mourn every loss, and as much as we humanly can, we try to avoid losing fighters," he insisted. "But at this early stage of our young country, it's of the utmost importance we make political gains with the United Nations, and particularly with the United States, and the Second World War Allies, including Russia. Good luck to you and your men, Amnon." His hand clutched Amnon's right shoulder. "And when the Arabs attack, give them hell!" he urged in parting.

As soon as Amnon arrived in Mea Shearim, he got hold of his deputy, and they went to check the five-story building, located about half a kilometer from the Mea Shearim intersection. The building had two entrances, one on each side, but like all the other houses on the street, there was no front entrance facing the street. From the outside, the building appeared to be divided into two sets of apartments, one set on the left, the other on the right, one entrance serving the left side apartments, the other the right.

They walked up to the fifth floor on the west side first; an elderly man opened the door. When Amnon explained he needed to look out his northern window, he let them in. Just as Amnon had thought, he could clearly see the entire length of the Ramallah road straight in front of them. He estimated the distance to be from one and a half kilometers at the bottom of the road to three kilometers at the top.

The road from Sheik Jarrach, the Arab quarter on the eastern side of Beit Israel, climbed a hill toward Ramallah. From the top of the hill it vanished as it ran down to a valley. "We certainly have plenty of road to cover. The Beza machine gun will blow apart any traffic," Amnon announced.

They then went around to the other side of the building, up the five flights, and entered the fifth floor apartment. The view from that window was the same. And when Amnon checked the wall between the two apartments, he found it was built from cement blocks. When the war resumed, he knew the moment they started firing from that building, heavy artillery would be aimed at them. He had to find a way to move the Beza from one apartment to the other, and from floor to floor, quickly and efficiently to make it more difficult for the enemy to fire back at them with accuracy. Amnon told this to Yaakov, his deputy.

"We need to cut open the walls between the apartments on the top three floors. Get men to help you break through on each floor. Make sure the openings are wide enough to accommodate the size of the Beza. I'll go check on the other front," Amnon instructed as he departed, little knowing his deputy would meet resistance from the residents when he came back with a number of men.

Amnon hastened to where his unit had been dropped off and made sure the men were completely out of sight from any direction. Then he called all deputy commanders into a corner and while they sat on the floor, Amnon explained they needed to take over from the elders on watch, and to be prepared for an Arab assault.

"Our intelligence reports suggest the main Arab forces are militias with limited support from the Arab Legion. It's my opinion that when the Arabs attack us, they'll use the two wide streets leading to Mea Shearim rather than go through the houses. We've been through this before. An attacking army can't be bogged down by house-to-house combat."

"I also assume they won't bombard Arab houses to minimize damage to Arab property. So here's my plan…

"I want the streets on both sides of the police station booby trapped with hand grenades. This must be done at night, two nights before this ceasefire ends. Place one man at each window in every house on both sides of the two streets, and at least two men on the ground at each house behind the wall fence, facing the street."

" I want one man at ground level at the back of each house in case any infiltrators come from the rear. Arab assaults have always come during the day, hardly any after dark. But they may change their tactics this time around, so be sure to be as ready at night as during the day."

"You have plenty of flare guns. In case of a night assault, use them to light up the streets. I want you to be especially alert during the early morning hours, because military operations typically start when one side believes the other side is asleep or tired."

"The men positioned on the ground should control the booby-trapped grenades. And remember; don't activate them until a main body of Arabs has come through, not a minute before. You know our strategy: let them get through thinking there's little or no opposition. Wait until you can smell their breath then attack with everything you've got."

"And we now have semi and automatic rifles, Bren guns, plus plenty of ammunition. I also want all of our movements taking place at night so that the enemy doesn't see you, and from here on in, I want absolutely no one on the streets during the day. Let it look like the area is isolated. Any questions?"

After receiving a unanimous affirmative, Amnon went back to the five-story building to find an enormous argument going on between his deputy and many residents blocking the entrances.

"They won't let us in to open the walls," Yaakov complained.

Infuriated, Amnon took out his revolver and fired two shots into the ground, yelling, "The next bullets will be fired at you. Get out of my face and leave the building. You have exactly one hour. Hostilities are starting in two days. Are you waiting to be killed here?"

Amnon's furious face and mood must have convinced them, for they let the men through and went packing. As Amnon passed them, he roared, "If you lock up the water supply the way you did last time, I will personally blow up your homes when the war is over!"

Amnon's men proceeded to open the walls between the apartments on the three top floors. All windows in the building had steel shutters. He made sure they were closed, but it was easy to peek through the thin slats in the shutters and see the target area.

The Beza machine gun was brought in and found to be lower than any of the windowsills, which meant it had to be lifted up in order to be operated. Amnon eyed the dining tables in each of the apartments; there was no way they could fire without mounting the machine gun on something to get it high enough. The dining room tables would do well, Amnon decided, and sent the men to bring sand bags. He instructed them to leave ten bags in each apartment, next to the northern window. Unfortunately, a smooth table was not the ideal location for the Beza machine gun, which meant that powerhouse would have to be held down while being fired.

Tuesday, July 6, 1948

Amnon arranged for leaflets to be distributed to all residents of the area. The leaflets clearly stated the Arabs were planning to attack Mea Shearim when the cease-fire was over, and instructed the residents to move out of their homes no later than Wednesday night, July 7th; anyone staying behind would be shot by his men should they interfere. Amnon noticed people moving out as soon as the pamphlets were distributed.

The exodus continued until almost everyone was gone. Amnon found one old man and his wife still in the building. He hugged Amnon and said he and his wife would stay in their ground floor apartment, no matter what, to pray for their success. He told Amnon he didn't want to pray for them from a distance. Amnon told him it might become very dangerous, but the old man didn't seem to care.

The Beza machine gun was delivered with one hundred cases of ammunition. Amnon had it taken to the third floor, and stationed two men with it. As to the ammunition, Amnon distributed enough cases to each floor on both sides of the building, and what remained was placed to the rear of the apartments.

The men mounted the Beza on a dining room table and secured it with sand bags.

Amnon

Cracking the shutters, Amnon took careful aim at the top of the Ramallah Road. All he needed were ten shots to determine the accuracy of the target.

As long as they could shoot from that building, there'd be no traffic on the Ramallah road. Amnon was convinced that as soon as they began hitting enemy traffic, the building would become a major target for their six and two pounder cannons. Amnon and that special Beza unit were ready. All the necessary passages between the apartments were open, and sand bags were ready next to each window, as well as the tables supporting the machine gun.

As it got dark, Amnon's men went into action. Each soldier was carrying his weapon, a case of grenades, and wire. His unit replaced the seniors, who were sent back to base, and preparations began. Amnon walked from one house to the next, examined each window and each opening, and made sure every location with a view of the street was covered by at least one soldier.

Wednesday, July 7, 1948

Food supplies were delivered, along with a few dozen pairs of boots in different sizes. Amnon was overjoyed to see the boots; the pair he was wearing was virtually gone, their soles looked as though they'd been shaved off. Amnon instructed a couple of his men to move the food and the boots to the front at night. As darkness fell, Amnon went to inspect the houses facing the valley to the east, as well as the houses along both sides of the streets.

His men were busy setting up the booby-trapped hand grenades, carefully covering each grenade with whatever rubbish or stones they could find. The wires were tucked carefully along the curb. Since the streets hadn't been cleaned in weeks, it wasn't too difficult to camouflage the wires or grenades. Amnon returned to the five-story building, found a comfortable bed in one of the apartments, and slept through the night.

Saturday, July 10, 1948

Exactly at midnight, Arab firepower aimed at all Jewish areas of Jerusalem began with a vengeance. It continued throughout the night nonstop. Soon after midnight, Arab army trucks began rolling down Ramallah Road toward Jerusalem. Their lights were on, and as soon as they appeared at the top of the hill, the Beza started spraying the road with heavy fire. Within seconds, two of the trucks exploded, and the light from the flames allowed Amnon's men to concentrate their fire on the rest of the convoy. Trucks went off the road and crashed left and right.

In the distance, fires and explosions shattered the darkness. They kept the pressure on for another half hour until they saw no more movement of any kind. At this point Amnon had the Beza moved to the fifth floor on the opposite side of the building. In five minutes, the Beza was set up and ready; however, Amnon's men didn't have to renew firing, as all traffic on the Ramallah road stopped.

Within the hour, six pounder shells were fired in the direction of the five-story building. It was still dark, and obviously the enemy couldn't see well enough to properly aim, and none of the shells hit the building. The fires were beginning to die down, and Amnon assumed that whatever manpower in that convoy had managed to escape death or injury would either continue their trip, or help the wounded. Amnon then ordered his men to fire at the general target every thirty seconds for no more than ten seconds on each clip, then move the Beza to another window on the other side of the building, and onto another floor, fire again, switching floors every third time. That activity continued non-stop for hours and days.

At 5:00am, without any previous warning by a typical softening artillery barrage, a major assault took place on the Mea Shearim police station area. Just as Amnon predicted, the assault was launched through the two streets behind the station that led to the intersection, it began with armored vehicles firing straight ahead into the street and beyond, giving cover to hundreds of Arab soldiers following behind.

"Armored cars without infantry backup are no use to an advancing army," Amnon had stated many times.

The defenders let the cars that were shooting go through. Amnon was amazed they didn't fire one bullet at the houses on either side of the booby-trapped streets. When the Arab infantry was in the center of the booby-trapped locations, Amnon's men set off all the grenades at once. The enemy's approach didn't surprise Amnon one bit -- he expected it; it was as if he could read their minds. Once the grenades were activated, the men started ferocious firing barrage stronger than ever before.

This time they had plenty of weapons and ammunition, which they used to their hearts' content. The Arabs scattered all over the place. Dozens fell to the ground, while others tried to find cover in the doorways of the houses, which none of them managed to reach, due to Amnon's ground personnel. The armored cars, realizing what had happened, turned around, and began firing at the houses indiscriminately. They were showered with hand grenades, and within minutes all the cars were disabled.

Whatever was left of the attacking infantry was fleeing the scene. Amnon's men kept shooting them down until the last man was out of sight. The streets were littered with bodies. The armored cars, now facing east, could see what had happened to their men, and stopped firing. Amnon had one of his men who was fluent in Arabic instruct the men inside the armored cars to come out with their hands up. They did. They were walked into the Mea Shearim police station, and after a thorough search, locked up.

Amnon sent two men to check that all the booby trap grenades had indeed gone off, and at the same time had the armored cars pushed forward by one of the cars that hadn't been totally incapacitated, creating a barricade out of them at the edge of the street. Within minutes, all the men were back at their positions in case another assault was mounted. This time, however, thinking the Arabs might change tactics, Amnon doubled the number of men at the rear of the houses. But no assault came.

Meanwhile, dawn had come and gone; the sun was up. Amnon ran to his Beza building, which was being bombarded by endless shells. Running from floor to floor, he dashed from one side of the building to the other until he found his men. For the first time, he saw what had happened the night before on the top of the Ramallah road.

Burned army trucks blocked the road, and many others were stuck in the ravines on both sides. Daylight let Amnon and his men see the results of the Beza machine gun. The ground was covered with the bodies of dead or wounded soldiers. Seeing no traffic whatsoever, they stopped firing. However, the enemy's two and six pounder shells still kept coming steadily at the building. Amnon was surprised at the number of shells that missed the building altogether, and wondered where they'd landed.

A two or six-pounder could penetrate solid stone, concrete wall, or steel plate. Apart from creating a huge noise, like a flying missile, depending upon the thickness of its target, it makes one hole upon penetration and another when it exits. Most shells fired at this building went in one side and out the rear. The only damage to people would be if someone got hit by a shell or flying stone.

Amnon ordered his men to fire during the day only if they saw anything moving on the Ramallah road, otherwise to stay quiet; at night, he instructed them to continue to spray the road about every thirty seconds. Amnon contemplated shooting flares from his Sanhedriah position to illuminate part of the road at night, but then decided against it. It was quiet on that section of the front. Why stir things up? His guess was that the command of the Arab Legion was using the Police Academy building, and that British personnel were still in it, so they didn't want any fighting there.

While all of this was happening in Jerusalem, Syrian and Iraqi forces were on the march again in the north. Not only were all their assaults repelled, the Israel Defense Forces captured the entire lower Galilee, including the city of Nazareth. And in the central part of the country, the cities of Ramleh, and Lydda were captured along with dozens of Arab villages. The Egyptian armies were contained in the south.

The United Nations was again very active, trying to arrange a permanent cease-fire. The newly established Israeli Government felt that the United Nations should force Egypt out of the area, thus avoiding bloodshed.

Tuesday, July 13, 1948

Amnon inspected his entire line of defense. Everything was in place. The northern sector, from Mea Shearim to Sanhedriah, was quiet, but the sector south of Mea Shearim was being fired upon without letup. This time, though, Amnon's men returned fire with fervor. They had weapons and ammunition, and one by one his snipers took out many shooting Arabs. There were no assaults anywhere in that section, all the way to the Old City.

Finally, through the intervention of one of the foreign consuls in Jerusalem, Arab ambulances were allowed to pick up their dead and wounded from the streets behind the Mea Shearim police station. Their damaged armored cars, with an Israeli flag atop one, were a standing monument to the defender's success.

The Beza machine gun continued firing at the Ramallah Road every night. There was no traffic on that road day or night. The pressure was kept up.

The Beza building, as they were used to calling it, continued to be pounded day and night. There were more holes in the building than Amnon could count. Fortunately, none of his men were hurt.

Sunday, July 18, 1948
　　The United Nations succeeded in arranging a cease-fire, this time, they said, a permanent one. The cease-fire was to go into effect on July 19, 1948. There was no more activity on the fronts of Jerusalem. Firing slowly died down in the course of the night.

Monday, July 19, 1948
　　All had quieted down. As the day wore on, residents began flocking back to their homes. The old couple that had remained in their apartment had a few near misses, but were in good spirits. The old man wouldn't let Amnon out of his sight. He felt so proud, even though he was too old to fight or be of any help. Amnon was in the building, helping his men clean the Beza, when the first residents arrived. Then the last thing in the world he'd have expected occurred. He was attacked by most of the residents! They shouted at him and his men, screamed at them, cursed and insulted them for destroying their precious furniture. The dining room tables, and coffee tables, that Amnon's men had used as bases for the Beza had been unavoidably damaged, some beyond repair. There was also plenty of damage from the endless pounding of the building.
　　Amnon told his men to pack up and leave, and if anyone tried to harm them, they had his authority to shoot in self-defense. As Amnon was about to leave the building, he was stopped by one Orthodox man demanding his name address, and number. Amnon gave it to him, and told him to remember him as the one who had saved his life, then walked away in disgust.
　　If he ever had any positive feeling toward the Orthodox Jews, Amnon lost it right there. The scene of the Hassidic men wanting to cross to the Arab side, on that very street, flashed across his mind. Amnon was totally disgusted as he walked away. He couldn't begin to figure out what made those people tick. Not one of them was an active soldier. None participated in the war effort. None had as much as a scratched fingernail. And despite the fact that the Haganah or the Israel Defense Forces had saved their lives, they had the brassbound gall to curse them for unavoidable damage to their furniture!
　　"What about my furniture? What about my belongings? What about my sacrifice, my hardship, my involvement in bringing thousands of Jewish survivors home, the sleepless nights, the fear, the not knowing if I would be alive the next hour? What about my parents, who didn't know if I was alive or dead? They don't have to worry about their sons and daughters, because they aren't in the army or the Haganah," Amnon fumed. "They are nowhere, as far as I'm concerned. Yet these people locked up the water supply and I had to blow it up so my men and I could have some drinking water." Never in his life had Amnon been so fed up with those ultra religious people.
　　Amnon was informed that in a few days his units would be transferred to a less stressful area, so they could rest after the ordeal of the past few days.

266

Amnon

This was good news, for mentally and physically Amnon was worn out and badly needed a rest. Firing and hostilities had completely stopped, and there wasn't much to do except to wait for whatever came next.

Telling his men to stay on alert, as surprises could always happen, Amnon decided to visit his parents, who were surely worried about him.

As usual, his mother smothered him with hugs and kisses. His father wasn't home. He'd gone to Tel Aviv to meet with someone in the government, hoping that they'd enlist his services. Amnon sat down, as usual, at the dining room table. His mother made a glass of tea, this time with a little bit of sugar, and a slice of lemon. They talked for hours. Amnon told her about the various battles, how they defended against each assault, and how they'd prepared for the next.

She asked about Jewish fatalities and wounded. Her face saddened when she heard the names of some of the men who fell. With tears in his eyes, he told her about the bravery of those wonderful young men. He sorely missed them, and their deaths would be a heavy burden he'd carry with him for the rest of his life. Amnon could see each of their smiling faces, full of enthusiasm and idealism.

"What a pity that so many young lives were sacrificed to make a homeland of our own," he said to his mother.

Thinking of the parents of the fallen men, Amnon wondered how in the world he'd be able to face them. He knew he'd have to see them sooner or later.

His mother noticed him getting depressed, and quickly changed the subject. "Your father," she began, "could be of such help to the newly formed government. He's a first class administrator, and the Israeli government would greatly benefit from his background and experience."

Yes, she did change the subject, and they began to talk about how their lives would be shaped after the war. Immigration to Israel was in full swing, and all of the detainees in Cyprus, and elsewhere had been brought home. There was plenty of work ahead; they had to reconstruct all the war-damaged farms, settlements, and city buildings, build new housing projects for the arriving immigrants, build new industries, and further expand their farming.

It was dark when Amnon left his mother. It felt good to be able to walk the streets of Jerusalem without fearing a stray bullet or long-range bombardment. After a twenty-minute walk, Amnon reached Mea Shearim and rejoined his men. This was his first opportunity to talk with his Polish/Russian men after their first battle experience.

They were elated. The news of survivors arriving in Israel by the thousands made them feel special and proud. They hugged and kissed each other. Amnon told them in a few days they'd be transferred to another location where they could all have a well-earned rest.

There was a lot of cleaning up to do, but they still kept an eye on the front. They never knew what might happen without notice. This time, however, the Arabs had learned it wasn't so simple to lick Israel. The State of Israel still had the Egyptian armies to deal with, but Amnon's understanding was that this would come in due course.

One interesting development was that under pressure from the United

Nations, the Egyptians agreed to cease hostilities in the vicinity of Jerusalem. Their armies actually retreated from the Ramat Rachel area.

Saturday, July 31, 1948
   Intelligence reports confirmed there was no more Arab military activity. Arab residents also began to return to their homes around the front line, a good sign. Amnon's units were ordered to pack up and were taken by military buses, of all places, to Ramat Rachel, to replace the units which had fought the Egyptians. They, too, were exhausted from days of heavy fighting, and Amnon had no idea where they were being transferred. All he knew was that a truce with Egypt was in effect, and that in Ramat Rachel they could all have a rest and relax. Ramat Rachel was on top of a hill from which Amnon could see the edge of Bethlehem. The landscape was magnificent. He stood for a while at the edge of the kibbutz grounds, enjoying the beautiful southern scenery, the rolling mountains and valleys. He called his men, busy setting up camp, to come enjoy the view with him.
   When their camp was set up, Amnon designated watch shifts, and began to tour the kibbutz. Most of the buildings had been heavily damaged during the battles, and weren't at that moment able to house anyone. In time, however, Amnon thought it would be a great place for a vacation.
   A few days before the war ended, the newly created Ministry of Finance introduced the new Israeli currency.
   "This is the real sign that we're a nation like any other, with our own currency," Amnon declared happily. One Israeli pound was worth four United States dollars. Regrettably, it didn't stay that way long. The national bureaucracy was beginning to form. In the past, the Yishuv was used to having a leadership in the form of the Jewish Agency for Palestine, as it was known, which was a quasi government. With the establishment of the State of Israel, new departments were announced, Interior, Finance, Immigration Absorption, Agriculture, Foreign affairs, and Defense. At Ramat Rachel, they were still very far from all that reality, and hearing of those developments over the radio, Amnon wasn't able to form a very clear picture in his mind. Moreover, since he was still on one of the fronts, he wasn't yet part of the country.
   Amnon suddenly began to think of the future.
   "*I need to finish my high school, and I need to go college. But what should I study?*" Amnon wondered. There were many positions in the military, but he didn't even want to think of staying in the army.
   "*When will I be discharged?*" was his question of the day. But he had no answers. Amnon had a hard time even thinking of what he'd like to do, or be, in the future.
   Amnon suddenly realized that having spent the past five years in the Resistance movement and army, hadn't exactly prepared him for any career other than the military.
   "*What do I want to do with my life?*" Amnon kept asking himself. He had no idea in those days, for uncertainty was still in the air. While every single person in Israel was hoping for peace, no one knew if the Arabs would honor

their permanent ceasefire agreement.

The first night in Ramat Rachel, Amnon was very pensive. His cot was hard and not conducive to a restful sleep. During the night, it got quite cool and a gentle breeze caressed him. Realizing that for the first time in years he had actually begun to think about things other than war, the creation of the Homeland and independence, Amnon was suddenly enveloped by a strange feeling.

"In a few months I'll be nineteen. Where have all the years gone? With no time to think about myself, I haven't had time to realize I've become a man, and a very mature man at that," Amnon mused. He suddenly felt as though his childhood had been stolen from him; he could barely remember having any fun.

"Surely," Amnon thought, *"my life will be renewed soon, since the war is finally over, and I'll become a civilian. But when?"* As of that moment, he had no idea. Then he began thinking of the early days in the Haganah, and his recruitment.

"We're very interested in you because of your language skills," Amnon had been told. But he couldn't remember when those skills were used. He did feel proud of everything he had done. He felt his sacrifice was justified. Indeed, he was only one of many who gave up their youth for the ideal of creating a Jewish homeland, a home for the persecuted, and the survivors of the world's worst atrocities. In reality, just the fact that he'd helped bring home the wandering Jews, whose homes, families, and lives were destroyed, was worth the effort.

"Let the State of Israel stand as a memorial monument to the Holocaust," Amnon proudly declared.

Thursday, August 5, 1948

Amnon and his units were transferred again, this time to the Sha'ar Hagai area. Here they were driven on the old road between Jerusalem and Tel Aviv, the one on which he'd defended so many convoys. Burned and disabled cars were still where they'd been left, except many had been pushed off the road. The frontline with the Arabs was just a kilometer away. Again, there wasn't much to do. They kept their weapons clean, they patrolled the area, and kept watch for any movement on the other side. There wasn't any.

Monday, August 30, 1948

Last week Amnon and his men had been transferred once again, this time to the old Ramleh police station building, the army's local headquarters. There was little to do, so Amnon decided to kill some time by touring the building. It was quite big, and spread over a great deal of territory. He walked from room to room, exploring the many desks and filing cabinets left by the British. To his surprise, in one cabinet he found a dozen cans of corned beef. He brought them down to the kitchen, and sent one of his men to the city of Ramleh with instructions to buy eggs, if he could find any. He did, and Amnon proceeded to make corned beef omelets, using all the cans and all the eggs. They had a ball.

The next morning, as Amnon's men were looking across the huge meadow at the back of the police station, they noticed a cow wandering toward their building. The cow was grazing, slowly getting closer. One of his men who was the son of a butcher, went out and brought the cow in. The next thing Amnon knew, he'd slaughtered the cow, and for days they ate beef until it came out of their ears.

Kol Israel reported that both the United States and Russia were sending special representatives to Israel.

"This is the ultimate proof that we're now a nation like any other," Amnon thought, *"When foreign countries begin to set up their embassies in our country."*

Meanwhile, Count Bernadotte, the United Nations mediator, was working on his report. The newly issued Israeli currency was then in full circulation. The government announced that Golda Meir was appointed as Israel's Ambassador to Russia. Politically, Amnon felt that the little new nation was making great strides.

On the ground, the Israeli army was preparing a plan to uproot the Egyptian armies that had been contained in the south. United Nations or not, the plan was to kick them out. It was going to be a major offensive, Amnon was told. Date and time were not yet established.

Saturday, September 18, 1948

A member of Lehi assassinated Count Bernadotte in Jerusalem. The Israeli Government declared Lehi an illegal organization. What steps were to be taken against that organization were not known. Apparently, Bernadotte had been going to recommend to the United Nations that Israel receive the north of the country, and the Arabs the south, namely, the Negev, and Jerusalem was to become a separate entity. Additionally, all Arabs would be allowed to return to their previous homes. It was obvious that such recommendations didn't sit well with anyone, yet the Jewish mainstream population preferred diplomacy to murder. One news item did bother the Yishuv greatly. The United States foreign secretary announced his government's acceptance of Count Bernadotte's recommendations.

Sunday, October 10, 1948

Another move, this time to the mountainous region west of Jerusalem, the very same mountains that he'd canvassed sometime ago. His instructions were to set up camps on each mountain, as he had sketched, so that when the boundaries of Israel were drawn at the United Nations, Israel could claim that territory. Several trucks delivered camping and other equipment outside kibbutz Kiriat Anavim, and once again, they were loading mules for the journey to various mountains where roads didn't exist. This time, however, they were instructed to build mountain paths for future jeep traffic.

Some of the Polish boys were familiar with road construction, and immediately volunteered to work on the project. Amnon made copies of the map he was given, and they set out in five different directions. Amnon assigned his old group to the northern mountain, which they reached after an entire night of travel. He assigned one road expert to each unit, and told his men to start the path project as soon as their camps had been set up, working from the encampment

270

area toward the Tel Aviv-Jerusalem road.

Once they'd pitched their tents, built a mobile kitchen, and dug out a few trenches for security, they began the path construction. Amnon stood at the top of the mountain and looked south towards the Tel Aviv-Jerusalem road. He conferred with his young Polish soldier, whose only knowledge of road construction was that he had been a laborer working under Russian military command on building roads. They decided on the route the path should follow, and began. The men cleared brush, stones, rocks, and, sometimes, cut down trees. Progress was slow, but by the end of the day they had gone down about a quarter of the mountain.

Tuesday, October 19, 1948

To celebrate Amnon's birthday, one of his men who regularly took the mule trip to the kibbutz for food supplies brought back a bottle of wine. At nineteen, even though he was full of energy, Amnon felt like an old man. He supposed that on birthdays people tend to review their lives, and as he looked back on his all he could see was hardship, hard work, and endless personal sacrifice, intermingled with the suffering faces of Holocaust survivors.

It was a strange mixture of issues and feelings, yet he felt a deep connection with the Jewish fate. One particular aspect of his looking back was the realization he had missed the normal life of a teenager. Joining the Haganah had turned him into a man at the early age of fourteen. Looking back at all he'd done helping save Jewish lives and giving the survivors back their dignity made him feel good. Just knowing he'd played a part, however small, in the creation of the Jewish homeland made him feel even better, and Amnon was quite content.

While reminiscing about the past, Amnon again began to think about the future. The unanswered question was whether peace would last, and if so, when would he be discharged from the army. At the time, Amnon thought it was premature to think beyond that. But he couldn't help thinking that if the Arabs finally realized they couldn't defeat Israel, perhaps they'd agree to the United Nations' plan for the partition of the country. He could almost make himself believe that if they were to agree, they could all live in peace. The land was certainly sufficient for all of them.

But knowing the British and their anti-Jewish Mufti had both planted and nurtured the abiding hatred that caused the division between the easily led Arabs, and the Jews, Amnon had strong doubts. The Arabs lived according to the Code of Hammurabi, which translated to 'an eye for an eye, a tooth for a tooth and a life for a life.' That further translated to a vengeance-oriented mentality that might well cause them to seek vengeance for their defeats, thus negating all efforts for a lasting peace treaty brokered by the United Nations. Arabs were not known for their logic or practicality, so it was pointless trying to think which way they might move.

However, to paraphrase a famous rough-riding American president, whose best-known advice was to 'speak softly, but carry a big stick,' Amnon believed it best, when dealing with scorpions, to always stay alert and carry a heavy club.

It rained all afternoon and well into their dinnertime. Though the food was plain and wholesome, it was extremely bland, and Amnon thought wistfully of his mother's wonderful cooking. Just the thought of it brought tears to his eyes, how he missed her! Suddenly, Amnon felt an urge to see her, and resolved to do so in the next few days.

After the meal, the wine was opened, and each of them had a drink. The guys told Amnon he was their best friend, and how much they appreciated his constant concern for their welfare. It was a very touching evening. Amnon felt at home with those men, some of whom had been with him for years.

Rain continued to slash down, and they were getting soaked, for there was no place to hide from it. Inside the tents, the ground was soaking wet, and small streams of water ran from one end to the other. There was nothing they could do but wait it out. Amnon went to bed in his army cot, and undoubtedly thanks to the wine, actually slept without waking all night long.

It was still raining in the morning, but not as hard; looking up, he saw the sky was still gray. They had hard-boiled eggs, bread, some farmer's cheese, and water to wash it down. They couldn't light a fire, so there was no hot tea.

Despite the constant drizzle, after breakfast they either walked or rode the mules to the place they'd stopped the previous day, and went to work clearing the path. As the clearing work progressed, they moved further and further away from their encampment. Since the encampment would be used as a point of settlement in the final decision of boundaries, they couldn't move it, so every day they moved further from camp.

Building a rough dirt road, no matter how wide was backbreaking. The most difficult part was where the road needed switchbacks because of the steep inclines in parts of the mountain. First, they sort of drew a line showing where the road should be, marked it with stones, and finally began clearing the path. When they encountered large rocks blocking their way, they either had to break them up, if possible, or else build the road snaking around them.

They worked very hard. As the mountains grew steeper, their progress became correspondingly slower, for they had to cut out parts of the slope to make room for a path. At the end of each day they returned to their encampment, where whoever had been on watch that day had a meal ready for them. Later, they simply collapsed onto their cots to sleep like rocks through the night.

The weather was not overly cooperative. During the three weeks of road building, they endured many rainy and drizzly days. It did however help cool them down from the heat of hard labor. By the end of the third week, they had completed a dirt road that was two meters wide, and led from the mountaintop to the Jerusalem-Tel Aviv road. The final trip was made on mule back, at the end of which Amnon was sure the mules were pleased to be back in their barn where better food and plenty of water awaited them.

They filled the jeep that was ready for them with supplies and inaugurated the dirt road to their mountain. It was a long and tedious trip, but in an hour and ten minutes, they'd reached their destination. The guys were elated. They sang and danced around the jeep, and then Amnon brought out his big surprise, a cake that the kibbutz had baked for them to celebrate that special occasion. The cake was gone long before dinner was served.

As a matter of habit, they went looking for the mules, which were usually grazing around the encampment, to give them their evening water, when they realized they were no longer with them. They missed those wonderful animals; they'd become so close to them. After all, they were part of their family.

At the kibbutz, Amnon heard the great news that the Egyptian armies had been defeated and pushed back to the Gaza strip. The entire Negev had been recaptured, and the Israeli Defense Forces were en route to the Galilee to complete the conquest of the northernmost and final sector. It was believed that that operation would be completed by the end of the month.

Amnon wanted so much to be part of the forces battling Egypt, but he had no say in that matter at all. Since the days of the convoys, Amnon had been assigned to the Jerusalem area, and it appeared that's where he would stay. Desert fighting wasn't his background or experience. Obviously, his command felt his strength and specialty focused on fighting in mountains and inhabited regions. As much as he wanted to be everywhere and fight every battle, Amnon could do neither. In his heart, he was pleased he'd at least done his share.

Wednesday, November 10, 1948

Amnon was still king of the mountain. It was very boring, with not a thing to do except wait. The Israeli Government was very active on the political front, as there remained many issues requiring attention. In particular, the newly appointed mediator, Mr. Ralph Bunche, told the United Nations Israel must evacuate the Negev Desert, and retreat to the positions it held before the offensive against Egypt began. He also asked the Security Council to impose sanctions against Israel if it did not comply.

Israel didn't need that type of mediation, and it didn't comply with this demand. The American representative to the United Nations disagreed with Ralph Bunche, stating the situation was not reversible. Though Israel defied a United Nations order to retreat from the Negev, the feared sanctions weren't imposed after all.

Through the kibbutz, Amnon was in weekly contact with his commander, seeking a change that didn't come. Bored, he read numerous books borrowed from the kibbutz library, just to keep his mind active while waiting for some telephone wire he'd requested.

The jeep trips actually helped harden the dirt road they'd built. The road began to show signs of life, for occasionally they had to stop the jeep to clear away rocks that must have hurtled down from higher up the mountain. In time, Amnon became familiar with every turn in the road, every tree and bush.

When Amnon finally received the telephone wire he'd requested, he took two men with him on the trip to the mountaintop, and together they stretched the wire all the way from the kibbutz to their summit encampment and then connected it to the kibbutz telephone system. From then on, they were connected to the rest of the world. That accomplished, there wasn't much else for him to do.

Telling his commander he'd be taking a day off, Amnon drove to

Jerusalem and visited with his parents. He also wanted very much to visit the parents of his very best childhood friend, Izhar, who had been killed in one of the Galilee battles, as Amnon had only recently learned. They'd been very close during the days of the Resistance, even before they joined the Haganah, and Amnon felt he needed to visit with his parents.

Izhar had been their only son, and while Amnon knew it would be a very difficult visit, he decided to stop at Izhar parents' house before visiting with his own parents. Izhar's family lived in a single-family home, just a few blocks from Amnon's parents' apartment building. As he crossed the yard that separated the street from their front door, Amnon passed the cherry tree whose fruit Izhar and he had eaten so many times. In his memory's eye, Amnon clearly saw the two of them picking and eating the cherries.

Amnon's eyes were still wet when Izhar's mother opened the front door. At first she didn't recognize Amnon. Dumbstruck with grief, Amnon could neither move nor utter a word as they stood silently facing each other for a moment. Suddenly, she called his name in great surprise, grabbed Amnon's hand, and pulled him into a hug. While she held him in a long embrace, Amnon heard her calling her husband, and he slowly regained his senses.

Izhar's father shook Amnon's hand warmly, and asked him in. They talked for a long time, and Amnon didn't notice the sun set, or darkness descend. He hadn't the courage to ask them where Izhar was killed. Eventually he learned Izhar was killed in a battle fighting the Syrians in the Galilee. Amnon described the many battles he'd been involved in, and the last days of the convoys, and they kept pressing him for more details. But Amnon was getting very tired, and finally got the courage to tell them he hadn't seen his parents yet. Promising to visit them again in the near future, with tears in their eyes, they said their goodbyes, and Amnon headed out to his jeep, very much enjoying passing through the old neighborhood on the way. Then he got into the jeep and drove to his parent's apartment. It was such a pleasant drive he actually wished his parents lived further away so he could drive longer in Rehavia. It was a cool November night, the Jerusalem air dry and crisp. Amnon loved it.

Amnon reached his parents' house within five minutes, and, as always, was warmly greeted by his mother. His father, however, seemed very upset. Amnon learned that his request to serve the newly created government of Israel had been denied. He couldn't believe it. He was in shock. He refused to accept the new reality.

He kept saying over and over, "What have I done wrong? I served the Jewish Agency for years. I put myself in danger hundreds of times working for the British government. Time and again helped arrange immigration certificates for people they wanted to bring in. I provided vital insider information. I gave up my position, and decided to stay in Israel to be part of our country. I have experience in government no one here possesses. Yet they don't want me!"

"Did they say why?" Amnon asked.

"They said I was rejected because I wasn't a member of the Histadrut [Labor union]."

"That makes no sense at all," Amnon said, "They know damn well that as an employee of the British Government, you couldn't be a member of the Histadrut. There has to be another reason. What do you suspect?"

"I believe the mere fact I worked for the British is their problem. I also believe they want their people to take all the top positions, whether they have the experience or not."

Amnon felt sorry for him. Here was a man who was selected to join the British Government when Palestine became a British Mandate. Just as the first British High Commissioner for Palestine was a Jew, the British sought other Jews to participate in its Palestinian affairs following the issuance of the famous Balfour Declaration, which was intended to help create a Jewish homeland in Palestine.

"What are you going to do?" Amnon asked.

"I still have people I haven't approached yet. I'm going to fight this," he said. "I can't go back to England now. It's out of the question."

Amnon could barely keep his eyes open, and begged to be excused. He went to bed wondering how his father would resolve his dilemma. At least he had a good pension he could live on.

Amnon felt very lazy when he woke up, and decided to stay in bed. He propped himself up on another pillow, wondering whether there was any way he could help his father. He decided to talk to his commander about him later that day. As he lay there thinking of the future, his mother walked in carrying the morning newspaper, which described the Egyptian situation in great detail. The Israeli Defense Forces had entered the Sinai Peninsula, pushing back the Egyptian armies.

The United Nations, which the Yishuv hoped would press Egypt to leave territories it had captured, wasn't in fact trying to do that. Israel also wanted them out of the Gaza strip. While a truce existed with the other Arab countries, Egypt had not yet agreed to it. At least the good news was that the Egyptian armies had been defeated. Capturing part of the Sinai would surely serve as leverage in the political situation to come.

Thursday, November 18, 1948

When Amnon left his parents' apartment, he went straight to the Jerusalem headquarters. Yoav, his commander, wasn't there, and wouldn't be back before the end of the month. Amnon met many men he hadn't seen in a long time, and also learned who'd been killed. Having been tucked away in the mountains west of Jerusalem for some time, he hadn't been informed about many things that were going on.

A major change was the disbandment of the Palmach, the commando section of the Haganah. It became part of the Israeli Defense Forces. Amnon couldn't find anyone who might be helpful to his father, so he left. He needed some air, so he took a long walk, passing from sector to sector, enjoying watching people going about their business. Workmen were everywhere, busily repairing damages from the recent bombardment.

Most workers were older, since the younger men hadn't been released from service yet. Many shops along Jaffa Road and the Machne Yehuda market were open. Thursday was usually a big shopping day in preparation for the Sabbath. Feeling satisfied from the long excursion, Amnon walked to his jeep, and drove back to camp.

That week the government announced the results of the first census conducted in Israel. Over 780,000 Jews were counted, an increase of about 100,000 persons since the beginning of the year. The number of Arabs living in Israel was around 70,000. Also announced that week was the establishment of El Al, the Israeli airline.

Driving to his camp, Amnon couldn't stop reflecting on the news.

"We're now an independent country with a democratically elected government. We have our own army, a tiny navy, new-minted currency, and our own airline. We sure move fast," he thought.

As usual, soldiers were waiting at various corners looking for a lift. Amnon had room for three, but he wasn't going far, so he couldn't be much help to anyone. He passed through Romema, Givaat Shaul, and then was on the road to Tel Aviv. Within twenty minutes he got to his newly built dirt road, and followed it to the kibbutz, he picked up a few items and some supplies, and drove to the encampment.

Tuesday, November 30, 1948

The Security Council of the United Nations pressured the Arab countries to start negotiating a permanent armistice with Israel. The Government of Israel consented immediately. However, before agreeing to remove military forces from many areas of the country, the Israeli Defense Forces captured the entire eastern part of the Negev Desert all the way to the Dead Sea. November ended with the report that Israel had applied for membership in the United Nations, as well as Amnon receiving information that all his units in the mountain areas would be returning to base sometime the following week. Amnon wondered where their base was, for he'd never had one before.

Friday, December 17, 1948

Amnon and his men were transferred from the mountains to the Talpiot barracks, the same one he had earlier attacked, and demolished its weapons storage. There wasn't much to do; there was talk that with the strengthening of the armistice, the army would begin discharging soldiers. Amnon was approached by the higher military command, and offered a high-ranking position in the army as a career soldier. He immediately rejected their offer, for he had no interest in continuing his life in military service.

Amnon asked when he might reasonably expect to be discharged, but couldn't get an answer. The Government of Israel didn't want to discharge its armies until it felt absolutely secure with a permanent armistice. A great deal depended on the Arab's attitude toward peace and tranquility. Amnon and his men spent the days doing very little. All the men received passes for two or three days at a time, and went to visit family and friends. Amnon did the same. After visiting his parents for a few hours, he took the bus to Tel Aviv, and enjoyed two days at the beach. Walking to the beach, he came across a very old friend of his.

Amnon

They used to live in the same neighborhood during kindergarten. He introduced Amnon to his wife, whom he'd married just a few days ago. He'd been wounded in a battle with the Egyptians, and his leg was in a cast. He told Amnon it wasn't serious, and he should be completely healed in a couple of weeks.

On his second leave from the barracks, Amnon walked through Mea Shearim, and passed by the frontline he knew so well. The northern wall of the five-story Beza building hadn't been repaired yet. There were countless artillery shell holes in that wall, and he wondered how his men had been so lucky that not a one of them was hit.

Deciding to check whether the old couple was still there, Amnon knocked on their door. The old man opened the door and greeted him warmly, but he didn't look too good. He told Amnon his wife had been very ill, and the end was probably near. Despite his agony, he invited Amnon in, and they talked for a while. Amnon had often thought about that old man, for he resembled the mental image of the grandfather he never knew.

After leaving him, Amnon continued to walk towards Sanhedriah. It was cold, and his jacket wasn't warm enough, but that stroll held special feelings and meaning for Amnon, and he greatly enjoyed it. From Sanhedriah Amnon took the bus to the center of the city, and walked along Ben Yehuda Street all the way to the top of the hill. From there he turned left to his parents' apartment.

Arab leaders, meeting in Beirut, appointed King Abdullah of Trans-Jordan king of Palestine.

"*Now here's a strange announcement. I can't figure this one out,*" Amnon thought. Then he remembered the secret meeting rumored to have taken place between someone in the Jewish leadership and the king.

"*Could they possibly have agreed that since the rest of Palestine was going to be Arab territory, that part of Palestine would be Trans-Jordan's price for staying out of the way, as it were?*" Amnon decided the subject was too difficult for logical speculation.

The talk in town focused on the United Nations rejecting Israel's application for membership in that world body, and the ejection of Egyptian forces from the last few pockets of territory they held.

Friday, December 31, 1948

As the year came to an end, Amnon did the same thing he'd done every year of his life for as far back as he could remember -- he reviewed the events of the past year. What a year it had been! Arab militias attacked Jewish settlements and cities all over Palestine; Arabs also attacked traffic all over the country. Traveling anywhere in Palestine could only take place in convoys; no one dared travel alone. Jerusalem was cut off.

Finally, the day came when the British abandoned Palestine. In the war that followed their departure, the Haganah went on the defensive, which quickly turned into an offensive. Throughout Palestine, from pre-Independence days well into the period after the Declaration of Statehood, the Haganah's offensive captured vital areas for the existence of the Yishuv. The State of Israel more or less followed the original partition plan the Arabs had rejected. Finally, the Arabs were defeated.

Over 100,000 new immigrants arrived, and the incoming stream continued at a rate of about 1,000 a day. Israel made a home for the survivors and other Jews who wanted to become part of the new homeland. It was a year of great bloodshed; the Yishuv suffered thousands of deaths and wounded. But the goals of the entire population of the land were achieved.

Sitting on an empty gasoline can near one of the fences that surrounded the barracks, looking at the dirt road they'd followed in one of their assaults, Amnon took some time to seriously ponder his future.

"Soon I'm going to be discharged," he thought, *"so where do I go from here, and what am I going to do?"* Even though he hadn't done much of anything since he left the mountains, Amnon felt emotionally and physically drained from everything he'd experienced in the past five years.

He suddenly thought of Shmuel, who came to recruit him, telling him what an asset he would be to the Haganah with all his languages. When Amnon asked himself if they ever used his language skills, he had to laugh. *"Was it merely a ploy to get me? I'll never know,"* he thought. Certainly, Amnon knew he had to complete his education, but how, and where, he had no idea. Along with so many other unanswered questions, Amnon didn't know if he wanted to live with his parents.

But in the question of housing he knew that he had no alternative, for housing was not to be found anywhere, and the only place for him to go was his parents' apartment. Over 100,000 immigrants were living in sheds, makeshift tents, and in most military barracks, like sheep. And, although Amnon had enjoyed being in the kibbutzim during the days of Resistance and the war, he didn't want to join a kibbutz either, for he didn't feel he belonged there. Amnon was a city boy, and a city boy he was going to remain.

Amnon's thoughts then turned to the survivors. How difficult it must be for them to be absorbed into life in Israel. While many of the survivors knew some Hebrew, most didn't. They spoke fluent Yiddish, but the everyday life of the country was conducted in Hebrew, and most people refused to talk or do business in any other language than Hebrew. What's more, how does a broken person who has lost everything, from family members to possessions, and arrived in this country penniless, get started?

Although Amnon knew he hadn't been complaining, he ordered himself to never complain. *"Look around at others who are much worse off than you are, and you'll grab back your own problems."* It was less than productive looking back into the past and stumbling over the present while also trying hard to see into the future, when he had no answers to any of his questions.

As he sat there daydreaming, the main issues became crystal clear.

"We have literally done the impossible, with the greatest achievement in our nation's history. We are now an independent country, standing, for the most part, on the ancient site of the Land of Israel. We now have our own Homeland. The Jews of the world can now look at Israel with pride, and no one shall ever again think of us as, or call us, nomads," Amnon told himself. *"The people of*

Amnon

Israel, their children and their children's children have something to look up to. True, what a price we had to pay, and what sacrifice. But we have turned the age-old dream into reality."

The thought of the country having become a Jewish State with its own government, police, and military forces, pulled Amnon out of his doldrums, and he again felt ready to take on the dragons of the world. Chin up, shoulders back and head high, Amnon decided to stop thinking about the past, and pursue whatever objectives he'd be designing for himself. The only nightmare that followed him bore the names and faces of his lost friends and comrades who paid the highest price for those achievements.

Tuesday, February 1, 1949

January was very sluggish for Amnon, with little if any activity. While other army units were helping to set up camps for the newly arriving immigrants, his units were kept around Jerusalem, which saw only a trickle of newcomers. Despite their having reached a cease-fire agreement with the Trans-Jordanians and the Arab Legion, Amnon knew that the Israeli Government was still uneasy with the situation in Jerusalem. While Amnon and his units weren't on active alert, they were there and ready just in case, because from time to time Arab snipers fired from across the border.

The first elections, the greatest occurrence of all in the new life of the young State of Israel, took place during January. The MAPAI (labor) party won 35% of the vote. MAPAM (another labor party) received 15%. There were 25 tickets running for the Knesset. Amnon could never understand why the Yishuv had more than one labor party, and even more difficult for him to grasp was the number of political parties the people of the land had to deal with.

Israel was such a small nation, less than one million strong, and it had twenty-five political parties!

"*Total insanity*," Amnon thought.

But despite the over abundance of political competition, an air of democracy abounded. As a nation, Israel knew from the start democracy was the right way of life. On the other hand, their Arab neighbors didn't even know what democracy meant.

The Egyptians took their defeat hard. Maybe the other Arab countries did as well, but it wasn't as pronounced as the Egyptians. At the beginning of January, Egyptian navy ships shelled Tel Aviv. The United Nations mediator, Ralph Bunche, exerted a lot of pressure on the Egyptian Government, which finally agreed to a serious cease-fire, and eventually signed an armistice agreement. All meetings with Arab countries took place on the Island of Rohdes, Greece, and each country signed a separate agreement with Israel.

The United States announced a one hundred million dollar loan to Israel. At the same time, Britain, and many other countries officially recognized the new State of Israel. In Amnon's opinion, Britain's recognition of the State of Israel marked the final defeat of British colonialism in the Middle East. He couldn't help thinking how seriously Britain's imperialistic and colonial policies had damaged them and the Jews. But as Britain had officially recognized the State of

279

Israel at the United Nations, the road was opening for normalization, and hopefully, everlasting peace.

The Cyprus chapter of the immigration story came to an end with the last of the detainees coming home to Israel. An exchange of Arab and Jewish prisoners also took place, and all the men and women who surrendered in the Gush Etzion area, as well as the Old City of Jerusalem returned home. Huge feelings of relief started to sweep over all the people of Israel, and though the word 'normalization' cropped up everywhere, Amnon couldn't help think the past five years had been anything but normal.

They had become used to living under constant tension in abnormal situations. Amnon couldn't see anyone easily jumping from one era to the other.

"It will take quite some time before our lives will be normalized," Amnon said to his friends. At the same time, Amnon knew that well over one hundred thousand persons would like nothing better than to have a normal life!

Three days later, Amnon received his discharge from the army. His life as member of the Resistance, a lifesaver, a fighting soldier, a builder, and a fervent believer in the Zionist cause to establish a Jewish Homeland, would change forever.

EPILOGUE

Amnon's mother passed away in Tel Aviv, on September 2, 1980 at the age of 80. Among her papers and her many writings, Amnon found the following script, which he translated from French:

THE MIRACLE

"Singing, dancing, elated fortune, hearts full of abundant joy, feeling every moment the grace. The fortune is so great, and what a fortune, and what a well merited gift, with so much suffering, expectation, the torment, and the patience, we the chosen children of God, after 2000 years, this great miracle is accomplished."

"Palestine, our dear and holy country, is ours. Understand, a sweet and holy mystique which envelops our horizon is in the sky where the angels sing and dance at the glory of God. He forgave his children after so many hard years. His children are free at last; free to live with their heads high, and with human dignity."

"The joy is in the air. Every day, and every moment of the day, we should remember to thank God for what he has done for us. Pardoned at last, and guarding from generation to generation the sad and painful memory of our six million brothers who were murdered in the 20th century, in a time when civilization was at its peak, these horrible deeds, in cold blood, and so calmly, were accomplished, while the entire world was watching with open eyes."

"Be happy, for after the deluge comes the calm. Thank with your whole being, sing and dance, fill the air with happiness, for today is the day. The day of the birth, forever, of this 15th day of May, of the sacred gift which was given us on a golden platter, the State of Israel."

Amnon cried and cried when, after so many years had passed, he read those holy words written so many years ago. What a wonderful soul his mother was. May she rest in peace.

Daniel Rosenfeld

ACKNOWLEDGEMENT:

I was reminded of some of the dates by The Twentieth Century in Eretz Israel
By Mordechai Naor.